D1571789

APPROXIMATION THEORY

APPROXIMATION THEORY

Proceedings of a Symposium held at
Lancaster, July 1969

Edited by

A. TALBOT

Department of Mathematics,
University of Lancaster, England

1970

ACADEMIC PRESS LONDON AND NEW YORK

ACADEMIC PRESS INC. (LONDON) LTD
Berkeley Square House
Berkeley Square,
London, W1X 6BA

U.S. Edition published by
ACADEMIC PRESS INC.
111 Fifth Avenue,
New York, New York 10003

Library of Congress Catalog Card Number: 76-117118
SBN: 12-682250-6

PRINTED OFFSET PHOTO-LITHOGRAPHY IN GREAT BRITAIN BY
THE WHITEFRIARS PRESS LIMITED, LONDON AND TONBRIDGE

PREFACE

In the age of the computer, Approximation Theory is flowering at an unprecedented rate, and it has grown tremendously since Chebyshev first applied a novel kind of mathematical thinking to the optimal design of a steam-engine linkage more than a century ago.

This book contains more than twenty papers presented at an international symposium on the subject, which was organised at the suggestion of Professor E.H. Lloyd, Head of the Mathematics Department of the University of Lancaster, and held at the University during 21-25 July 1969.

Two of the principal invited speakers were, unfortunately, for different reasons unable to be present: C. Lanczos, who was recovering from a serious illness, and E.V. Voronovskaya, who at the last moment was prevented from making the journey from Leningrad. Their absence was much regretted by all participants. However, a copy of Professor Voronovskaya's paper is included in this volume, and is I believe the first account in English of a powerful method which she has developed over a long period. It is perhaps worth noting that although there were no participants from the U.S.S.R. at the symposium, we had the pleasure of welcoming speakers from four other countries of Eastern Europe, and their papers appear in these Proceedings.

Two of the papers presented (by E.L. Ortiz and J. Blatter) have not been included here since the manuscripts could not be made available in time. They will be published elsewhere in due course.

The symposium sessions were chaired by Dr. M.J.D. Powell, of the Atomic Energy Research Establishment, Harwell, Professor A. Young, of the New University of Ulster and Professor C.W. Clenshaw, then of the National Physical Laboratory, Teddington and now at the University of Lancaster, as well as by several of the contributors, namely Professor E.W. Cheney, Dr. P. Rabinowitz, Professor P.J. Davis, Professor J.R. Rice, and Dr. D.C. Handscomb. My thanks are due to all of these, especially to Professor A. Young, who until his departure from the University of Liverpool, cooperated with Professor Lloyd and myself in the early organisation of the symposium. I wish to record also my appreciation of the generous financial support given by the Royal Society and by the New University of Ulster.

In editing the papers, I have borne in mind the importance of minimising the time interval between the occurrence of a conference and the publication of its proceedings. Nevertheless I have endeavoured by repeated scrutiny to eliminate errors of all sorts, and trust that not too many still remain.*

With so many different authors, from many different countries, there were bound to be some variations in notation. I have not attempted to standardise this, but only to impose as far as possible a uniform layout style. In particular, I have not interfered with the rich variety of the spellings of the name Chebyshev. There is, possibly, one innovation in symbols: the end of a proof is (sometimes) denoted by the symbol // .

The papers have been grouped into sections for convenience. The groupings do not correspond to those in the symposium sessions, which were partly determined by practical factors of transitory significance.

I must finally record my gratitude to Mrs. S.A. Brennan and Miss J. Unsworth for their help in making the Symposium run so smoothly, and again, and especially Miss Unsworth, for carrying out the arduous task of typing the manuscript.

A. Talbot.

* NOTE ADDED IN PROOF

A number of further errors have been detected, and they are listed on pp. 355-356.

CONTENTS

Page

IV PRACTICAL TECHNIQUES

V APPROXIMATION IN ABSTRACT LINEAR SPACES

VI APPROXIMATION BY LINEAR OPERATORS

ERROR ESTIMATES FOR BEST POLYNOMIAL APPROXIMATIONS

G. M. Phillips

(University of St. Andrews)

1. The interpolating property

I will consider the problem of estimating the error in certain best polynomial approximations to a function $f(x)$ on $[-1,1]$. The results obtained may be extended to any finite interval $[a,b]$ by making a linear change of variable. First, for minimax approximation (also called uniform or Chebyshev approximation) we write in the usual notation

$$E_n(f) = \inf_{q \in \Pi_n} \|f - q\|_\infty. \tag{1}$$

In (1), Π_n denotes the set of polynomials with real coefficients of degree at most n and the norm denotes the supremum over $[-1,1]$. Several estimates for $E_n(f)$ were given by D. Jackson, who obtained the first of his results in 1911. An example of a theorem of Jackson type is

Theorem 1

If $f(x)$ is continuous on $[-1,1]$,

$$E_n(f) \leq 6\omega(1/n). \tag{2}$$

In (2), ω denotes the modulus of continuity of f. It may be noted from the definition of ω that the proof of Theorem 1 also proves Weierstrass' theorem. Theorem 1 is proved in Rivlin [10]. For other theorems of Jackson type, see Cheney [2].

Another estimate of $E_n(f)$ is due to Meinardus [5]:

Theorem 2

If $f^{(n+1)}(x)$ is continuous on $[-1,1]$, then $\exists\ \xi \in [-1,1]$ such that

$$E_n(f) = |f^{(n+1)}(\xi)|/2^n(n+1)! \tag{3}$$

A simple proof of Meinardus' theorem, given by Phillips [7], depends on the property that the best minimax polynomial approximation interpolates $f(x)$ at $n+1$ points on $[-1,1]$. The main purpose of this paper is to seek a theorem which will extend that of Meinardus to estimate the error of best L_p polynomial approximations ($p \geq 1$).

It may be observed that, when we depart from minimax approximation to consider best L_p polynomial approximation, we still have the interpolatory condition. For L_1 approximation, the interpolation property is well known: see, for example, Rice [9]. This is also true of L_2 approximation, as may be seen in Davis [3]. For any value of p, $1 < p < \infty$, we may appeal to the characterising property of L_p approximation. This states that a necessary and sufficient condition for $q^*(x) \in \Pi_n$ to be the best L_p approximation to a continuous function $f(x)$ on $[-1,1]$ is that

$$\int_{-1}^{1} x^r |f(x) - q^*(x)|^{p-1} \operatorname{sgn}[f(x) - q^*(x)]dx = 0, \tag{4}$$

for $r=0,\ldots,n$. This result is proved in Timan [11] for the more general case where the approximating functions are linear combinations of functions belonging to a Chebyshev set. From (4), it is clear that, if $q^*(x)$ is the best approximation, $f(x) - q^*(x)$ must change sign at least once in $[-1,1]$. Let us assume that sign changes occur only at $x_0,\ldots,x_k$ in the interior of $[-1,1]$, where $k < n$. Then the function

$$(x-x_0)\ldots(x-x_k) \quad \operatorname{sgn}[f(x) - q^*(x)]$$

has constant sign, and so

$$\int_{-1}^{1} (x-x_0)\ldots(x-x_k) \; |f(x) - q^*(x)|^{p-1} \operatorname{sgn}[f(x) - q^*(x)]dx$$

is non-zero, which contradicts (4). Thus there exist $n+1$ points in $[-1,1]$, say $x_0^*,\ldots,x_n^*$, at which $q^*(x)$ interpolates $f(x)$.

Now let

$$\delta_n^{(p)} = \inf_{(x_i)} ||(x-x_0)\ldots(x-x_n)||_p, \tag{5}$$

where

$$||g||_p = \{\int_{-1}^{1} |g(x)|^p dx\}^{1/p},$$

i.e. the L_p norm of g. Let $\tilde{x}_0,\ldots,\tilde{x}_n$ denote the abscissae for which the infimum in (5) is attained. The existence of the minimising abscissae is discussed by Nikolskii [6], who shows that the $\tilde{x}_i$ are distinct and belong to

$[-1,1]$. We will use $\tilde{q}(x)$ to denote the interpolating polynomial for $f(x)$ constructed at $\tilde{x}_0, \ldots, \tilde{x}_n$.

We now need to extend the notation used in (1) and put

$$E_n^{(p)}(f) = \inf_{q \in \Pi_n} \|f - q\|_p. \tag{6}$$

From now on we shall assume that $f^{(n+1)}(x)$ is continuous on $[-1,1]$. By definition,

$$E_n^{(p)}(f) = \|f - q^*\|_p. \tag{7}$$

Using the well-known relation for the error in the interpolating polynomial, we deduce from (7) that

$$E_n^{(p)} \geq \|(x-x_0^*)\ldots(x-x_n^*)\|_p \cdot \min_{-1 \leq x \leq 1} |f^{(n+1)}(x)|/(n+1)!$$

From this inequality and (5), we obtain

$$E_n^{(p)}(f) \geq \delta_n^{(p)} \min_{-1 \leq x \leq 1} |f^{(n+1)}(x)|/(n+1)! \tag{8}$$

Also, from (6) we may argue that

$$\begin{aligned} E_n^{(p)}(f) &\leq \|f - \tilde{q}\|_p \\ &\leq \delta_n^{(p)} \max_{-1 \leq x \leq 1} |f^{(n+1)}(x)|/(n+1)! \end{aligned} \tag{9}$$

From (8) and (9) we now have:

Theorem 3

If $f^{(n+1)}(x)$ is continuous on $[-1,1]$ and p is fixed, $1 \leq p \leq \infty$, then $\exists\, \xi \in [-1,1]$ such that

$$E_n^{(p)}(f) = \delta_n^{(p)} |f^{(n+1)}(\xi)|/(n+1)! \tag{10}$$

It is clear that in (10) ξ depends in general on f, n and p. The number $\delta_n^{(p)}$, which is independent of f, will be estimated later. It is easy to extend (10) to deal with approximation on any finite interval $[a,b]$. In an obvious notation, we find that

$$E_n^{(p)}(f,a,b) = \delta_n^{(p)} \left(\frac{b-a}{2}\right)^{n+1+1/p} |f^{(n+1)}(\xi)|/(n+1)! \tag{11}$$

2. The cases p=1,2,∞

When $p=\infty$, we have the well-known result that (in the above notation) the $\tilde{x}_i$ are the zeros of the Chebyshev polynomial,

$$T_{n+1}(x) = \cos\{(n+1)\cos^{-1}x\}$$

and $\delta_n^{(\infty)} = 1/2^n$.

When $p=1$, the $\tilde{x}_i$ are the zeros of the Chebyshev polynomial of the second kind,

$$U_{n+1}(x) = \{\sin(n+2)\cos^{-1}x\}/\sin(\cos^{-1}x).$$

Timan [11] attributes this result to A. A. Markov. It follows that $\delta_n^{(1)} = 1/2^n$.

When $p=2$, the $\tilde{x}_i$ are the zeros of the Legendre polynomial of degree $n+1$. This follows from the orthogonality property of the Legendre polynomials and is easier to verify than the above results for $p = 1$ and $p = \infty$. Also,

$$\delta_n^{(2)} = \left(\frac{2}{2n+3}\right)^{\frac{1}{2}} 2^{n+1}\Big/\binom{2n+2}{n+1}. \tag{12}$$

3. General values of p

Not so much appears to be known about $\delta_n^{(p)}$ for values of $p\neq 1,2,\infty$. See, for example, Nikolskii [6]. It might be conjectured that the minimising polynomials, for fixed p and varying n, are orthogonal on $[-1,1]$ with respect to some simple weight function. This is true for $p=1,2,\infty$ where the sets of polynomials are orthogonal with weight functions $(1-x^2)^{1/2}$, 1, $(1-x^2)^{-1/2}$ respectively. By direct calculation, Burgoyne [1] shows by a counter-example that, in general, the weight function is not $(1-x^2)^{1/p-1/2}$. He also calculates $\delta_n^{(p)}$ and the zeros of the minimising polynomials for $p=2,3,\ldots,7$ and $n=1,2,\ldots,6$.

We may, however, derive inequalities for $\delta_n^{(p)}$ as follows. First,

$$\delta_n^{(p)} \leq \|2^{-n}T_{n+1}\|_p < 2^{-n}.2^{1/p}.$$

Secondly, we may use the inequality

$$2^{-1/p}\|g\|_p > 2^{-1/p'}\|g\|_{p'},$$

for $p > p' > 0$, assuming that both integrals exist and that $g(x)$ is not a constant function. This result is given in Hardy et al. [4]. Hence, for $p > 1$,

$$2^{-1/p}\,\delta_n^{(p)} > \tfrac{1}{2}\,\|(x-\tilde{x}_0)\dots(x-\tilde{x}_n)\|_1$$
$$\geq 2^{-(n+1)}.$$

Therefore, for $1 < p < \infty$,

$$1/2^{n+1-1/p} < \delta_n^{(p)} < 1/2^{n-1/p}. \tag{13}$$

Timan [11] quotes these inequalities for the case $p=2$.

4. Extension to piecewise approximations

Let us now partition $[a,b]$ into k sub-intervals at $a=x_0 < x_1 < \dots < x_k=b$. Let us define

$$E_{n,k}^{(p)}(f,a,b) = \inf\,\{\sum_{i=1}^{k}\int_{x_{i-1}}^{x_i} |f(x) - q_i(x)|^p dx\}^{1/p} \tag{14}$$

where the infimum is over all $q_i \in \Pi_n$ and all partitions of $[a,b]$ into k sub-intervals. A simple induction argument on k shows that there exist polynomials q_i and a partition of $[a,b]$ on which the infimum (14) is attained. It is also clear that, for the infimum, $q_i(x)$ must be the best L_p approximation to $f(x)$ on $[x_{i-1},x_i]$. We may also deduce that all terms in the summation in (14) must be equal. This argument is also the basis of an algorithm for constructing the best approximation described by (14).

We have, therefore, using (11), that

$$E_{n,k}^{(p)}(f,a,b) = \{\sum_{i=1}^{k}[\delta_n^{(p)}\left(\frac{x_i-x_{i-1}}{2}\right)^{n+1+1/p}|f^{(n+1)}(\xi_i)|/(n+1)!]^p\}^{1/p}, \tag{15}$$

where $\xi_i \in [x_{i-1},x_i]$, and the k terms are all equal. Using this fact, and the fact that $\sum(x_i-x_{i-1}) = b-a$, it is easy to show that, for $i=1,\dots,k$,

$$(x_i-x_{i-1})^{n+1+1/p}\,|f^{(n+1)}(\xi_i)| \leq \left(\frac{b-a}{k}\right)^{n+1+1/p}\max_{-1\leq x\leq 1}|f^{(n+1)}(x)|,$$

and to derive similarly an inequality in the opposite direction, with max replaced by min. Hence there exists a number $\xi \in [a,b]$ such that

$$E_{n,k}^{(p)}(f,a,b) = \delta_n^{(p)}\left(\frac{b-a}{2k}\right)^{n+1+1/p}k^{1/p}\,|f^{(n+1)}(\xi)|/(n+1)! \tag{16}$$

This result holds for $1 \leq p \leq \infty$ and $k=1,2,3,\dots$.

We can also obtain an asymptotic result for large k and fixed n. Let us further assume that $f(x)$ cannot be represented exactly by a polynomial of degree n on any sub-interval of $[a,b]$. Then, as $k \to \infty$, the length of the largest sub-interval $[x_{i-1},x_i]$ must tend to zero. We can then deduce from (15) that

$$\lim_{k\to\infty} k^{n+1}E_{n,k}^{(p)}(f,a,b) = \delta_n^{(p)} \left\{\tfrac{1}{2}\int_a^b |f^{(n+1)}(x)|^{1/(n+1+1/p)}dx\right\}^{n+1+1/p} /(n+1)! \tag{17}$$

This result, which holds for $1 \leq p \leq \infty$, generalises a result of Ream [8], who gave (17) for n=1 and p=2,∞.

Acknowledgement

It is a pleasure to thank Dr. Frank Deutsch for helpful discussions on L_1 approximation.

References

1. BURGOYNE, F. D. 'Practical L_p polynomial approximation'. Math. of Comp., 21 (1967), pp. 113-115.
2. CHENEY, E. W. Introduction to Approximation Theory. McGraw-Hill, 1966.
3. DAVIS, P. J. Interpolation and Approximation. Blaisdell, 1963.
4. HARDY, G. H., LITTLEWOOD, J. E. and POLYA, G. Inequalities. Cambridge University Press, 1934.
5. MEINARDUS, G. Approximation von Funktionen und ihre numerische Behandlung. Springer, 1964. English trans., Approximation of Functions: Theory and Numerical Methods. Springer, 1967.
6. NIKOLSKII, S. M. Quadrature Formulae. Hindustan Publ. Corp., 1964. (Transl. from Russian.)
7. PHILLIPS, G. M. 'Estimate of the maximum error in best polynomial approximations'. Comp. J., 11 (1968), pp. 110-111.
8. REAM, N. 'Note on "Approximation of curves by line segments"'. Math. of Comp., 15 (1961), pp. 418-419.
9. RICE, J. R. The Approximation of Functions, Vol. 1: Linear Theory. Addison-Wesley, 1964.
10. RIVLIN, T. J. An Introduction to the Approximation of Functions. Blaisdell, 1969.
11. TIMAN, A. F. Theory of Approximation of Functions of a Real Variable. Pergamon Press, 1963. (Transl. from Russian.)

ORTHOGONAL POLYNOMIAL APPROXIMATION METHODS IN NUMERICAL ANALYSIS

J. C. Mason

(University of Toronto)

1. Introduction

The remarkable properties of the Chebyshev polynomials of the first kind have been exploited in a number of methods for solving problems in various areas of numerical analysis, such as the approximation of functions, numerical integration, and the numerical solution of differential and integral equations. These methods are often referred to as "Chebyshev methods" and are usually based on techniques of Chebyshev polynomial interpolation or Chebyshev series expansion. Information about most of the available methods may be found by reference to the texts of Fox and Parker [11], Clenshaw [4], and Snyder [22]. A strong theoretical justification for the methods has been given by Powell [19], who shows that, in the approximation of explicit functions, close relationships can be established between minimax approximations (i.e. approximations that are best in the Chebyshev norm) and approximations produced by Chebyshev methods. However, there is an absence in the literature of unifying definitions and theories for the methods. Precisely what does one mean by "Chebyshev methods"? Can they be related directly to the Chebyshev norm? Can corresponding approximation methods be found for other norms, such as L_1 and L_2, and, if so, do they have useful applications?

The purpose of the present paper is to clarify and extend the Chebyshev theory by giving definitions of two specific types of approximation methods in each of the three norms L_∞, L_1, and L_2. "Methods of (I) type" will be defined by unique interpolation criteria, and "methods of (S) type" will be defined by unique series expansion criteria. Methods which correspond to the Chebyshev, L_1, and L_2 norms will be called "Chebyshev methods", "L_1 methods", and "L_2 methods", respectively. Almost all orthogonal polynomial approximation methods in the literature will fit conveniently into these classifications, usually as Chebyshev methods of (I) or (S) type. The unified theory will be based on the existence of a unique system of "canonical polynomials" for each norm coinciding in the case of the Chebyshev norm with the Chebyshev polynomials of the first kind. Theoretical results will be presented, for the approximation of explicit functions, which demonstrate that resulting approximations are either best approximations or "near-best approximations" in the relevant norm. Convergence in norm will also be established.

Special emphasis will be placed on the L_1 norm, since its properties are not very widely known, and in particular we shall discuss a significant class of "normal functions" for which sequences of best approximations may be determined directly by interpolation. The practical value of the L_1 theory will be demonstrated in a rigorous analysis of methods of Clenshaw-Curtis type for the indefinite integration of given functions.

2. Basis for a unified theory

The accuracy of an approximation $f_n(x)$ to a given function $f(x)$ will be measured by a continuous norm of the difference $f-f_n$. Unless otherwise stated, the discussion will be restricted to functions in the space $C[a,b]$ (i.e. functions continuous on the finite interval $[a,b]$), to approximations f_n which are polynomials of degree n in x, and to the Chebyshev (or L_∞), L_1, and L_2 norms. The three norms are defined as follows:

$$L_\infty \text{ norm :} \qquad \| f-f_n \|_\infty = \max_{-1\le x\le 1} |f-f_n| ,$$

$$L_1 \text{ norm :} \qquad \| f-f_n \|_1 = \int_{-1}^{1} |f-f_n|\,dx \quad ,$$

$$L_2 \text{ norm :} \qquad \| f-f_n \|_2 = \left\{ \int_a^b (f-f_n)^2 \omega dx \right\}^{\frac{1}{2}}$$

In the case of the Chebyshev and L_1 norms, the interval $[a,b]$ is taken to be $[-1,1]$, for convenience. In the case of the L_2 norm, we include a weight function $\omega(x)$ such that ωf is integrable on $[a,b]$ for every f in $C[a,b]$ and ω possesses a positive integral on every sub-interval.

With the above restrictions it can be guaranteed in each of the three norms that there exists a unique best approximation f_n^B of degree n to f for every n (see Rice [21]). Moreover, the sequence $\{f_k^B\}$ $(k = 0,1,2,\ldots)$ of best approximations converges in norm to f, as expressed by the following theorem (compare page 116 of Cheney [1]):

Theorem 2.1

In (i) the L_∞ norm, (ii) the L_1 norm, and (iii) the L_2 norm, the sequence $\{f_k^B\}$ of best approximations converges in norm.

Proof. By Weierstrass's theorem (see for example page 66 of [1], there exists a sequence $\{f_k\}$ of approximations convergent in the L_∞ norm to f. Hence the sequence of best L_∞ approximations must also converge in the L_∞ norm. This proves (i). Now the sequence $\{f_k\}$ also converges in both L_1 and L_2, because

$$\| f-f_k \|_1 = \int_{-1}^{1} |f-f_k| dx \leq 2\| f-f_k \|_\infty,$$

and

$$\| f-f_k \|_2 = \left\{\int_a^b (f-f_k)^2 \omega dx\right\}^{\frac{1}{2}} \leq \left\{\int_a^b \omega dx\right\}^{\frac{1}{2}} \| f-f_k \|_\infty$$

Hence the sequences of best approximations corresponding to each of the norms L_1 and L_2 must also converge in those respective norms. //

In addition to being important in their own right, best approximations are valuable as a standard for the rigorous assessment of other approximations. Specifically, we define two types of approximations which are comparable to best approximations according to absolute and relative criteria, respectively.

Definition 2.2. A polynomial f_n of degree n is said to be a "near-best approximation to f by an absolute distance α_n" in a given norm if

$$\| f-f_n \| \leq \| f-f_n^B \| + \alpha_n.$$

Definition 2.3. A polynomial f_n of degree n is said to be a "near-best approximation to f by a relative distance ρ_n" in a given norm if

$$\| f-f_n \| \leq (1 + \rho_n) \| f-f_n^B \|.$$

The latter concept is a generalization of a term "near-minimax", introduced by Fraser [12]. We also use this term, but in both absolute and relative senses, as follows:

Definition 2.4. A polynomial f_n is said to be a "near-minimax approximation to f by an absolute (or relative) distance" if it is near-best by the same absolute (or relative) distance in the Chebyshev norm.

Ideally, the statement of the approximation problem would include a specification of bounds on the permitted values of absolute or relative distances associated with near-best approximations, thus defining classes of "acceptable approximations". In forming near-best approximations, we shall simply try to make corresponding distances "as small as we can". If a sequence $\{\alpha_k\}$ or $\{\rho_k\}$, corresponding to a sequence $\{f_k\}$ of the near-best approximations, can be found which converges to zero, then the convergence in norm of $\{f_k\}$ can be guaranteed immediately by Theorem 2.1. In the case of relative distances, however, it is not usually possible to obtain a sequence which converges to zero, and we aim instead to find a sequence $\{\rho_k\}$ which diverges suitably slowly. The convergence in norm of $\{f_k\}$ can still be guaranteed in this case, provided that $\| f-f_k^B \|$ can be shown to tend to zero more rapidly than ρ_k^{-1}.

In order to prescribe a unique scheme for interpolation and series expansion, we define a system of "canonical polynomials" in any norm as follows:

<u>Definition 2.5</u>. A "canonical polynomial" ϕ_n of degree n in any given norm is a best monic polynomial approximation of degree n to the zero function in that norm.

Clearly there exists a unique system of canonical polynomials in every L_p norm ($1 \leq p \leq \infty$). More significantly, we shall show in §§ 3, 4 and 5 that the canonical polynomials appropriate to L_∞, L_1, and L_2 form the following explicit <u>orthogonal</u> systems:

$$L_\infty : \quad \phi_0(x) = 1, \ \phi_k(x) = 2^{1-k} T_k(x) \ (k = 1,2,\ldots),$$

$$L_1 : \quad \phi_k(x) = 2^{-k} U_k(x) \quad (k = 0,1,2,\ldots),$$

where T_k and U_k are the Chebyshev polynomials of the first and second kinds, respectively,

L_2 : $\{\phi_k(x)\}$ is the complete monic polynomial system orthogonal with respect to the weight function $\omega(x)$ on $[a,b]$. Thus two specific polynomial approximations f_n^I and f_n^S of degree n, corresponding respectively to interpolation and series expansion criteria, may be defined uniquely in each of the norms L_∞, L_1, and L_2 as follows:

f_n^I is defined as the interpolating polynomial to f at the n+1 zeros of $\phi_{n+1}(x)$;

f_n^S is defined as the partial sum of the series expansion of f in $\{\phi_k\}$.

These two approximations form the basis of our entire discussion of Chebyshev, L_1, and L_2 methods.

The "model function" f for approximation by f_n^I and f_n^S is a polynomial of exact degree n+1, and in particular a monic polynomial of degree n+1. For such a function it is easy to verify from Definition 2.5 that

$$f_n^I \equiv f_n^S \equiv f_n^B , \tag{1}$$

and thus the "canonical" interpolation and expansion schemes yield the best approximation. More generally, f_n^I and f_n^S are both essentially the best approximation if f has a rapidly convergent expansion in $\{\phi_k\}$:

$$f = \sum_{i=0}^{\infty} a_i \phi_i .$$

In this case,

$$f - f_n^S = \sum_{i=n+1}^{\infty} a_i \phi_i \simeq a_{n+1} \phi_{n+1},$$

and hence

$$f_n^I \simeq f_n^S \simeq f_n^B . \tag{2}$$

By more detailed discussions, it is possible to relate f_n^I and f_n^S <u>rigorously</u> to f_n^B for much wider classes of functions f. Indeed in §§ 3, 4, and 5 we shall present a fairly comprehensive selection of old and new theoretical results which demonstrate that for each of the three norms there is a significant class of functions f for which each of the sequences $\{f_k^I\}$ and $\{f_k^S\}$ is either a sequence of best approximations or a sequence of approximations near-best by appropriate distances. The convergence in norm of the sequences $\{f_k^I\}$ and $\{f_k^S\}$ will also be discussed.

3. The Chebyshev norm and Chebyshev polynomials of the first kind

The canonical polynomials for the Chebyshev norm on [-1,1] are

$$\phi_0(x) = 1, \ \phi_k(x) = 2^{1-k} T_k(x) \quad (k = 1,2,\ldots), \tag{3}$$

where T_k is the Chebyshev polynomial of the first kind defined by the relation

$$T_k(x) = \cos k\theta \text{ where } x = \cos \theta. \tag{4}$$

This assertion is an immediate consequence of the well-known minimax property of the Chebyshev polynomials (see for example page 61 of [1]). From the relation (4) we may easily deduce that the system $\{\phi_k\}$ is orthogonal with respect to the weight function $(1-x^2)^{-\frac{1}{2}}$ on $[-1,1]$. The polynomial approximations f_n^I and f_n^S introduced in §2 appropriate to L_∞ are thus the interpolating polynomial to f at the zeros of $T_{n+1}(x)$ and the partial sum of the Chebyshev series expansion, respectively. The results of Powell [19], which relate f_n^I and f_n^S to f_n^B, may be expressed in terms of our definition of "near-minimax" as follows:

Theorem 3.1

If f is in $C[-1,1]$, then f_n^I is near-minimax by a relative distance

$$\rho_n = \rho_n^I = \frac{1}{n+1} \sum_{i=0}^{n} \tan \frac{(i+\frac{1}{2})\pi}{2(n+1)} .$$

Asymptotically, $\rho_n^I \sim \frac{2}{\pi} \log n$.

Theorem 3.2

If f is in $C[-1,1]$, then f_n^S is near-minimax by a relative distance

$$\rho_n = \rho_n^S = \frac{1}{2n+1} + \frac{2}{\pi} \sum_{i=1}^{n} \frac{1}{i} \tan \frac{\pi i}{2n+1} .$$

Asymptotically, $\rho_n^S \sim \frac{4}{\pi^2} \log n$.

The distances ρ_n^I and ρ_n^S in these theorems increase very slowly with n. Indeed Powell [19] has tabulated a number of values of the quantities $v(n) = 1+\rho_n^I$ and $u(n) = 1+\rho_n^S$, and both are less than 6 for all n less 500. Thus for most practical purposes f_n^I and f_n^S are acceptable substitutes for f_n^B. To establish the convergence in norm of $\{f_k^I\}$ and $\{f_k^S\}$, we make use of a sharp theorem due to Jackson (to be found in [1] as part of Jackson's Theorem V) which describes the nature of the convergence of $\|f-f_n^B\|$:

Theorem 3.3

If f is in $C[-1,1]$ and has modulus of continuity ω, then

$$\| f-f_n^B \| < \omega\left(\frac{\pi}{n+1}\right) .$$

From Theorems 3.1, 3.2, 3.3 we may immediately deduce:

Theorem 3.4.

If $\omega(\delta) \log \delta \to 0$ as $\delta \to 0$, then $\{f_k^I\}$ and $\{f_k^S\}$ converge in norm to f.

In the case of the sequence $\{f_k^S\}$, we may prove a comparable convergence result by making direct use of the theory of Fourier series, as follows:

Theorem 3.5.

If f is continuous and of bounded variation on $[-1,1]$, then $\{f_k^S\}$ converges in norm to f.

Proof. The function $g(\theta) = f(\cos\theta)$ is continuous and of bounded variation on $[-\pi,\pi]$. A result of Titchmarsh ([23], p.410) therefore ensures the uniform convergence of the Fourier expansion of $g(\theta)$ on any interval interior to $[-\pi,\pi]$. Since $g(\theta)$ is periodic in θ, the uniform convergence extends to the whole interval $[-\pi,\pi]$. Now $g(\theta)$ is even in θ, and therefore its Fourier expansion is

$$g(\theta) = \tfrac{1}{2} a_0 + \sum_{i=1}^{\infty} a_i \cos i\theta, \text{ where } a_i = \frac{2}{\pi} \int_0^{\pi} g(\theta) \cos i\theta \, d\theta.$$

Applying the transformation $x = \cos\theta$ and using relation (4) we deduce that $f(x)$ has the Chebyshev series expansion

$$f(x) = \tfrac{1}{2} a_0 T_0(x) + \sum_{i=1}^{\infty} a_i T_i(x),$$

which converges uniformly (i.e. in the L_∞ norm) on $[-1,1]$. //

Theorems 3.1 and 3.2 enabled us to compute relative distances ρ_n, corresponding to the near-minimax approximations f_n^I and f_n^S, which were appropriate to all continuous functions f. In practice it is usually possible a posteriori to compute smaller relative distances for particular functions f. Indeed if any approximation f_n has the property that $f-f_n$ changes sign at least n+1 times in $[-1,1]$, then we may exploit a well-known result of de la Vallée Poussin (Cheney [1], p.77):

Theorem 3.6.

If $f-f_n$ assumes alternately positive and negative values at n+2 consecutive points η_i of $[-1,1]$, then

$$\| f-f_n^B \| \geq \min_i |f(\eta_i) - f_n(\eta_i)|.$$

From this result we easily deduce:

Corollary 3.7.

If $f-f_n$ changes sign at n+1 consecutive points x_i (i = 1,...,n+1) of [-1,1] and if the greatest value of $|f-f_n|$ in $[x_i, x_{i+1}]$ is attained at the point ξ_i (i = 0,...,n+1), where $x_0 = -1$ and $x_{n+2} = 1$, then f_n is near-minimax by the relative distance

$$\rho_n = [\max_i|\lambda_i|/\min_i|\lambda_i|] - 1$$

where

$$\lambda_i = f(\xi_i) - f_n(\xi_i).$$

<u>Proof</u>. By definition, $\| f-f_n \| = \max_i|\lambda_i|$, and by Theorem 3.6, $\| f-f_n^B \| \geq \min_i|\lambda_i|$. Hence the result follows immediately from Definition 2.3.

4. The L_1 norm and Chebyshev polynomials of the second kind

It is known (see for example [1], p.222) that $2^{-k}U_k(x)$ is the best monic polynomial approximation of degree k to zero in the L_1 norm on [-1,1], where U_k is the Chebyshev polynomial of the second kind defined by the relation

$$U_k(x) = \sin(k+1)\theta/\sin\theta \quad \text{where } x = \cos\theta. \tag{5}$$

Hence the canonical polynomials for L_1 form the system

$$\phi_k(x) = 2^{-k}U_k(x) \quad (k = 0,1,2,\ldots). \tag{6}$$

From relation (5) we may easily deduce that $\{\phi_k\}$ is orthogonal with respect to the weight function $(1-x^2)^{\frac{1}{2}}$ on [-1,1]. The canonical property of the polynomials $\{U_k\}$ is in fact a special case of a more powerful theorem (Rice [21], p.112) which asserts that, under suitable conditions, the best L_1 approximation f_n^B to any f is just the polynomial f_n^I that interpolates f at the zeros of U_{n+1}:

Theorem 4.1

If f is in C[-1,1] and $f-f_n^I$ has exactly n+1 changes of sign in [-1,1] occurring at the zeros of U_{n+1}, then f_n^I is the best approximation

f_n^B to f.

In order to be able to apply Theorem 4.1 precisely, we shall make some appropriate definitions.

Definition 4.2. The polynomial f_k^I is said to be a "normal interpolant" if $f-f_k^I$ has exactly k+1 changes of sign in [-1,1] occurring at the zeros of U_{k+1}.

Definition 4.3. A function f is said to be "totally normal in L_1" on [-1,1] if, for every $k \geq 0$, f_k^I is a normal interpolant.

Definition 4.4. A function f is said to be "partially normal in L_1" on [-1,1] if, for every k in some infinite subsequence of the positive integers, f_k^I is a normal interpolant.

Clearly these definitions may be adjusted to be appropriate to any required interval [a,b] by a suitable transformation. From the definitions and Theorem 2.1 we immediately deduce:

Corollary 4.5

If f is totally normal in L_1, then $f_k^I \equiv f_k^B$ for every k and $\{f_n^I\}$ converges in norm.

Corollary 4.6

If f is partially normal in L_1, then some subsequence of $\{f_k^I\}$ is a sequence of best approximations and converges in norm.

We believe that the functions f which are totally or partially normal together form a significant class, although we have been unable to characterize this class precisely in terms of more standard specifications. It is simple, however, to show that a number of standard functions belong to the class. Specifically, if f has infinitely many derivatives all of which (or a subsequence of which) have no changes of sign on [-1,1] then f is totally (or partially) normal in L_1 on [-1,1] as a consequence of the formula

$$f(x) - f_k^I(x) = \frac{1}{(k+1)!} \phi_{k+1}(x)\, f^{(k+1)}(\xi) \text{ for some } \xi \text{ in } [-1,1].$$

Examples of totally normal functions of this type are:

on [-1,1] : e^x , $(x+3)^{-1}$;

on [0,1] : $\cos \frac{1}{2}\pi x$, $\log(1+x)$, $\sqrt{(1+x)}$.

Function f and Interval	Classification of Interpolants f_k^I		Suggested Classification of f
	Normal for k = ...	Not Normal for k = ...	
(i) $J_{2/3}(x)$ [0,1]	0,1,2,3,4,5, 6,7,8,9,10.		T.N.
(ii) $\tan^{-1}x$ [0,1]	0,1,3,4,5,6,8,9.	2,7,10.	P.N.
(iii) $(1+25x^2)^{-1}$ [-1,1]	1,3,5,7,9.	0,2,4,6,8,10.	P.N.
(iv) $(1-x)/(1+4x^2)$ [-1,1]	1,3,5,7,9.	0,2,4,6,8,10.	P.N.
(v) $x^{1/3}$ [-1,1]	0,2,4,6,8,10.	1,3,5,7,9.	P.N.
(vi) $\cos(4x+1)$ [-1,1]	4,6,7,8,9,10.	0,1,2,3,5.	P.N.
(vii) $\cos(10x+1)$ [-1,1]	10.	0,1,2,3,4,5, 6,7,8,9.	P.N.
(viii) $\begin{cases} e^x & [0,1] \\ e^{-x}-e^{-1}+e & [1,2] \end{cases}$	0,1,3,5,7,9.	2,4,6,8,10.	P.N.
(ix) $\begin{cases} e^x & [0,1] \\ e^{-x}-e^{-1}+e & [1,3] \end{cases}$	1,4.	0,2,3,5,6,7, 8,9,10.	Not P.N.
(x) $\begin{cases} e^x & [0,1] \\ e^{-x}-e^{-1}+e & [1,2] \\ e^x-e^2+e^{-2}-e^{-1}+e & [2,3] \end{cases}$	2,4.	0,1,3,5,6,7, 8,9,10.	Not P.N.
T.N. = totally normal, P.N. = partially normal.			

Table 1. Analysis of f and $\{f_k^I\}$ in L_1.

It is also easy to construct functions which are not totally normal on a particular interval. Indeed all even (or odd) functions have this property on [-1,1], since, for such functions, f_k^I is not a normal interpolant when k is even (or odd). However, even or odd functions can still be partially normal on [-1,1], and the function $\cos \frac{1}{2}\pi x$ is an example.

In Table 1 we have analyzed f_k^I for k = 0,1,...,10 for a number of functions f. We certainly expect any function with a rapidly convergent series expansion to be at least partially normal, and indeed we see from example (i) that the Bessel function $J_{2/3}(x)$ is apparently totally normal. More surprisingly, the function $x^{1/3}$, which does not have a bounded derivative, seems to be partially normal. It is also interesting to note that, while the "piecewise-exponential" function (viii) (which has a discontinuous derivative) appears to be partially normal, the similar function (ix) does not. Finally, we remark that our negative results for the more complicated piecewise-exponential function (x) are consistent with earlier results of Usow [24].

When the conditions of Theorem 4.1 are satisfied, we generally expect the zeros of $f-f_n^I$ to be simple. However, we now give an illustrative class of examples in which this is not always the case. Consider the function

$$f(x) = p_n(x) + \frac{1}{n+2} U_{n+1}(x) + \frac{C_n}{2n+4} U_{2n+3}(x), \tag{7}$$

where $p_n(x)$ is some polynomial of degree n and C_n is a constant. Both $\frac{1}{n+2} U_{n+1}$ and $\frac{1}{2n+4} U_{2n+3}$ have maximum magnitudes of unity, and so f can be expected to behave like a function with a convergent or divergent $\{U_k\}$ expansion according as C_n is small or large. If, in our usual notation, f_n^S denotes the partial sum of degree n of the expansion of f in $\{U_k\}$, then it follows from (7) that

$$f_n^S \equiv p_n \tag{8}$$

Now it may easily be verified from the definitions (4) and (5) of T_k and U_k that

$$U_{2n+3}(x) = 2U_{n+1}(x)\, T_{n+2}(x) \tag{9}$$

and hence, from (7), that

$$f(x) - p_n(x) = \frac{1}{n+2} U_{n+1}(x) H(x) \tag{10}$$

where $H(x) = 1 + C_n T_{n+2}(x)$.

From (8) and (10) it follows that

$$f_n^I \equiv f_n^S \equiv p_n. \tag{11}$$

For $|C_n| > 1$, H has n+2 changes of sign in [-1,1] and therefore Theorem 4.1 is not applicable. However, for $|C_n| \leq 1$, H does not change sign, and we may deduce from (10), (11) and Theorem 4.1 that

$$f_n^I \equiv f_n^S \equiv f_n^B \equiv p_n \tag{12}$$

Although f_n^I is a normal interpolant for every C_n with $|C_n| \leq 1$, the behaviour of $f-f_n^I$ in the limiting cases $C_n = \pm 1$ is remarkable. In the latter cases H has a total multiplicity of n+2 real zeros occurring in [-1,1], but all the zeros of H, with the exception of $x = \pm 1$, are in fact double zeros of H and in addition simple zeros of U_{n+1}. Thus approximately half the zeros of U_{n+1} are triple zeros of $f-f_n^I$, and the remaining zeros are all simple zeros.

We now turn our attention away from interpolating polynomials and study the partial sum f_n^S of the series expansion of f in Chebyshev polynomials of the second kind. The approximation f_n^S will be shown to be near-best in a relative sense as a particular example of a more general result (compare Powell [19]):

Theorem 4.7

Suppose f is in C[a,b], and let f_n^ω be the partial sum of degree n of the expansion of f in the system $\{q_k\}$ of polynomials (q_k of degree k) orthonormal with respect to the weight function $\omega(x)$ on [a,b]. Then f_n^ω is near-best in the L_1 norm on [a,b] by the relative distance

$$\rho_n = K_n = \int_a^b \max_{a \leq y \leq b} \left|\omega(y) \sum_{k=0}^{n} q_k(x)\, q_k(y)\right| \, dx. \tag{13}$$

Proof. Define $\varepsilon_n^\omega \equiv f-f_n^\omega$, and $\varepsilon_n^B \equiv f-f_n^B$. Then $\varepsilon_n^\omega-\varepsilon_n^B$ is a polynomial of degree n, and expanding in $\{q_k\}$,

$$\varepsilon_n^\omega(x) - \varepsilon_n^B(x) = \sum_{k=0}^{n} q_k(x) \int_a^b \omega(y)[\varepsilon_n(y)-\varepsilon_n^B(y)]q_k(y)dy.$$

Since ε_n^ω is orthogonal to q_k for $k = 0,1,\ldots,n$, we deduce that

$$\varepsilon_n^\omega(x) = \varepsilon_n^B(x) - \int_a^b \varepsilon_n^B(y) \, [\omega(y) \sum_{k=0}^n q_k(x) \, q_k(y)] \, dy.$$

Applying Hölder's inequality and the triangle inequality,

$$|\varepsilon_n^\omega(x)| \leq |\varepsilon_n^B(x)| + \int_a^b |\varepsilon_n^B(y)|dy. \max_{a\leq y\leq b} |\omega(y) \sum_{k=0}^n q_k(x) \, q_k(y)|.$$

Integrating with respect to x,

$$\| \varepsilon_n^\omega \|_1 \leq (1+K_n) \| \varepsilon_n^B \|_1,$$

and the theorem is proved.

In the case in which $\{q_k\}$ are the Chebyshev polynomials of the second kind (suitably normalized), the following Lemma gives a simple but clear description of the behaviour of K_n with n:

Lemma 4.8

If $\omega(y) \equiv \sqrt{(1-y^2)}$ and $[a,b] \equiv [-1,1]$ in (13), then

$$(n+1) \leq K_n \leq \frac{4}{\pi} (n+1)$$

<u>Proof</u>. In this case $q_k(x) = \sqrt{2/\pi} \, U_k(x)$ for every k, and hence

$$K_n = \frac{2}{\pi} \int_{-1}^1 \max_{-1\leq y\leq 1} |\sqrt{(1-y^2)} \sum_{k=0}^n U_k(x)U_k(y)|dx.$$

Let x = cos v and y = cos t; then by the formula (5) for U_k,

$$K_n = \frac{2}{\pi} \int_0^\pi \max_{0\leq t\leq \pi} | \sum_{k=0}^n \sin(k+1)v \, \sin(k+1)t|dv. \tag{14}$$

(i) Now $\max_{0\leq t\leq \pi} | \sum_{k=0}^n \sin(k+1)v \, \sin(k+1)t| \geq \sum_{k=0}^n \sin^2(k+1)v$, since the right hand side is attained when t=v.

Thus $K_n \geq \frac{1}{\pi} \sum_{k=0}^n \int_0^\pi [1-\cos 2(k+1)v]dv = n+1.$

(ii) Also, since $|\sin(k+1)t| \leq 1$, we deduce from (14) that

$$K_n \leq \frac{2}{\pi} \sum_{k=0}^n \int_0^\pi |\sin(k+1)v|dv.$$

Letting $v_j = j\pi/(k+1)$, and splitting the integral,

$$\int_0^\pi |\sin(k+1)v|\,dv = \sum_{j=0}^{k} \int_{v_j}^{v_{j+1}} |\sin(k+1)v|\,dv$$

$$= \sum_{j=0}^{k} \left|\int_{v_j}^{v_{j+1}} \sin(k+1)v\,dv\right| = \sum_{j=0}^{k} \frac{2}{k+1} = 2.$$

Hence $K_n \leq \frac{2}{\pi}.(n+1).2 = \frac{4}{\pi}(n+1)$. //

Applying Lemma 4.8, we immediately deduce the corollary of Theorem 4.7 that we specifically require:

Corollary 4.9

The approximation f_n^S is near-best in L_1 on $[-1,1]$ by the relative distance $\rho_n = \frac{4}{\pi}(n+1)$.

We believe that it should be possible to show that f_n^S is near-best by a relative distance smaller than $\frac{4}{\pi}(n+1)$, possibly a distance of the order of $\log n$ or $n^{\frac{1}{2}}$. However, we note that, as a consequence of the tightness of Lemma 4.8, any essential improvement in Corollary 4.9 would necessitate an improvement in the general form K_n obtained in Theorem 4.7.*

Without making any further assumptions about the smoothness of f, we may prove the convergence in norm of $\{f_k^S\}$ by applying the theory of Fourier series (compare Theorem 3.5):

Theorem 4.10

If f is in $C[-1,1]$, then $\{f_k^S\}$ converges in the L_1 norm.

Proof. The function $g(\theta) = \sin\theta.f(\cos\theta)$ is continuous on $[-\pi,\pi]$, and it is also odd and periodic in θ. Thus $g(\theta)$ has a Fourier expansion of the form

$$g(\theta) \sim \sum_{i=0}^{\infty} a_i \sin(i+1)\theta, \tag{15}$$

where $a_i = \frac{2}{\pi}\int_0^\pi g(\theta)\sin(i+1)\theta\,d\theta$, (16)

which converges in the L_2 norm on $[0,\pi]$ (by a standard result in Fourier series; see for example Titchmarsh [23], p.424.) Convergence in an L_p norm implies convergence in an L_q norm for every q such that $1 \leq q \leq p$ (Handscomb [13], p.12), and hence (15) converges in the L_1 norm on $[0,\pi]$. Thus

* Since this paper was written, such an improvement has been obtained, and is indicated in a Supplement at the end of the paper.

$$\lim_{k\to\infty} \int_0^{\pi} |g(\theta) - g_k(\theta)| d\theta = 0, \tag{17}$$

where $g_k(\theta) = \sum_{i=0}^{k} a_i \sin(i+1)\theta$. (18)

Since $|\sin\theta| = \sin\theta$ throughout $[0,\pi]$, we may rewrite (17) in the form

$$\lim_{k\to\infty} \int_0^{\pi} \sin\theta \left| f(\cos\theta) - \frac{g_k(\theta)}{\sin\theta} \right| d\theta = 0 \tag{19}$$

Applying the transformation $x = \cos\theta$ to (16) and using the formula (5) for U_i, we obtain

$$a_i = \frac{2}{\pi}\int_{-1}^{1} \sqrt{(1-x^2)} f(x) U_i(x) dx.$$

Thus a_i is the coefficient of U_i in the expansion of f in the orthogonal polynomials $\{U_k\}$, and from (18) and (5) it follows that

$$g_k(\theta) = f_k^S(x)\sin\theta.$$

Applying the transformation $x = \cos\theta$ to (19) we conclude that

$$\lim_{k\to\infty}\int_{-1}^{1} |f(x)-f_k^S(x)| dx = 0. \quad //$$

5. The L_2 norm and orthogonal polynomial systems

A fundamental theorem on best approximation in an inner-product space ([1], p.14) is the following:

Theorem 5.1

Let $\{q_0,\ldots,q_n\}$ be a complete orthonormal set in an inner-product space with norm defined by $||h|| = \sqrt{<h,h>}$. Then $\Sigma c_i q_i$ is a best approximation to an element f in the space if and only if $c_i = <f,q_i>$.

A straightforward application of Theorem 5.1 characterises the canonical polynomials in L_2:

Corollary 5.2

The canonical polynomials in the L_2 norm on $[a,b]$ form the complete monic polynomial system $\{\phi_k\}$ orthogonal with respect to the weight function $\omega(x)$ on $[a,b]$.

The polynomial approximations f_n^I and f_n^S may now be defined in the usual way, and by Theorem 2.1 we immediately deduce from Theorem 5.1:

Corollary 5.3

If f is in C[a,b], then the sequence $\{f_k^S\}$ is precisely the sequence $\{f_k^B\}$ of best L_2 approximations, and $\{f_k^S\}$ converges in the L_2 norm.

The best known result in the literature about the interpolating polynomials $\{f_k^I\}$ is probably the convergence theorem due to Erdös and Turán ([1], p.137):

Theorem 5.4

If f is in C[a,b], then $\{f_k^I\}$ converges in the L_2 norm.

We have not been able to determine absolute or relative distances such that $\{f_k^I\}$ is a sequence of near-best approximations in L_2 according to our definitions. However, it is possible to prove the following result:

Lemma 5.5

Suppose that $\{x_i\}$ $(i = 0,1,\ldots,n)$ are the zeros of ϕ_{n+1}, and let

$$\ell_i(x) = \prod_{j\neq i} \frac{x-x_j}{x_i-x_j} \quad \text{and} \quad \omega_i = \int_a^b \omega(x)[\ell_i(x)]^2 dx.$$

Define $\varepsilon_n^I = f-f_n^I$ and $\varepsilon_n^B = f-f_n^B$. Then, if f is in C[a,b],

$$\| \varepsilon_n^I \|_2^2 = \| \varepsilon_n^B \|_2^2 + \alpha_n \tag{20}$$

$$\text{where } \alpha_n = \sum_i \omega_i [\varepsilon_n^B(x_i)]^2. \tag{21}$$

<u>Proof</u>. Applying the Lagrange interpolation formula to $\varepsilon_n^I - \varepsilon_n^B$:

$$\varepsilon_n^I(x) = \varepsilon_n^B(x) - \sum \ell_i(x)\varepsilon_n^B(x_i). \tag{22}$$

Now $\{\ell_i\}$ is an orthogonal set ([1], p.137), and ε_n^B is orthogonal to $\{\ell_i\}$. Hence (20) is obtained by squaring (22), multiplying by ω, and integrating over [a,b]. //

Thus, for the comparison of f_n^I and f_n^B, the square of the L_2 norm seems to be a particularly appropriate measure of approximation. Adopting the analogous definition to 2.2 for the term "near-best by an absolute distance" in the squared L_2 norm, we conclude from Lemma 5.5 that f_n^I is near-best by the absolute distance α_n (defined by (21)) in this measure. Clearly this α_n is optimal because of the equality in (20), but we have not been able to characterize its asymptotic behaviour as a function of n. We note that α_n tends to zero, as an immediate consequence of (20) and Theorem 5.4, and we observe that α_n is the square of a weighted <u>discrete</u> least squares norm of ε_n^B taken over the interpolation points.

6. Definitions of Chebyshev, L_1 and L_2 methods

The approximation of an explicit function f in the Chebyshev, L_1, and L_2 norms has been discussed in detail in §§2-5, and the two specific approximations f_n^I and f_n^S have been shown to be best or near-best approximations provided that f belongs to a suitably restricted class of continuous functions. Let us now consider the more general problem of approximating a function f defined implicitly by a mathematical equation

$$E(f) = 0 \quad \text{for all } x \text{ in } [a,b] \tag{23}$$

subject to m boundary conditions

$$B_i(f) = 0 \quad \text{at } x = x_i \ (i = 1,\ldots,m). \tag{24}$$

(Equation (23) could, for example, be an integral equation or an ordinary differential equation.) We wish to determine directly from (23) and (24) a set of (n+1) parameters defining a polynomial approximation f_n of degree n ($\geq$ m). Typically, f_n is represented in one of the two forms

$$f_n = \sum_{i=0}^{n} a_i x^i \qquad \text{with parameters } \{a_i\} \tag{25}$$

or

$$f_n = \sum_{i=0}^{n} c_i \phi_i(x) \quad \text{with parameters } \{c_i\}, \tag{26}$$

where $\{\phi_k\}$ is an appropriate canonical polynomial system. We shall specify two general methods for obtaining approximations f_n analogous to the approximations f_n^I and f_n^S of §2.

<u>Definition 6.1</u>. A "method of (I) type" in a given norm for the problem (23) and (24) is a method which determines the (n+1) parameters of f_n from the following system of algebraic equations:

$$E(f_n) = 0 \quad \text{at each of the n-m+1 zeros of } \phi_{n-m+1}(x)$$

and $\quad B_i(f_n) = 0 \quad \text{at } x = x_i \ (i = 1,\ldots,m),$

where $\{\phi_k\}$ are the canonical polynomials appropriate to the given norm.
Definition 6.2. A "method of (S) type" in a given norm for the problem (23) and (24) is a method which determines the n+1 parameters of f_n to satisfy the boundary conditions

$$B_i(f_n) = 0 \quad \text{at } x = x_i \quad (i = 1,\ldots,m)$$

and to eliminate the leading n-m+1 coefficients in the expansion of $E(f_n)$ in the canonical polynomials $\{\phi_k\}$ appropriate to the given norm.
Definition 6.3. Methods of (I) or (S) type in the Chebyshev, L_1, and L_2 norms are termed "Chebyshev methods", "L_1 methods", and "L_2 methods", respectively.

The approximation of an explicit function f may be regarded as a particular example of the problem (23) and (24) in which a function g is defined by the equation

$$E(g) \equiv g-f = 0 \tag{27}$$

subject to no boundary conditions. For this problem the methods of (I) and (S) type defined above can easily be seen to yield the approximations f_n^I and f_n^S, respectively. Thus the definitions 6.1, 6.2, and 6.3 provide a generalization of the methods of §§2-5. The definitions could be extended to cover functions of more than one variable, by performing interpolation at a vector product of zeros of canonical polynomials in the (I) methods and by forming multi-dimensional expansions in $\{\phi_k\}$ in the (S) methods (see Mason [16]). We also remark that the methods of (I) and (S) type are essentially particular examples of well-known general methods of continuous approximation, namely "collocation methods" and "Galerkin methods". These general methods are discussed in detail under the unifying formulation of the "method of weighted residuals" in an expository paper of Finlayson and Scriven [9].

Most of the polynomial approximation methods proposed in the literature fit conveniently into our classifications in Definitions 6.1 and 6.2. Examples of Chebyshev methods of (I) type are the selected points method of Lanczos [14] for linear ordinary differential equations, the corresponding method of Wright [25] for nonlinear ordinary differential equations (see also Clenshaw [6]), and the method of Mason [16] for linear partial differential equations. Examples of Chebyshev methods of (S) type are the tau method of Lanczos [14] and the Chebyshev series method of Clenshaw [2] for linear ordinary differential equations, the method of Clenshaw and Norton [5] for nonlinear ordinary differential equations, and the method of Mason [18] for separable partial differential equations and in particular [17] for the heat equation. In addition, methods have been proposed for numerical integration, integral equations, and first order ordinary differential equations which are based on the polynomials $\{U_k\}$ and may be classified as L_1 methods. We shall discuss these methods in more detail in [7.]

Although we should normally expect all methods of (I) (or (S)) type in a given norm to produce the same approximate solution f_n to a given problem (23) and (24), the methods may differ in their techniques and parametric representations. For example, subject to appropriate boundary conditions, the Lanczos tau method and Clenshaw's Chebyshev series method yield the same approximation f_n for an ordinary differential equation (see Fox [10]). But, whereas Lanczos' method adopts the representation (25) and equates powers of x in $E(f_n)$, Clenshaw's method use the representation (26) and equates coefficients of $\{\phi_k\}$ in $E(f_n)$.

Two other topics should be mentioned in connection with methods of (I) and (S) type. Firstly, rational approximations analogous to f_n^I and f_n^S may be found to an explicit function f by Chebyshev rational interpolation and "Maehly's method" (see Snyder [22]), respectively. Secondly, telescoping procedures based on the minimax property of the Chebyshev polynomials have been developed for polynomial expansions by Lanczos [14] and for continued fraction expansions by Maehly [15] (see also Ralston [20]).

Finally, we must make some remarks about the choice of norm in polynomial approximation methods. In continuous (as opposed to discrete) approximation, the data is normally regarded as being exact, and it is then appropriate to measure approximations in the Chebyshev norm. Hence for the implicit problem (23) and (24) we should generally expect to adopt a Chebyshev method rather than an L_1 or L_2 method. However, there are classes of problems in which the Chebyshev norm of $f-f_n$ relates rather naturally to the L_1 or L_2 norm of $E(f_n)$, and then L_1 or L_2 methods are particularly appropriate. Such a class of problems will be the subject of discussion in [7].

7. L_1 methods of indefinite integration

Several polynomial approximation methods have been proposed for the determination of the indefinite integral

$$f(x) = \int_{-1}^{x} g(x)dx \quad \text{for } x \text{ in } [-1,1] \tag{28}$$

of a given continuous function $g(x)$. An original method was developed by Clenshaw and Curtis [3], a modified version was introduced by Filippi [8], and a variety of possible variants of the method were compared from an empirical point of view by Wright [26]. All polynomial approximation methods have the effect of forming an approximation f_{n+1} of degree n+1 to f by integrating an approximation g_n of degree n to g, and the various variants of the Clenshaw-Curtis method determine g_n by interpolating g at a chosen set of n+1 points. As interpolation points, Clenshaw and Curtis chose the zeros of $(1-x^2)U_{n-1}$, Fillippi chose the zeros of U_{n+1}, and Wright also considered the zeros of T_{n+1}.

Now the function f may alternatively be defined by the equation

$$E(f) \equiv f'-g = 0 \quad \text{for } x \text{ in } [-1,1] \tag{29}$$

subject to the initial condition

$$f(-1) = 0. \tag{30}$$

Following the discussion of §6, we may now define methods of (I) and (S) type for determining a polynomial approximation f_{n+1} of degree n+1. To allow greater freedom, we shall replace the initial condition (30) on f_{n+1} by

$$f'_{n+1}(-1) = \delta_n, \tag{31}$$

where δ_n is a chosen constant of integration. The methods of (I) type for (29) and (31) consist of integrating the interpolating polynomial g_n^I of degree n to g at the zeros of a canonical polynomial ϕ_{n+1}, and the methods of (S) type consist of integrating the partial sum g_n^S of degree n of the expansion of g in canonical polynomials $\{\phi_k\}$. Clearly the methods of (S) type have a distinct disadvantage in efficiency compared to the methods of (I) type, since they require the evaluation of the n+1 integrals defining the first n+1 Chebyshev series coefficients of g.

With the above definitions, all variants of the Clenshaw-Curtis method are methods of (I) type for (29) and (31). Filippi's method is an L_1

method, Wright's T_{n+1} method is a Chebyshev method, and the Clenshaw-Curtis method is an L_1 method for (29) and (31) subject to additional boundary conditions

$$f'_{n+1} = g \quad \text{at } x = \pm 1. \tag{32}$$

In fact, Clenshaw and Curtis [3] describe their method as a Chebyshev series method in which the n+1 integrals defining Chebyshev coefficients are approximated by appropriate sums. Thus a theoretical study of methods of both (I) and (S) types is relevant to an analysis of the variants of the Clenshaw-Curtis method.

Now the real objective in polynomial approximation methods for (29) is not to minimize a norm of $E(f_{n+1})$ but rather to minimize a norm of $f-f_{n+1}$. Assuming that $g(x)$ is known exactly, and adopting the Chebyshev norm, we wish to minimize

$$\varepsilon_n = \| f-f_{n+1} \|_\infty. \tag{33}$$

From (28) and (31),

$$\varepsilon_n = \| -\delta_n + \int_{-1}^{x} (g-g_n)dx \|_\infty \tag{34}$$

$$\leq |\delta_n| + \| \int_{-1}^{x} |g-g_n| dx \|_\infty = |\delta_n| + \int_{-1}^{1} |g-g_n| dx$$

Thus,

$$\varepsilon_n \leq \bar{\varepsilon}_n \tag{35}$$

where $\bar{\varepsilon}_n = |\delta_n| + \| g-g_n \|_1$. (36)

It is convenient to use this bound $\bar{\varepsilon}_n$ on ε_n as a measure in the assessment of the polynomial approximation methods, for the theoretical results of §4 on the L_1 norm are then directly applicable. In particular, since $\bar{\varepsilon}_n$ is minimized for any fixed δ_n when g_n is a best L_1 approximation to g, we may immediately obtain from Theorem 4.1 and Definition 4.2:

Theorem 7.1

If g_n^I is a normal interpolant to g in L_1 on $[-1,1]$, then the measure $\bar{\varepsilon}_n$ is minimized for any fixed constant of integration δ_n when the

L_1 method of (I) type is applied to (29) and (31).

Thus Filippi's method is the best polynomial approximation method for the problem (28) with respect to the measure $\bar{\varepsilon}_n$. Moreover, by applying Theorems 4.5 and 4.6 to (35) and (36), we deduce that under suitable conditions this method is uniformly convergent:

Theorem 7.2

Suppose the L_1 method of (I) type (i.e. Fillippi's method) is applied to (29) and (31) for $k = 0,1,2,\ldots$, giving a sequence $\{f_{k+1}\}$ of approximations to f and a corresponding sequence $\{\delta_k\}$ of constants of integration. If g is totally normal (or partially normal) in L_1 and if $\{\delta_k\}$ converges to zero, then the sequence $\{f_{k+1}\}$ (or some subsequence converges uniformly to f on $[-1,1]$.

In the methods of (I) and (S) type, the function $g-g_n$ is highly oscillatory, and so the bounds $\bar{\varepsilon}_n$ on ε_n, which is based on the bound $\int|g-g_n|dx$ for $|\int(g-g_n)dx|$, is necessarily very pessimistic. Thus the measure $\bar{\varepsilon}_n$ would at first sight appear to be an unrealistic substitute for ε_n. However, our main concern is that the minimization of $\bar{\varepsilon}_n$ should be closely related to the minimization of ε_n. In §§2-5 we used as a model function a polynomial of exact degree n+1, and this led to strong theoretical results for much wider classes of functions. If we adopt the same model for the function g in (28), then it is possible to choose a constant of integration δ_n for this model function so that both $\bar{\varepsilon}_n$ and ε_n are simultaneously minimized. Hence the choice of the measure $\bar{\varepsilon}_n$ is justified, and in general we may reasonably expect the minimization of $\bar{\varepsilon}_n$ to lead to a "near-minimization" of ε_n. The required result is as follows:

Theorem 7.3

If g is a monic polynomial of degree n+1, then both $\bar{\varepsilon}_n$ and ε_n are minimized when the L_1 method of (I) type (i.e. Filippi's method) is applied to (29) and (31) with the fixed constant of integration

$$\delta_n = (-1)^{n+1}/2^{n+1}(n+2) \tag{37}$$

<u>Proof</u>. We know immediately by Theorem 7.1 that $\bar{\varepsilon}_n$ is minimized for any fixed δ_n, and in particular for δ_n given by (37), when Filippi's method is applied.

Now $g-g_n$ is a monic polynomial of degree n+1, and we may therefore define a polynomial p_{n+2} of degree n+2 uniquely from the relations

$$p'_{n+2} = g-g_n, \qquad p_{n+2}(-1) = -\delta_n. \tag{38}$$

From (34) and (38) we deduce that

$$\varepsilon_n = || -\delta_n + \int_{-1}^{x} (g-g_n)dx||_\infty = || p_{n+2} ||_\infty$$

Clearly p_{n+2} has leading coefficient $(n+2)^{-1}$ and therefore by the canonical property of the Chebyshev polynomials of first kind in L_∞, ε_n is minimized over all such polynomials p_{n+2} when

$$p_{n+2} = T_{n+2}/2^{n+1}(n+2) \tag{39}$$

But $\{U_k\}$ and $\{T_k\}$ are connected ([22], p.23) by the relation

$$T'_k = k\, U_{k-1}, \tag{40}$$

and, therefore, when (38) and (39) hold,

$$g-g_n = U_{n+1}/2^{n+1}$$

Hence ε_n is minimized when g_n interpolates g in the zeros of U_{n+1}, which corresponds to an application of Filippi's method. From (38) and (39), the constant δ_n must be chosen to be

$$\delta_n = -p_{n+2}(-1) = (-1)^{n+1}/2^{n+1}(n+2). \quad //$$

Turning our attention now to methods of (S) type, we may apply Theorems 4.9 and 4.10 directly to (35) and (36). Assuming only that g is continuous, we obtain:

Theorem 7.4

If δ_n is chosen as zero for all g_n, then the measure $\bar{\varepsilon}_n$ for the L_1 method of (S) type satisfies

$$\bar{\varepsilon}_n \leqslant [1 + \frac{4}{\pi}(n+1)] . \ \bar{\varepsilon}_n^B ,^*$$

where $\bar{\varepsilon}_n^B$ is the minimum value of $\bar{\varepsilon}_n$ over all g_n.

* A stronger result is given in the Supplement.

Theorem 7.5

If the L_1 method of (S) type is applied to (29) and (31) for $k = 0,1,2,\ldots$ and if the sequence $\{\delta_k\}$ of constants of integration is chosen to converge to zero, then the sequence $\{f_{k+1}\}$ converges uniformly to f on $[-1,1]$.

A practical comparison of the various methods of Clenshaw-Curtis type has already been made by Wright [26], and, if constants of integration are suitably adjusted, his tabulated results can be seen to confirm the overall superiority of Filippi's method for the indefinite integration of his chosen selection of functions. We observe that, for practical degrees of approximation, almost all the functions considered by Wright are totally or partially normal as an immediate consequence of the discussions of §4 or the results of Table 1, and therefore all our theoretical results are applicable.

The present discussion of L_1 methods of indefinite integration is also relevant in a wider context. The form (28) can serve as a model for a Fredholm integral equation, and the alternative form (29) and (30) as a model for a first order ordinary differential equation. Thus we might expect L_1 methods to have certain advantages over Chebyshev methods in both of these more general classes of problems. Such methods have in fact already been advocated in the literature. Firstly, Elliott [7] describes a generalization of the Clenshaw-Curtis method for Fredholm integral equations, which involves interpolation at the zeros of $(1-x^2)U_{n-1}$. Secondly, Lanczos [14] suggests the use of the polynomial T'_{n+1}, which by (40) is just a constant multiple of U_n, in place of T_n in his tau method for a first order ordinary differential equation. For the latter problem, Fox [10] proposes a very similar procedure of applying a Chebyshev method to an integral of the differential equation.

Supplement

By applying Fubini's theorem in the analysis of §4, J. Freilich and J.C. Mason have shown (in a paper to appear) that

$$\| f-f_n^{\omega}\|_1 \leq (1+K_n).\| f-f_n^B\|_1, \tag{41}$$

where

$$K_n = \max_{a\leq y\leq b} \int_a^b \omega(y)\left|\sum_{k=0}^{n} q_k(x)q_k(y)\right|dx \tag{42}$$

and f_n^{ω}, f_n^B are as defined in §4.

In the case of the Chebyshev polynomials of the second kind, it can be proved from (42) that

$$\frac{4}{\pi^2}\log \frac{1}{2}(n+1) < K_n < 3 + \log(n+1). \tag{43}$$

Thus the partial sum f_n^S of the Chebyshev series of the second kind is near-best in the L_1 norm by a relative distance of the order of log n.

These new results provide substantial improvements to Theorem 4.7, Lemma 4.8, and Corollary 4.9.

A corresponding improvement can be incorporated in §7 in the analysis of L_1 methods of indefinite integration. Specifically, in Theorem 7.4 the stronger inequality

$$\bar{\varepsilon}_n < [4 + \log(n+1)].\bar{\varepsilon}_n^B$$

is valid and can replace the inequality presently given.

Acknowledgments

This research work was supported in part by the National Research Council of Canada. The programming assistance of Mr. I. Farkas of the University of Toronto is gratefully acknowledged.

References

1. CHENEY, E.W. Introduction to Approximation Theory. McGraw Hill, 1966

2. CLENSHAW, C.W. 'The numerical solution of linear differential equations in Chebyshev series'. Proc. Camb. Phil. Soc., 53 (1957), pp.134-149.

3. CLENSHAW, C.W., and CURTIS, A.R. 'A method for numerical integration on an automatic computer'. Num. Math., 2 (1960), pp.197-205.

4. CLENSHAW, C.W. Chebyshev Series for Mathematical Functions. Math. Tab. Nat. Phys, Lab. 5, H.M. Stationery Office, 1962.

5. CLENSHAW, C.W. and NORTON, H.J. 'The solution of non-linear ordinary differential equations in Chebyshev series'. Comp. J., 6 (1963), pp. 88-92.

6. CLENSHAW, C.W. 'The solution of van der Pol's equation in Chebyshev series', in Greenspan, D. (Ed.) Numerical Solutions of Nonlinear Differential Equations, pp.55-63. Wiley, 1966.

7. ELLIOTT, D. 'A Chebyshev series method for the numerical solution of Fredholm integral equations'. Comp. J., 6 (1963), pp.102-111.

8. FILIPPI, S. 'Angenäherte Tschebyscheff--Approximation einer Stammfunktion--eine Modifikation des Verfahrens von Clenshaw and Curtis' Num. Math., 6 (1964), pp.320-328.

9. FINLAYSON, B.A., and SCRIVEN, L.E. 'The method of weighted residuals --A review'. Appl. Mech. Revs., 19 (1966), pp.735-748.

10. FOX, L. 'Chebyshev methods for ordinary differential equations'. Comp. J., 4 (1962), pp.318-331.

11. FOX, L., and PARKER, I.B. Chebyshev Polynomials in Numerical Analysis. Oxford Univ. Press, 1968.

12. FRASER, W. 'A survey of methods of computing minimax and near-minimax polynomial approximations for functions of a single independent variable.' J. Assoc. Comp. Mach., 12 (1965), pp.295-314.

13. HANDSCOMB, D.C. (Ed.). Methods of Numerical Approximation. Pergamon Press, 1966.

14. LANCZOS, C. Applied Analysis. Prentice-Hall, 1956.

15. MAEHLY, H.J. 'Methods for fitting rational approximations, Part I'. J. Assoc. Comp. Mach., 7 (1960), pp.150-162.

16. MASON, J.C. 'Chebyshev Polynomial approximations for the L-membrane eigenvalue problem'. SIAM J. Appl. Math., 15 (1967), pp.172-186.

17. MASON, J.C. 'A Chebyshev method for the numerical solution of the one-dimensional heat equation'. Proc. A.C.M. Nat. Conf. 1967, pp.115-124. Thompson Book Co., Washington, D.C.

18. MASON, J.C. 'Chebyshev methods for separable partial differential equations'. Proc. I.F.I.P. Congress 68. North-Holland, 1969.

19. POWELL, M.J.D. 'On the maximum errors of polynomial approximations defined by interpolation and least squares criteria'. Comp. J., 9 (1967), pp.404-407.

20. RALSTON, A. 'On economization of rational functions'. J. Assoc. Comp. Mach., 10 (1963), pp. 278-282.

21. RICE, J.R. The Approximation of Functions, Vol. I. Addison Wesley, 1964.

22. SNYDER, M.A. Chebyshev Methods in Numerical Approximation. Prentice-Hall, 1966.

23. TITCHMARSH, E.C. The Theory of Functions, 2nd Edition, Oxford Univ. Press, 1939.

24. USOW, K.H. 'On L_1 approximation I: Computation for continuous functions and continuous dependence'. SIAM J. Num. Anal., 4 (1967), pp.70-88.

25. WRIGHT, K. 'Chebyshev collocation methods for ordinary differential equations'. Comp. J., 6 (1964), pp.358-363.

26. WRIGHT, K. 'Series methods for integration'. Comp. J., 9 (1966), pp.191-199.

ASYMPTOTIC PROPERTIES AND THE CONVERGENCE OF NUMERICAL QUADRATURES

Jozef Miklosko

(Institute of Technical Cybernetics, Bratislava)

1. Introduction

The paper deals with certain asymptotic properties of interpolation quadratures and their convergence for functions with singularity.

Consider a Newton-Cotes type quadrature with weight function (WF) $w(x)$:

$$\int_a^b f(x)w(x)dx = \sum_{i=1}^{n} A_i^{(n)} f(x_i^{(n)}) + R_n(f), \tag{1}$$

and one of Gauss type with positive WF $W(x)$:

$$\int_a^b f(x)W(x)dx = \sum_{i=1}^{n} B_i^{(n)} f(x_i^{(n)}) + \overline{R}_n(f), \tag{2}$$

where the WF satisfy the required prerequisites, and in (1) for arbitrary nodes $x_i^{(n)} \in (a,b)$ we take

$$A_i^{(n)} = \int_a^b \frac{\omega_n(x)}{\omega_n'(x_i^{(n)})(x-x_i^{(n)})} w(x)dx \tag{3}$$

where $\omega_n(x) = \prod_{i=1}^{n} (x-x_i^{(n)})$, while in (2) we take

$$B_i^{(n)} = \int_a^b \frac{Q_n(x)}{Q_n'(x_i^{(n)})(x-x_i^{(n)})} W(x)dx = \frac{-a_{n+1}^{(n+1)}}{a_n^{(n)} Q_n'(x_i^{(n)}) Q_{n+1}(x_i^{(n)})} \tag{4}$$

where $\{Q_n(x)\}$ is the system of orthonormal polynomials (OP) with WF $W(x)$ on $[a,b]$ given in (13) and $x_i^{(n)}$ are the roots of $Q_n(x)$. Of $\{Q_n(x)\}$ and $W(x)$ it will be supposed that they are uniformly bounded on $[\alpha,\beta] \subset [a,b]$.

Further, the following concepts are used:

If

$$\lim_{n\to\infty} \sum_{i=1}^{n} A_i^{(n)} f(x_i^{(n)}) = \int_a^b f(x)w(x)dx \tag{5}$$

then the quadrature (1) is convergent for the function f(x).

The measurable function f(x) is said to be integrable with w(x) if $\int_a^b f(x)w(x)dx < \infty$. It is obvious that if $f(x) = w(x)/W(x)$ then $\int_a^b f^2(x)W(x)dx < \infty$.

The function f(x) satisfies at the point t the Dini-Lipschitz condition (DLC) if for all sufficiently small values of $|h|$ the inequality

$$|f(t + h) - f(t)| \leqslant M|\log|h||^{-\gamma-1}$$

holds, where γ,M are positive constants.

2. Asymptotic properties of coefficients (3) and (4)

Theorem 1

Suppose that for each $n > n_o$ $\exists\{x_i^{(n)}\}_{i=1}^{n} \in (\alpha,\beta) \subset [a,b]$ such that for the OP system $\{Q_n(x)\}$ we have

$$\sum_{j=1}^{n} Q_k(x_j^{(n)})Q_\ell(x_j^{(n)}) = \begin{cases} 0, & k\neq\ell \\ c_n, & k=\ell \end{cases} \quad (k,\ell = 0,1,\dots,n-1). \tag{6}$$

Select these $x_i^{(n)}$ as the nodes in (1). If the function w(x)/W(x) is integrable with w(x) and satisfies DLC uniformly in $[\alpha,\beta]$, and if c_n^{-1} is bounded as $n \to \infty$, then for every i

$$A_i^{(n)} = \frac{w(x_i^{(n)})}{c_n W(x_i^{(n)})} + \varepsilon_i^{(n)} \tag{7}$$

where $\varepsilon_i^{(n)} \to 0$ as $n \to \infty$.

Proof. The polynomial of (n-1)-th degree $\ell_i(x) = \omega_n(x)/\omega_n'(x_i^{(n)})(x-x_i^{(n)})$ occurring in (3) can be expressed in the form

$$\ell_i(x) = \sum_{j=0}^{n-1} b_j Q_j(x). \tag{8}$$

On substituting $x = x_i^{(n)}$ into (8) for i=1,2,...n, since $\ell_i(x_i^{(n)}) = 1$, $\ell_i(x_k^{(n)}) = 0$ we obtain the system of linear equations

$$\begin{bmatrix} Q_0(x_1^{(n)}) & \cdots & Q_{n-1}(x_1^{(n)}) \\ \vdots & & \vdots \\ Q_0(x_i^{(n)}) & \cdots & Q_{n-1}(x_i^{(n)}) \\ \vdots & & \vdots \\ Q_0(x_n^{(n)}) & \cdots & Q_{n-1}(x_n^{(n)}) \end{bmatrix} \begin{bmatrix} b_0 \\ \vdots \\ \vdots \\ \vdots \\ b_{n-1} \end{bmatrix} = \begin{bmatrix} 0 \\ \vdots \\ 1 \\ \vdots \\ 0 \end{bmatrix} \tag{9}$$

from which b_j is to be determined, $j=0,1,2,\ldots n-1$. To calculate b_k equations (9) are successively multiplied by $Q_k(x_i^{(n)})$, $i=1,2,\ldots n$ and the equations thus obtained are added. We get

$$\sum_{\ell=0}^{n-1} b_\ell \sum_{j=1}^{n} Q_\ell(x_j^{(n)})Q_k(x_j^{(n)}) = Q_k(x_i^{(n)})$$

which under the presupposition (6) simplifies to $b_k = Q_k(x_i^{(n)})/c_n$. By substituting this into (8) we obtain

$$\ell_i(x) = \frac{1}{c_n} \sum_{j=0}^{n-1} Q_j(x_i^{(n)})Q_j(x)$$

thus getting from (3)

$$A_i^{(n)} = \frac{1}{c_n} S_{n-1}(x_i^{(n)}) \tag{10}$$

where

$$S_{n-1}(x_i^{(n)}) = \sum_{j=0}^{n-1} \int_a^b w(x)Q_j(x)dxQ_j(x_i^{(n)}) \tag{11}$$

is the value at $x_i^{(n)}$ of the partial sum of the development of the function $w(x)/W(x)$ into a Fourier series by means of OP $\{Q_n(x)\}$. Since the presuppositions of the theorem guarantee the uniform convergence of this series to $w(x)/W(x)$ in (α,β), $|S_{n-1}(x) - w(x)/W(x)| < \varepsilon$ for $n > n(\varepsilon)$ and all $x \in (\alpha,\beta)$, in particular for $x_i^{(n)}$. Thus $|A_i^{(n)} - w(x_i^{(n)})/c_nW(x_i^{(n)})| < \varepsilon c_n^{-1}$ for $n > n(\varepsilon)$, and since c_n^{-1} is bounded, (7) follows.

Theorem 2

Let the nodes $\{x_i^{(n)}\}$ in (1) be the roots of $\{Q_n(x)\}$ i.e. OP with WF $W(x)$ on $[a,b]$. If the function $w(x)/W(x)$ is integrable with $w(x)$ and satisfies DLC uniformly in $[\alpha,\beta] \subset [a,b]$ then for every i such that for $n > n_o$, $x_i^{(n)} \in (\alpha,\beta)$,

$$A_i^{(n)} = B_i^{(n)} \frac{w(x_i^{(n)})}{W(x_i^{(n)})} + \xi_i^{(n)} \tag{12}$$

where $\xi_i^{(n)} \to 0$ as $n \to \infty$.

Proof. Consider OP $Q_n(x)$, $n=0,1,\ldots$ in the form

$$Q_n(x) = \sum_{i=0}^{n} a_{n-i}^{(n)} x^{n-i} = a_n^{(n)} \omega_n(x). \tag{13}$$

For the system $\{Q_n(x)\}$ the Christoffel-Darboux identity holds, i.e.

$$(x-y) \sum_{j=0}^{n} Q_j(x)Q_j(y) = \frac{a_n^{(n)}}{a_{n+1}^{(n+1)}} (Q_{n+1}(x)Q_n(y) - Q_n(x)Q_{n+1}(y)).$$

On substituting in it the root of $Q_n(x)$ i.e. $y=x_i^{(n)}$ then, after multiplication with $w(x)/Q_n'(x_i^{(n)})$, and integration, we obtain for (3)

$$A_i^{(n)} = \frac{-a_{n+1}^{(n+1)}}{a_n^{(n)} Q'(x_i^{(n)}) Q_{n+1}(x_i^{(n)})} \sum_{j=0}^{n-1} \int_a^b w(x)Q_j(x)dx Q_j(x_i^{(n)}) \tag{14}$$

and thus considering (4) and the partial sum (11) of the uniformly convergent Fourier series we obtain (12). //

Provided that Theorem 1 or 2 is valid, we now formulate (using the same symbols):

Theorem 3

For a fixed i, suppose that for $n > n_1$ $x_i^{(n)} \in I_i \subset (a,b)$ and $|w(x_i^{(n)})| \geq |w_i| > 0$ where $\operatorname{sgn} w(x_i^{(n)}) = \operatorname{sgn} w_i$. If the Fourier series of $w(x)/W(x)$ by means of $\{Q_n(x)\}$ converges uniformly in I_i then from a certain n,

$$\operatorname{sgn} A_i^{(n)} = \operatorname{sgn} w(x_i^{(n)}). \tag{15}$$

Proof. From (7) or (12) we have

$$A_i^{(n)} = C_i^{(n)} \frac{w(x_i^{(n)})}{W(x_i^{(n)})} - \sum_{j=n}^{\infty} a_j Q_j(x_i^{(n)}) \tag{16}$$

where $C_i^{(n)} = \frac{1}{c_n}$ or $B_i^{(n)}$, and the a_j are expansion coefficients for w/W.

Let $w(x_i^{(n)}) \geq w_i > 0$, $n > n_1$. If $W(x) \leq M_i$ on I_i then there exists $\varepsilon > 0$ such that

$$w_i > M_i \varepsilon. \tag{17}$$

It follows from the uniform convergence of the Fourier series of the function $w(x)/W(x)$ that $\exists\, n_2 = n_2(\varepsilon)$ such that $|\sum_{j=n}^{\infty} a_j Q_j(x)| < \varepsilon$ holds for all $x \in I_i$ and $n > n_2$. Thus if $n > \max(n_1, n_2)$ we get from (17)

$$w(x_i^{(n)}) > W(x_i^{(n)}) \sum_{j=n}^{\infty} a_j Q_j(x_i^{(n)}).$$

Since c_n, $B_i^{(n)}$ and $W(x_i^{(n)})$ are positive numbers, from (16) we get (15).

The proof for $w_i < 0$ is similar. //

Theorem 4

Let the function $w(x)/W(x)$ be bounded on (a,b). If the Fourier series of this function by means of $\{Q_n(x)\}$converges uniformly in (a,b) then the quadrature (1) converges for every continuous function ($f(x) \in C[a,b]$).

<u>Proof</u>. We find, for an arbitrary fixed $\varepsilon > 0$, n_o such that for $n > n_o$ $|\sum_{j=n+1}^{\infty} a_j Q_j(x_i^{(n)})| < \varepsilon$ holds, where $x_i^{(n)}$ are roots of $Q_n(x)$. Thus from (16) follows the estimate

$$|A_i^{(n)}| \leqslant B_i^{(n)}(M + \varepsilon) \tag{18}$$

where $|w(x)|/W(x) \leqslant M$ on (a,b). By adding the inequalities (18) for $i=1,2,\ldots n$ we obtain $\sum_{i=1}^{n} |A_i^{(n)}| \leqslant W(M + \varepsilon) = K_o$ where $W = \int_a^b W(x)dx$. Since for $r=1,2,\ldots$ $\sum_{i=1}^{r} |A_i^{(r)}| \leqslant K = \max\left(\max_{m=1(1)n_o} \sum_{i=1}^{m} |A_i^{(m)}|,\ K_o\right)$, then (1) converges for $f(x) \in C[a,b]$. //

The following theorem handles the quadrature (2) with equal coefficients.

Theorem 5

Let $\ell_i(x)$ in (8) given in the form

$$\ell_i(x) = \sum_{j=0}^{n-1} b_j^{(i)} Q_j(x) \tag{19}$$

where $\{Q_n(x)\}$ is the system of OP for $W(x)$ on $[a,b]$. Then for $\ell=1,2,\ldots n$,

$$B_i^{(n)} = \sum_{j=0}^{n-1} (b_j^{(i)})^2. \tag{20}$$

If (6) holds for the system $\{Q_n(x)\}$ where $x_i^{(n)}$ are roots of $Q_n(x)$

then for i=1,2,...n,

$$B_i^{(n)} = \frac{1}{c_n} . \tag{21}$$

Proof. Consider the integral

$$J_i = \int_a^b \ell_i^2(x)W(x)dx \tag{22}$$

for i=1,2,...n. Since $\ell_i^2(x)$ is a polynomial of degree 2n-2 we obtain, by applying (2), $J_i = B_i^{(n)}$. On substituting (19) into (22) then, following rearrangement by utilizing the properties of orthonormal polynomials $\{Q_n(x)\}$ we get (20). If (6) holds then $b_j^{(i)} = Q_j(x_i^{(n)})/c_n$ and thus from (20) we have

$$B_i^{(n)} = \frac{1}{c_n^2} \sum_{j=0}^{n-1} Q_j^2(x_i^{(n)}). \tag{23}$$

Since for $B_i^{(n)}$ in (2) we have $B_i^{(n)} = \left[\sum_{j=0}^{n-1} Q_j^2(x_i^{(n)})\right]^{-1}$, then from (23) we get (21). //

From Theorem 5 follows

Theorem 6

If $x_i^{(n)}$ in (2) are roots of OP $Q_n(x)$ then (6) holds only if $\{Q_n(x)\}$ is a normalized system of Chebyshev polynomials of 1st kind transformed into [a,b].

Proof. It is proved in Krylov [5] that on [-1,1] there exists no WF different from $1/\sqrt{1-x^2}$ such that formula (2) would have all coefficients equal. (Posse, Sonin). This proof can be easily generalized for [a,b] i.e. on [a,b] there exists no WF different from $1/\sqrt{(x-a)(b-x)}$ (with normalized system $\{T_n\left(\frac{2x-b-a}{b-a}\right)\}$) such that all $B_i^{(n)}$ would be equal.

Suppose the opposite of what the theorem asserts i.e. let there exist a system of OP $\{Q_n(x)\}$ on [a,b] with WF $W(x) \neq 1/\sqrt{(x-a)(b-x)}$ in which, if $x_i^{(n)}$ are roots of $Q_n(x)$, (6) holds. By Theorem 5, (21) holds, which contradicts the assertion already propounded.

Example 1. In (1) let a=-1, b=1, and WF w(x) be given, and let

a) $W(x) = 1/\sqrt{1-x^2}$ i.e. $\{Q_n(x)\}$ is a normalized system of Chebyshev polynomials of 1st kind, $T_n(x) = \cos(n \arccos x)$, with $x_i^{(n)} = \cos \phi_i$, $\phi_i = \frac{2i-1}{2n}\pi$, i=1,2,...n;

b) $W(x) = \sqrt{1-x^2}$ i.e. $\{Q_n(x)\}$ is a normalized system of Chebyshev polynomials of 2nd kind, $U_n(x) = \sin\{(n+1)\arccos x\}/\sqrt{1-x^2}$ with $x_i^{(n)} = \cos \psi_i$,

$\psi_i = \frac{i\pi}{n+1}$, $i=1,2,\dots n$.

Since in case a) $B_i^{(n)} = \frac{\pi}{n}$ (Mehler's formula) and in b) $B_i^{(n)} = \frac{\pi}{n+1} \sin^2 \psi_i$, then if the respective Fourier series converge uniformly, (12) gives

$$\text{a)} \quad A_i^{(n)} = \frac{\pi}{n} w(x_i^{(n)})\sqrt{1-(x_i^{(n)})^2} + \bar{\varepsilon}_i^{(n)} \tag{24}$$

and

$$\text{b)} \quad A_i^{(n)} = \frac{\pi}{n+1} w(x_i^{(n)})\sqrt{1-(x_i^{(n)})^2} + \bar{\bar{\varepsilon}}_i^{(n)} \tag{25}$$

Since in case a) (6) also holds, with $c_n = n/\pi$, (7) again yields (24).

Remarks. 1. With a concrete system of OP $\{Q_n(x)\}$ the conditions of uniform convergence of the function's development into a Fourier series can be formulated in a more concrete way. For the sake of generality the theorem from Alexits [1] has been adhered to.

2. From (10) and (14) we have, for every n, $\operatorname{sgn} A_i^{(n)} = \operatorname{sgn} S_{n-1}(x_i^{(n)})$ where $S_{n-1}(x_i^{(n)})$ is given by (11).

3. If in (1) coefficients $A_i^{(n)}$ are applied in the form of their asymptotic expressions (12), then the "asymptotic formula"

$$\int_a^b f(x)w(x)dx = \sum_{i=1}^{n} B_i^{(n)} \frac{f(x_i^{(n)})w(x_i^{(n)})}{W(x_i^{(n)})} + \bar{R}_n\left(\frac{fw}{W}\right)$$

is obtained, where

$$\bar{R}_n\left(\frac{fw}{W}\right) = R_n(f) - \sum_{i=1}^{n}\sum_{j=n+1}^{\infty} B_i^{(n)} f(x_i^{(n)})Q_j(x_i^{(n)})\int_a^b w(x)Q_j(x)dx,$$

being in fact formula (2) for the function $f(x)w(x)/W(x)$, i.e. if $w(x) = W(x)$ then $\bar{R}_n(f) = R_n(f)$.

4. Relation (25) can also be obtained thus: we may write (3) as $A_i^{(n)} = \int_0^{\pi} H(\psi)w(\cos\psi)d\psi$ where $H(\psi) = \ell_i(\cos\psi)\sin\psi$ is a sine polynomial of the n-th order [3], i.e. $H(\psi) = \sum_{j=1}^{n} b_j \sin j\psi$ where, since $\ell_i(\cos\psi_j) = \delta_{ij}$,

$$b_j = \frac{2}{n+1}\sum_{k=1}^{n} H(\psi_k)\sin j\psi_k = \frac{2}{n+1}\sin\psi_i \sin j\psi_i .$$

$A_i^{(n)}$ will thus be

$$A_i^{(n)} = \frac{\pi}{n+1}\sin^2\psi_i \sum_{j=1}^{n}\frac{2}{\pi}\int_{-1}^{1} w(x)U_{j-1}(x)dx U_{j-1}(x_i^{(n)}).$$

Supposing that the Fourier series by means of $\{U_n(x)\}$ of the function $w(x)/\sqrt{1-x^2}$ converges uniformly in $[-1,1]$, then (25) holds.

5. In Davis and Rabinowitz [2] is formulated the so called Circle Theorem: Let $W(x) = (1-x)^\alpha(1+x)^\beta$, $\alpha,\beta > -1$ and $x_i^{(n)}$ and $B_i^{(n)}$ be the nodes and coefficients of (2). Then $B_i^{(n)} \sim \frac{\pi}{n} W(x_i^{(n)})\sqrt{1-(x_i^{(n)})^2}$ as $n \to \infty$, where the index $i=i(n)$ has been selected in such a way that the points $x_i^{(n)}$ remain in a fixed interval lying in the interior of $[a,b]$. ($u_n \sim v_n$ means that $u_n/v_n \to 1$.)

It follows from the proved theorems that if the Fourier series of function $w(x)/W(x)$ converges uniformly on a fixed interval within $[a,b]$ then coefficients (3) for Examples 1a, 1b also satisfy the Circle Theorem.

It can be seen from (7) and (12) that under the given assumptions limit curves other than a circle can also be obtained.

6. Theorem 1 does not demand $x_i^{(n)}$ to be the roots of $Q_n(x)$. Theorems 5 and 6 state that if this is presumed then only the quadrature of Example 1a satisfies Theorem 1 and (21) whereby (2) becomes the already mentioned Mehler formula.

It is obvious that if integrals in (11) can be accurately calculated, precise formulae can be obtained for $A_i^{(n)}$. Here is an example of such procedure.

Example 2. On $[-1,1]$ let $w(x) = q_k(x)/\sqrt{1-x^2}$ where $q_k(x) = \left.\begin{matrix}\cos\\ \sin\end{matrix}\right\} \pi k(x+1)$, $k=1,2,\ldots$, and $W(x) = 1/\sqrt{1-x^2}$ i.e. $x_i^{(n)}$ are roots of $T_n(x)$ as in Example 1a.

If $q_k(x) = \cos \pi k(x+1) = (-1)^k \cos \pi kx$, coefficients (3), i.e. (10) and (14) respectively, have the form

$$A_i^{(n)} = \frac{(-1)^k\pi}{n}\left(\frac{1}{\pi}\int_{-1}^{1}\frac{\cos\pi kx}{\sqrt{1-x^2}}T_0(x)dxT_0(x_i^{(n)}) + \frac{2}{\pi}\sum_{j=1}^{n-1}\int_{-1}^{1}\frac{\cos\pi kx}{\sqrt{1-x^2}}T_j(x)dxT_j(x_i^{(n)})\right). \tag{26}$$

Since for $m > 0$ (see Granštejn I. S. and Ryžik I. M.: Tablicy integralov, Moscow, 1963, p. 850)

$$\int_{-1}^{1}\frac{\cos mx}{\sqrt{1-x^2}}T_p(x)dx = \begin{cases}(-1)^{p/2}\,\pi J_p(m), & p \text{ even}\\ 0, & p \text{ odd}\end{cases}$$

where $J_p(m)$ are Bessel functions of the first kind, then from (26) the precise formula is obtained

$$A_i^{(n)} = \frac{(-1)^k\pi}{n}\left\{J_0(\pi k) + 2\sum_{j=2(2)}^{N}(-1)^{j/2}J_j(\pi k)\cos j\phi_i\right\} \tag{27}$$

where N is the first even number $\leq n-1$, $j=2,4,6,\ldots N$.

With $q_k(x) = \sin \pi k(x+1) = (-1)^k \sin \pi kx$, noting that for $m > 0$ we have

$$\int_{-1}^{1} \frac{\sin mx}{\sqrt{1-x^2}} T_p(x)dx = \begin{cases} 0 & , p \text{ even} \\ (-1)^{(p-1)/2}\pi J_p(m), & p \text{ odd} \end{cases}$$

we obtain

$$A_i^{(n)} = \frac{(-1)^k 2\pi}{n} \sum_{j=1(2)}^{N} (-1)^{(j-1)/2} J_j(\pi k)\cos j\phi_i \tag{28}$$

where N is the first odd number $\leq n-1$, $j=1,3,5,\ldots N$.

The sums in (27) and (28) are the known partial sums of the Fourier series of functions $\cos \pi kx$, $\sin \pi kx$ respectively, from which it follows that $A_i^{(n)} \simeq \frac{\pi}{n} q_k(x_i^{(n)})$ which is in accord with (24).

The coefficients calculated from (27) and (28), respectively, can be applied in calculating the cosine or sine Fourier coefficients for $[0,2\pi]$ i.e. in the quadrature

$$\int_{-1}^{1} f(x)q_k(x)dx \simeq \sum_{i=1}^{n} A_i^{(n)} f(x_i^{(n)})\sqrt{1-(x_i^{(n)})^2}$$

especially with small values of k, when the method of the multiple use of one formula described in Miklosko [6] can not be utilized. The increase of n is practically unlimited in this case.

Theorem 7

If $w(x)$ and $W(x)$ are as in Example 2 then for $A_i^{(n)}$ from (27) or (28) respectively we have for every i

$$|A_i^{(n)}| < \frac{2\pi}{n} \exp\left(\frac{\pi k}{2}\right). \tag{29}$$

Proof. Since $|T_j(x)| \leq 1$ in $[-1,1]$ we have in both cases

$$|A_i^{(n)}| \leq \frac{2\pi}{n} \sum_{j=0}^{n-1} |J_j(\pi k)|.$$

Since (see Erdelyi, A. et al.: _Higher transcendental functions_, Vol. 2, McGraw Hill, 1953, p. 13)

$$|J_m(z)| \leq \left|\frac{z}{2}\right|^m \frac{\exp(|v|)}{\Gamma(m+1)}$$

for $m > -\frac{1}{2}$, $z=u+iv$ (u,v real) and thus $|J_m(\pi k)| \leq (\frac{\pi k}{2})^m/m!$ then

$$|A_i^{(n)}| < \frac{2\pi}{n} \sum_{j=0}^{\infty} \frac{(\pi k/2)^j}{j!} = \frac{2\pi}{n} \exp\left(\frac{\pi k}{2}\right).$$

Corollary 1

For every n, $\sum_{i=1}^{n} |A_i^{(n)}| < 2\pi \exp(\pi k/2) = K$, i.e. this quadrature converges for every $f(x) \in C[-1,1]$.

Corollary 2

By (29), $\lim_{n\to\infty} A_i^{(n)} = 0$.

3. Convergence for functions with singularity

Theorem 8

In quadrature (1) let a=-1, b=1. Let w(x) satisfy in [-1,1] these assumptions: w''(x) exists and is integrable, w'(x) has bounded variation. Let there exist δ, $0 < \delta \leq 1$, such that $w(x) \geq s > 0$ in $[1-\delta,1]$. If the nodes of integration $x_i^{(n)}$ are the roots of the Chebyshev polynomials $T_n(x)$, then for every n and for every i such that $x_i^{(n)} \in [1-\delta,1)$,

$$\frac{A_i^{(n)}}{w(x_i^{(n)})} < K(x_{i-1}^{(n)} - x_i^{(n)}) \tag{30}$$

where $x_0^{(n)} = 1$.

Proof. It follows from (24), and (10) and (14) respectively, that for every n

$$|A_i^{(n)}| \leq \frac{\pi}{n}(\sin \phi_i |w(x_i^{(n)})| + |R(\phi_i)|) \tag{31}$$

where

$$R(\phi_i) = \frac{2}{\pi}\sum_{m=n+1}^{\infty}\int_0^{\pi} F(\phi)\cos m\phi d\phi \cos m\phi_i \text{ and } F(\phi) = w(\cos\phi)\sin\phi.$$

It is proved in [6] that $\left|\int_0^{\pi} F(\phi)\cos m\phi d\phi\right| \leq \frac{d}{m^2}$, where $d = |w(-1)| + |w(1)| + \overset{\pi}{\underset{0}{V}}(F'(\phi))$. Since $\sum_{m=n+1}^{\infty}\frac{1}{m^{k+1}} < \frac{1}{kn^k}$ we get the estimate $|R(\phi_i)| < \frac{2d}{\pi n}$. Since $\sin\phi_i < \phi_i$ we get from (31)

$$|A_i^{(n)}| < \frac{\pi^2(2i-1)|w(x_i^{(n)})|}{2n^2} + \frac{2d}{n^2} \tag{32}$$

Now since $\sin\theta > 2\theta/\pi$ for $\theta \in (0,\pi/2)$, we have (see also Gautschi [4])

$$x_{i-1}^{(n)} - x_i^{(n)} = 2\sin\frac{(i-1)\pi}{n}\sin\frac{\pi}{2n} > \frac{4(i-1)}{n^2} \quad (1 < i \leq \tfrac{1}{2}(n+1)). \tag{33}$$

From (32) and (33) we obtain for i such that $x_i^{(n)} \in [1-\delta,1)$

$$\frac{A_i^{(n)}}{w(x_i^{(n)})} < (x_{i-1}^{(n)} - x_i^{(n)}) \left\{\frac{(2i-1)\pi^2}{8(i-1)} + \frac{d}{2(i-1)w(x_i^{(n)})}\right\} < (x_{i-1}^{(n)} - x_i^{(n)})C_1$$

where $C_1 = 3\pi^2/8 + d/2s$.

For i=1 we get the estimate $x_0^{(n)} - x_1^{(n)} > 1/2n^2$ which yields, when combined with (32),

$$\frac{A_1^{(n)}}{w(x_1^{(n)})} < (x_0^{(n)} - x_1^{(n)})C_2$$

where $C_2 = \pi^2 + 4d/s$.

Since $C_2 > C_1$, the assertion (30) with $K = C_2$ is proved. //

Now the theorem is expounded on the convergence of the general numerical quadrature with WF p(x) i.e.

$$\int_{-1}^{1} f(x)p(x)dx \approx \sum_{i=1}^{n} C_i^{(n)} f(x_i^{(n)}) = G_n(f)$$

for functions f(x) with singularity at x=1. Its presuppositions and its proofs differ from the theorem proved in Rabinowitz [7] in so far as we will not assume nonnegativity of p(x) on [-1,1], and $C_i^{(n)}$.

Theorem 9

Suppose given on [-1,1) the continuous functions f(x) and p(x) such that, for a certain $\delta_1 > 0$, the function f(x)p(x) will be nonnegative and nondecreasing in $[1-\delta_1,1)$, while $\lim_{t\to 1^-}\int_{-1}^{t} f(x)p(x)dx = I(fp) < \infty$. Let (34) with F for f converge for every $F(x) \in C[-1,1]$, i.e. $\lim_{n\to\infty} G_n(F) = I(Fp)$ where $-1 \leq x_n^{(n)} < x_{n-1}^{(n)} < \dots < x_1^{(n)} < x_0^{(n)} = 1$.

If $\exists n_1$, and $\delta_2 > 0$, such that for $n > n_1$ and for every i such that $1-x_i^{(n)} < \delta_2$

$$\frac{C_i^{(n)}}{p(x_i^{(n)})} \leq K(x_{i-1}^{(n)} - x_i^{(n)}), \tag{35}$$

and if $\exists n_2$, and $\delta_3 > 0$, such that for $n > n_2$ and for every i such that $1-x_i^{(n)} < \delta_3$

$$\text{sgn } C_i^{(n)} = \text{sgn } p(x_i^{(n)}), \tag{36}$$

then $\lim_{n\to\infty} G_n(f) = I(fp)$, i.e. quadrature (34) converges.

<u>Proof</u>. To each $\varepsilon > 0$ there exists $\delta_4 > 0$ such that $\int_{1-\delta_4}^{1} f(x)p(x)dx \leqslant \varepsilon$.

Let $n_o = \max(n_1, n_2)$ and $\delta = \min(\delta_1, \delta_2, \delta_3, \delta_4)$. Define the function

$$g(x) = \begin{cases} f(x), & x \in [-1, 1-\delta] \\ f(1-\delta), & x \in [1-\delta, 1]. \end{cases}$$

Since by (36), for $n > n_o$

$$\sum_{i=1}^{n} C_i^{(n)} f(x_i^{(n)}) \geqslant \sum_{i=1}^{n} C_i^{(n)} g(x_i^{(n)})$$

i.e. $G_n(f) \geqslant G_n(g)$ then, since $g(x) \in C[-1,1]$,

$$\liminf_{n\to\infty} G_n(f) \geqslant \liminf_{n\to\infty} G_n(g) = \lim_{n\to\infty} G_n(g) = I(gp) \geqslant I(fp) - \varepsilon.$$

Consider further that

$$G_n(f) = S_1 + S_2 \tag{37}$$

where

$$S_1 = \sum_{x_i^{(n)} \in [-1,1-\delta]} C_i^{(n)} f(x_i^{(n)}), \qquad S_2 = \sum_{x_i^{(n)} \in (1-\delta,1)} C_i^{(n)} f(x_i^{(n)}).$$

Since for $n > n_o$ and all i for which $1 - x_i^{(n)} < \delta$, $C_i^{(n)}$ and $g(x_i^{(n)})$ will be of equal signs, then

$$S_1 = \sum_{x_i^{(n)} \in [-1,1-\delta]} C_i^{(n)} g(x_i^{(n)}) \leqslant G_n(g), \qquad n > n_o.$$

Also, by (35) we have

$$\begin{aligned} S_2 &= \sum_{x_i^{(n)} \in (1-\delta,1)} \frac{C_i^{(n)}}{p(x_i^{(n)})} f(x_i^{(n)}) p(x_i^{(n)}) \\ &\leqslant K \sum_{x_i^{(n)} \in (1-\delta,1)} (x_{i-1}^{(n)} - x_i^{(n)}) f(x_i^{(n)}) p(x_i^{(n)}) \\ &\leqslant K \int_{1-\delta}^{1} f(x)p(x)dx \leqslant K\varepsilon. \end{aligned}$$

Thus we get from (37) $G_n(f) \leqslant G_n(g) + K\varepsilon$, and thus

$$\begin{aligned} \limsup_{n\to\infty} G_n(f) &\leqslant \limsup_{n\to\infty} G_n(g) + K\varepsilon \\ &= \lim_{n\to\infty} G_n(g) + K\varepsilon = I(gp) + K\varepsilon \leqslant I(fp) + K\varepsilon. \end{aligned}$$

From the obtained inequalities we have

$$I(fp) - \varepsilon \leq \liminf_{n \to \infty} G_n(f) \leq \limsup_{n \to \infty} G_n(f) \leq I(fp) + K\varepsilon,$$

i.e. $\lim_{n\to\infty} G_n(f) = I(fp)$. //

Remark. It is known that in order to make the Fourier series of a function $f(x)$ by means of Chebyshev polynomials $T_n(x)$ converge uniformly on $[-1,1]$ it is sufficient that $f(x)$ be continuous and of bounded variation on this interval. The function $w(x)/W(x) = w(x)\sqrt{1-x^2}$ in Theorem 8 is continuous. Since on $[-1,1]$ $w'(x)$ is bounded, then $w(x)$ satisfies Lipschitz's condition and thus has bounded variation. Since the even function $\sqrt{1-x^2}$ is monotonic on $[0,1]$, it also has bounded variation on $[-1,1]$ and thus the Fourier series of $w(x)\sqrt{1-x^2}$ converges uniformly on this interval. It follows by Theorem 4 that the quadrature of Theorem 8 converges for functions $f(x) \in C[-1,1]$. (This is proved also in [6].)

If for given $w(x) = p(x)$ we can prove tha assumption (36) in Theorem 9 then in this case (1) converges also for $f(x)$ with singularity at $x=1$.

References

1. ALEXITS, G. Convergence problems of orthogonal series. Akademiai Kiadó, Budapest, 1961, p. 35.
2. DAVIS, P. J. and RABINOWITZ, P. 'Some geometrical theorems for abscissas and weights of Gauss type'. J. Math. Anal. Appl., 2 (1961), pp. 428-437.
3. FEJER, L. 'Mechanische Quadraturen mit positiven Coteschen Zahlen'. Math. Z., 37 (1933), pp. 287-309.
4. GAUTSCHI, W. 'Numerical quadrature in the presence of a singularity'. SIAM J. Numer. Anal., 4 (1967), pp. 357-362.
5. KRYLOV, V. I. Priblizennoe vycislenie integralov. Izdatelstvo nauka, Moskva, 1967, p. 195.
6. MIKLOSKO, J. 'Numerical integration with Weight Functions cos kx, sin kx on $[0,2\pi/t]$'. Aplikace matematiky, 1969, p. 3.
7. RABINOWITZ, P. 'Gaussian integration in the presence of a singularity'. SIAM J. Numer. Anal., 4 (1967), pp. 191-201.

THE METHOD OF FUNCTIONALS AND ITS APPLICATIONS

E. V. Voronovskaya

(Electrotechnical Institute, Leningrad)

In 1955 I published a new theory, which united the problems of Tchebysheff approximation by algebraic polynomials into one problem on the basis of functional analysis. The essence of this method was presented to the Mathematical Congress in Moscow (1956).

From 1956 to the present date a series of new results has been published, which have confirmed the efficiency of the method in the solution of the above-mentioned classical problems.

The first part of this paper is a short summary of the principal ideas in the method of functionals. The second part contains modern results, dealing with applications of the theory.

PART I

THE METHOD OF FUNCTIONALS

In the space of algebraic polynomials $\{P_n(x)\}$ with the metric of Tchebysheff and the principal interval $[0,1]$ we examine linear functionals F_n, defined by n+1 arbitrary real numbers, that is

$$F_n = \mu_0, \mu_1, \ldots, \mu_n;\ F_n(x^i) = \mu_i;\ F_n(P_n) = \sum_0^n p_i \mu_i .$$

Let F_n have the norm

$$N = N(F_n) = \sup \frac{|F(P_n)|}{\max\limits_{[0,1]} |P_n|} ;$$

there always exists an extremal polynomial $Q_n(x)$ such that

$$\max_{[0,1]} |Q_n(x)| = 1$$

(Q_n is a "reduced" polynomial), and

$$F_n(Q_n) = +N.$$

Now we can apply such theorems, as those of Hahn-Banach and Riesz; this creates the first advantage in comparison to the classical approach.

We have proved the following result ([1], pp. 38-39):

> If F_n is not absolutely monotonic*, there exists one and only one number μ^*_{n+1}, that extends F_n to the space $\{P_{n+1}(x)\}$ in the "best" way, i.e. so that the norm is preserved: $N(\mu_0, \mu_1, \ldots, \mu_n, \mu^*_{n+1}) = N(F_n)$.

Corollary

> The best extension of F_n to the full space $C[0,1]$ is unique and creates a moment-sequence $\mu_0, \ldots, \mu_n, \mu_{n+1}, \ldots, \mu_p, \ldots,$
>
> $$\mu_p = \int_0^1 t^p dH(t); \quad \operatorname*{Var}_{[0,1]} H(t) < \infty,$$
>
> for which $Q_n(x)$ holds its properties.

We have the following result ([1], pp. 17-20):

> A moment-sequence functional $(\mu_p)_0^\infty$ has an extremal (or "attendant") polynomial if and only if the corresponding $H(t)$ is a step-function with a finite number of jumps; let their values be $(\delta_i)_1^s$ and the points of discontinuity, $(\sigma_i)_1^s$. Then the structure of $(\mu_p)_0^\infty$ is
>
> $$\mu_p = \sum_{i=1}^{s} \delta_i \sigma_i^p; \quad Q_n(\sigma_i) = \pm 1; \quad \operatorname{sgn} \delta_i = Q_n(\sigma_i) = \sum_{j=0}^{n} q_j \sigma_i^j;$$
>
> and the norm can be written in the following different forms:
>
> $$N = \operatorname*{Var}_{[0,1]} H(t) = \sum_1^s |\delta_i| = \sum_0^n q_j \mu_j = \sum_1^s \delta_i Q_n(\sigma_i) = \lim_{p \to \infty} \sum_{k=0}^{p} \binom{p}{k} |\mu_{k,p-k}|,$$
>
> where $\mu_{kr} = (-\Delta)^r \mu_k$.

Thus for every given F_n which is not absolutely monotonic there is a well-determined set of points $(\sigma_i)_1^s$ on $[0,1]$ - the jump-points of the function $H(t)$ corresponding to its unique best extension - which are also among the points of maximum deviation (or "knots") of the extremal polynomial $Q_n(x)$. We call the points σ_i the <u>true knots</u> of F_n, and if we indicate

---

* The finite sequence $\alpha_0, \alpha_1, \ldots, \alpha_n$ is called <u>absolutely monotonic</u>, when there exists an extension $\alpha_0, \ldots \alpha_n, \alpha_{n+1}, \ldots, \alpha_p, \ldots$ which is absolutely monotonic in the well known sense ([1], p. 25).

above each σ_i the sign of the corresponding δ_i, we obtain the <u>true distribution</u> $(\overset{\pm}{\sigma}_i)_1^s$ of F_n ([1], p. 39).

We emphasize: for F_n the δ_i (i.e. weights of the true knots) satisfy the system of linear equations (A), which in general is overdetermined ($s \leqslant n+1$):

$$\left.\begin{aligned} &\delta_1 + \delta_2 + \ldots + \delta_s = \mu_0 \\ &\delta_1\sigma_1 + \delta_2\sigma_2 + \ldots + \delta_s\sigma_s = \mu_1 \\ &\cdot \quad \cdot \quad \cdot \quad \cdot \quad \cdot \quad \cdot \quad \cdot \\ &\delta_1\sigma_1^n + \delta_2\sigma_2^n + \ldots + \delta_s\sigma_s^n = \mu_n \end{aligned}\right\} \qquad (A)$$

We introduce the following definitions: the resolvent

$$R_s(x) = \prod_1^s (x - \sigma_i),$$

its "quasi-square"

$$R_s^2(x) = \begin{cases} \prod_1^s (x-\sigma_i)^2 \text{ if } 0 < \sigma_1 < \ldots \sigma_s < 1. \\ x \prod_2^s (x-\sigma_i)^2 \text{ or } (1-x) \prod_1^{s-1} (x-\sigma_i)^2 \text{ for } \sigma_1 = 0 \text{ or } \sigma_s = 1. \\ x(1-x) \prod_2^{s-1} (x-\sigma_i)^2 \text{ if } 0 = \sigma_1 < \sigma_2 < \ldots < \sigma_s = 1. \end{cases}$$

and the two semiresolvents

$$R_{s_1}(x) = \prod_1^{s_1} (x - \overset{+}{\sigma}_i); \; R_{s_2}(x) = \prod_1^{s_2} (x - \overset{-}{\sigma}_i); \; s_1 + s_2 = s.$$

By means of these we can present the extremal polynomial in a constructive form ([1], p. 21): first of all we obtain by successive division $\phi(x), \psi(x)$ such that

$$\phi(x)R_{s_1}^2(x) + \psi(x)R_{s_2}^2(x) \equiv 2.$$

We have two cases:

1) If on $[0,1]$ $\phi(x) \geqslant 0$; $\psi(x) \geqslant 0$, the reduced attendant polynomial is

$$Q_n(x) = 1 - \phi(x)R_{s_1}^2(x) = -1 + \psi(x)R_{s_2}^2(x).$$

2) If the condition in 1) is not fulfilled, we have to construct a polynomial $\lambda(x)$ such that on $[0,1]$ we have

$$-\frac{\phi(x)}{R_{s_2}^2(x)} \leqslant \lambda(x) \leqslant \frac{\psi(x)}{R_{s_1}^2(x)}.$$

Here the "zone of reduction" has a breadth $L = 2/R_s^2(x)$, and we can take as our extremal polynomial

$$Q_n(x) = 1 - R_{s_1}^2(x)[\phi(x)+\lambda(x)R_{s_2}^2(x)] = -1 + R_{s_2}^2(x)[\psi(x)-\lambda(x)R_{s_1}^2(x)].$$

We note the existence of innumerable attendant polynomials of higher degree; their reciprocal dependence is always of the form

$$Q_p(x) = Q_n(x) + P(x)R_s^2(x) \quad (p \geq n),$$

that is, their difference is a multiple of $R_s^2(x)$. An attendant polynomial of lowest degree ($p \leq n$) for a given F_n is called a principal attendant polynomial.

Next we divide the set of all reduced $Q_n(x)$ into two classes ([1], p. 42), according to the number s of their knots. If $s \leq \frac{n}{2} + 1$, we have the class I, and if $s > \frac{n}{2} + 1$, the polynomial belongs to the class II. The same division is made for the true distribution of F_n. We state the important result: if F_n belongs to class II, its principal attendant polynomial is unique; (that statement is in general not true for F_n of class I).

In order to distinguish separate families of polynomials, belonging to class II, we introduce the following integer characteristics: n - the degree, s - the number of knots, p - the number of intervals such that the signs above σ_i, σ_{i+1} are identical. These united characteristics [n,s,p] constitute the "passport" of the polynomial, or its "pass". In exactly the same way we form the pass of the true distribution of F_n ([1], p. 74). In all cases we have the relation

$$s+p \leq n+1.$$

The array of passes, beginning with the highest (s = max for fixed n) is:

$$\begin{array}{ccccc} & & [n,n-1,0] & & \\ & [n,n,0] & & & \\ [n,n+1,0] & & [n,n-1,1] & \ldots\ldots & \\ & [n,n,1] & & & \\ & & [n,n-1,2] & & \end{array}$$

For every logically possible pass polynomials do exist ([1], p. 85).

We must note the essential properties of the pass [n,n+1,0] ([1], p. 45-48), consisting only of the two polynomials $\pm T_n^*(x) = \pm\cos n \arccos (2x-1)$. The largest possible s = n+1 affords them exceptional priviliges. Firstly, the system (A) for $\sigma_i = \tau_i = \sin^2(i\pi/2n)$ is well-determined. To establish the second advantage, we must turn to functionals with a variable parameter.

Let $F_n = \mu_0, \mu_1, \ldots, \mu_{n-1}, \Theta$; then there exists a well-defined interval $\mu_n' < \Theta < \mu_n''$ - the critical interval - such that for $\Theta \geqslant \mu_n''$ the attendant polynomial is $+T_n^*(x)$; for $\Theta \leqslant \mu_n'$ the attendant is $-T_n^*(x)$, and inside this interval the $\pm T_n^*(x)$ cannot be attendant, but for every two internal points Θ_1 and Θ_2 the attendant polynomials are <u>different</u>. Similar critical intervals exist for every $\mu_k (k > 0)$, with attendants $(-1)^{n-k}T_n(x)$ and $(-1)^{n-k-1}T_n(x)$, respectively, outside the critical interval.

We give here an example:

$$F_n = 0_0, 0_1, \ldots, 0_{n-2}, 1_{n-1}, \Theta; \ \mu_n' = \frac{n-1}{2}; \ \mu_n'' = \frac{n+1}{2}; \ \mu_n^* = \frac{n}{2} .$$

For the calculation of the μ_n', μ_n'' we have general formulas ([1], pp. 49-50).

Next we have to consider F_n with $m(< n+1)$ fixed and $n+1-m = \ell$ variable parameters (μ_0 is always fixed). We write $F_n = \{(\mu_{k_i})_{i=0}^{m-1}; (\Theta_i)_1^{\ell}\}$. Let its attendant polynomial for the values $\Theta_i = \Theta_i^{(0)}$ be $Q_n(x, \Theta_1^{(0)}, \ldots, \Theta_\ell^{(0)})$ of class II with the pass $[n,s;p]$, which is identical with the pass of $F_n(\delta_i \neq 0)$. We have the assertion: in the vicinity of $[\Theta_i^{(0)}]_1^{\ell}$, F_n and $Q_n(x, \Theta_1, \ldots, \Theta_\ell)$ have the same pass $[n,s,p]$. So we obtain an ℓ-dimensional set of points M_ℓ, where the same pass is maintained for both functional and polynomial. Moreover, the continuous alteration of the (Θ_i) produces continuous deformation of Q_n ([1], pp. 77-78). There arises the following question: under what conditions for two different points in M_ℓ do we have two different attendant polynomials? In this and only in this case we call the (Θ_i) <u>independent</u> ([1], pp. 79-80). The answer is: if m=s, the (Θ_i) are independent, if $m < s$, they are not; (if $m > s$, of course the independence holds). In the case m=s, $s + \ell = n + 1$, and the number of missing knots in (A) are replaced by the equal number of variables (Θ_i).

Another no less important question is: under what condition is M_ℓ complete? That is: when does the domain M_ℓ contain all the polynomials of the initial pass? This entirely depends upon the chosen basis of the functional. We can refer to the simplest case, - the pass $[n,s,0]$. The functional $0_0, 0_1, \ldots, 0_{s-2}, 1_{s-1}, \Theta_1, \ldots, \Theta_\ell$ (with $s+\ell = n+1$) determines in its M_ℓ all the polynomials of the pass ([1], pp. 84-85).

These results give the theory a second, decisive advantage in comparison to the classical approach: the possibility of defining, investigating and constructing reduced polynomials by means of the simplest linear functionals.

We now turn to the final problem, the analytic construction of attendant polynomials. We consider the general case of $F_n = \{(\mu_{k_i})_0^{s-1};\ (\Theta_i)_1^{\ell}\}$, where $s+\ell = n+1$. ([1], pp. 132-133). Then in M_ℓ, $Q_n(x,\Theta_1,\ldots,\Theta_\ell) = \sum q_i(\Theta_1,\ldots\Theta_\ell)x^i$ belongs to $[n,s,p]$.

The parameters (Θ_i) of the defining functional are not suitable for the purpose of analytic construction; we have to replace them by $(\theta_i)_1^{\ell}$, some of the coefficients of $Q_n(x,\Theta_1,\ldots,\Theta_\ell)$; let them be the highest coefficients:

$$Q_n(x,\theta_1,\ldots\theta_\ell) = \theta_\ell x^n + \theta_{\ell-1}x^{n-1} + \ldots + \theta_1 x^{n-\ell+1} + q_{n-\ell}(\theta_1,\ldots\theta_\ell)x^{n-\ell} + \ldots$$

Then we assert: 1) the equivalence of the (Θ_i) and the (θ_i), that is $\{Q_n(x,\Theta_1,\ldots,\Theta_\ell)\} \equiv \{Q_n(x,\theta_1,\ldots,\theta_\ell)\}$; 2) the existence of $\partial Q_n/\partial\theta_i$ $(i=1,2,\ldots,\ell)$. The principal analytical relations, which afford the required analytical construction, are:

$$\frac{\partial}{\partial\theta_k} Q_n = p_{k-1}(x)R_s(x) \quad (k=1,2,\ldots,\ell);$$

$$\frac{\partial}{\partial x} Q_n = \psi(x)R_s(x).$$

The polynomials $p_{k-1}(x)$ are of successive degrees $n-\ell+1,\ldots,n$; $\psi(x)$ is a rational function.

We have to make the following remarks:

1. The coefficients of $p_{k-1}(x)$ are determined algebraically by the condition that some of the coefficients of $\partial Q_n/\partial\theta_i$ vanish.

2. The structure of $\psi(x)$ must be settled beforehand by means of the defining functional.

We shall make a review of these formulae for the simplest case ([1], pp. 97-101). Let $s = n$, i.e. $\ell=1$; then the passes concerned are $[n,n,0]$ and $[n,n,1]$. Write $Q_n(x) = \theta x^n + y_{n-1}(\theta)x^{n-1} + \ldots + y_0(\theta)$. $R_s(x) = R_n(x)$, and

$$\frac{\partial Q_n}{\partial\theta} = R_n(x); \quad \frac{\partial Q_n}{\partial x} = \frac{n\theta(x-\lambda)}{x(x-1)} R_n(x),$$

where $\lambda = y_1/n\theta y_1'$.

The elimination of $R_n(x)$ gives:

$$x(x-1)\frac{\partial}{\partial x} Q_n = [n\theta x - \frac{y_1(\theta)}{y_1'(\theta)}]\frac{\partial}{\partial\theta} Q_n,$$

which yields the system:

$$(n-1)y_{n-1} - n\theta = n\theta y'_{n-1} - y_1/y'_1;$$
$$(n-2)y_{n-2} - (n-1)y_{n-1} = n\theta y'_{n-1} - y_1 y'_{n-1}/y'_1$$
$$(n-3)y_{n-3} - (n-2)y_{n-2} = n\theta y'_{n-3} - y_1 y'_{n-2}/y'_1$$
$$\cdot\quad\cdot\quad\cdot\quad\cdot\quad\cdot\quad\cdot\quad\cdot\quad\cdot\quad\cdot\quad\cdot\quad\cdot$$
$$y_1 - 2y_2 = n\theta y'_1 - y_1 y'_2/y'_1.$$

The form of the system is identical for both passes; the principal difference is in the situation of the root $\lambda(\theta)$, which for the case $[n,n,0]$ moves outside $[0,1]$; while for the different categories of the pass $[n,n,1]$, $\lambda(\theta)$ is localised in the corresponding intervals between the knots (τ_i) ([1], pp. 117-118). The boundary conditions also are quite different for the two cases.

Finally we underline the following general consequences:

1. The construction of differential equations for a chosen pass must be preceded by thorough qualitative investigation of the family, that is, one has to consider the general character of the continuous deformation of its members; this is needed to localize the roots of $\partial Q_n/\partial x$ and the shape of $\psi(x)$. All these problems can be solved by means of defining functionals.

2. The integration of the system requires the preliminary construction of all the polynomials of higher passes, as they afford the necessary boundary conditions.

3. The integration of such systems with partial derivatives is a very difficult task, if we desire to obtain an approximate analytical solution. It is otherwise, if we make use of electronic computers, and are satisfied by numerical results. This was done for $[n,n,0]$ in 1958 by the Polish mathematician Paszkovsky.

4. As it now stands we have the full right in all the theoretical applications of such polynomials to consider them as known; we are going to show, that a great many applications require only the polynomials of highest passes.

PART II

APPLICATIONS TO CLASSICAL PROBLEMS

1. <u>The problem of V. Markoff (1892)</u>: among polynomials in $\{P_n(x)\}$ whose coefficients satisfy the condition $\sum_0^n p_i\mu_i = A(\neq 0)$, to find the polynomial $Y_n(x)$ of least deviation from zero on $[0,1]$ and the value L of the

deviation; (μ_i) being given numbers.

If we create $F = \mu_0, \mu_1, \ldots, \mu_n$ with the attendant polynomial $Q_n(x)$ and norm N, we have $Y_n(x) = LQ_n(x)$; $LN = A$. ([1], pp. 135-140).

2. <u>The problem of Zolotareff-Psheborsky</u>: a similar problem with two linear conditions:

$$\sum \mu_i p_i = A (\neq 0),$$
$$\sum \nu_i p_i = B (\neq 0).$$

We must again find $Y_n(x)$ and L. ([1], pp. 140-145).

If we denote $F_1 = \mu_0, \ldots, \mu_n$; $F_2 = \nu_0, \ldots, \nu_n$ and $F_3 = \mu_0 + \Omega\nu_0, \ldots, \mu_n + \Omega\nu_n$, where $-\infty < \Omega < +\infty$, and $Q_n(x, \Omega)$ is the attendant polynomial for F_3, we have to solve the equation for Ω:

$$F_1(Q_n)/A = F_2(Q_n)/B.$$

Let the solution be $\Omega = \Omega_0$. Then $Y_n(x) = LQ_n(x, \Omega_0)$, and

$$\frac{1}{L} = \frac{F_1(Q_n)}{A} = \frac{F_2(Q_n)}{B}.$$

3. <u>Best approximation of analytic functions</u>. We assume that $f(x)$ can be developed in a Taylor series at every point of $[0,1]$. The polynomial of least deviation can be obtained by a finite number of tests. We are obliged to refer to our paper [2] for further details.

4. <u>Construction of trigonometric reduced polynomials</u>. Expansions on $[-\pi, +\pi]$ for reduced polynomials $\{C_n(\theta)\}$ and $\{S_n(\theta)\}$ of pure type are discussed in [3].

Polynomials $C_n(\theta) = \sum_0^n a_k \cos k\theta$ are easily constructed by the substitution

$$Q_n\left(\frac{1+\cos\theta}{2}\right) = C_n(\theta) \text{ for } 0 \leq \theta \leq \pi,$$

and then $C_n(-\theta) = C_n(\theta)$.

Polynomials $S_n(\theta) = \sum_1^n b_k \sin k\theta$ require an investigation of the reduced function $P_{n-1}(x)\sqrt{x(1-x)}$.

The mixed type $Y_n(\Theta)$ is more complicated to build and has been constructed in our paper [4]. After that, the trigonometric problems analogous to 1. and 2. are immediately solved by transferring the trigonometric conditions by means of given formulas to the corresponding algebraic case.

Much wider results can be obtained by using functionals containing μ_k as functions of a variable, that means, considering a functional-operator.

5. Trigonometric functionals. Let us consider the functionals ([1], pp. 169-172):

$$1)\ F_{\rho\ \cos} = 1,\ \rho \cos \phi,\ \rho^2 \cos 2\phi, \dots \rho^n \cos n\phi; \quad 0 \leq \phi \leq \pi$$
$$2)\ F_{\rho\ \sin} = 0,\ \rho \sin \phi,\ \rho^2 \sin 2\phi, \dots \rho^n \cos n\phi; \quad 0 < \phi < \pi$$

and their attendant polynomials $Q_n(x,\phi)$. (ρ = const.)

For that purpose we have to introduce the notion of "fictitious knots" of F_n; for example, if $F_n = 1, A, A^2, \dots, A^n$; $A > 1$ or $A < 0$, the knot A is fictitious. (The "true" knots all lie in [0,1].)

We have the following obvious theorem: If F_n has a fictitious structure with r knots, and s is the number of true knots, then always $s+r > n+1$, for in this case, the (μ_k) have a double structure, and if $s+r \leq n+1$ the system (A) gives for all $(\delta_i)_1^{s+r}$ the value zero.

Now we can return to our problem. We have

$$\rho^k \cos k\phi = \tfrac{1}{2}(\rho e^{\phi i})^k + \tfrac{1}{2}(\rho e^{-\phi i})^k;\ \rho^k \sin k\phi = \frac{1}{2i}(\rho e^{\phi i})^k - \frac{1}{2i}(\rho e^{-\phi i})^k.$$

That is, both functionals have fictitious structures, with r=2; then the number of true knots is $s \geq n$. A further investigation shows, that for $0 < \phi < \pi$, F_1 has n separate Tchebysheff segments and (n-1) Zolotareff intervals: that means, that all $Q_n(x,\phi)$ belong either to [n,n+1,0], or to [n,n,0]. We call such functionals stable. For F_2 we have similar results. In case $\rho = 1$ we immediately obtain the evaluation of Re $P_n(z)$ and Im $P_n(z)$ in the z-plane.

6. The functional for a derivative. ([1], pp. 157-169). We consider $P_n'(\xi)$ as a functional $F = 0,1,2\xi,3\xi^2,\dots,n\xi^{n-1}$; $-\infty < \xi < +\infty$. The investigation of F gives the following results: if ξ is outside [0,1], the attendant polynomials are $\pm T_n^*(x)$; on [0,1] there exist n separate T-segments, on the borders of which either δ_0 or δ_n vanishes; so that between such segments the attendance is transferred to the pass [n,n,0], and we may assert the stability of the functional. Further we get a precise majorant for the $P_n'(\xi)$ at every point ξ. The well known majorant, given by S. Bernstein, $|P_n'(\xi)| \leq n/\sqrt{\xi(1-\xi)}$ touches the precise one only at points, where $\sin n\theta = \pm 1$ ($\xi = \tfrac{1}{2}(1 + \cos \theta)$). The same problems for the derivatives of higher order were solved by my pupil, a postgraduate student

V. A. Gusev, in 1958. He also gave the following elegant theorem ([5]): for the derivative-functional of order K the sum of the lengths of all its T-segments on [0,1] is equal to K/n.

7. <u>The stability of functionals</u>. We can now put forward more general problems, for instance the question of necessary and sufficient conditions for the stability of a functional. We have recent results about this in my papers [6], [7].

8. <u>Other applications</u>. To conclude, I should like to mention a wide field of possible applications, that has not been explored in print even superficially, namely the problems of interpolation, beginning with the simplest case of Lagrange interpolation. This case can be easily connected with the question of best approximation, by means of Tchebysheff's alternation theorem; then the polynomial of best approximation $P_n(x)$ for $f(x)$ is also the polynomial of "best" interpolation with the best n+1 chosen points.

References

1. VORONOVSKAYA, E. V. <u>Method of functionals and its applications</u>. Leningrad, 1963. (In Russian.)
2. VORONOVSKAYA, E. V. 'On Chebyshev approximation of analytic functions by algebraic polynomials'. Dokl. Akad. Nauk SSSR, <u>121</u> (1958), pp. 206-209. (In Russian.)
3. VORONOVSKAYA, E. V. 'Extremal trigonometric polynomials and their applications'. Dokl. Akad. Nauk SSSR, <u>129</u> (1959), pp. 12-15. (In Russian.)
4. VORONOVSKAYA, E. V. 'Construction of extremal trigonometric polynomials of mixed type'. Dokl. Akad. Nauk SSSR, <u>179</u> (1968), pp. 768-771; transl. in Soviet Math. Dokl., <u>9</u> (1968), pp. 438-441.
5. GUSEV, V. A. 'Functionals of the derivative of an algebraic polynomial and a theorem of V. A. Markov'. Izv. Akad. Nauk SSSR, Ser. Mat., <u>25</u> (1961), pp. 367-384. (In Russian.)
6. VORONOVSKAYA, E. V. 'Some criteria for the stability of functionals'. Dokl. Akad. Nauk SSSR, <u>161</u> (1965), pp. 270-273; transl. in Soviet Math Dokl., <u>6</u> (1965), pp. 392-395.
7. VORONOVSKAYA, E. V. 'On Zolotarev stability of functionals'. Dokl. Akad. Nauk SSSR, <u>173</u> (1967), pp. 15-17; transl. in Soviet Math. Dokl., <u>8</u> (1967), pp. 304-306.

SOME REMARKS ON APPROXIMATION BY POLYNOMIALS WITH INTEGRAL COEFFICIENTS

L. B. O. Ferguson

(University of California, Riverside)

This paper is written in hopes of stimulating interest in a certain branch of approximation theory. The problem is that of uniformly approximating functions on a set X by polynomials whose coefficients are, in some sense, integers.

Possibly the first result along these lines is due to Pál [7] who showed that a continuous real-valued function f on $X = [-\alpha,\alpha]$, $0 < \alpha < 1$, is uniformly approximable by polynomials with coefficients in the ring Z of ordinary integers if and only if $f(0)$ is an integer.

This can be proved very easily as follows. Since the value at the origin of any polynomial with integral coefficients is an integer, the condition $f(0) \in Z$ is clearly necessary. To prove it is sufficient we can assume $f(0) = 0$ without loss of generality. Suppose $\varepsilon > 0$.

Since $0 < \alpha < 1$, there exists an odd positive integer k such that

$$\sum_{n \geq k} \alpha^n < \varepsilon/3. \tag{1}$$

Since k is odd, the function x^k separates the points of $[-\alpha,\alpha]$ and by the Stone-Weierstrass Theorem there is a polynomial p such that

$$\|p(x^k) - f(x)\| < \varepsilon/3 \tag{2}$$

where $\|\cdot\|$ is defined by

$$\|h\| = \sup_{x \in X} |h(x)|. \tag{3}$$

If we let p_1 be the polynomial p without the constant term we see from (2) that

$$\|p(x^k) - p_1(x^k)\| < \varepsilon/3. \tag{4}$$

Finally, if we define $[p_1]$ to be the polynomial p_1 with each coefficient replaced by its integral part we have, using (1),

$$\| [p_1](x^k) - p_1(x^k) \| < \varepsilon/3 \tag{5}$$

since the difference is a polynomial in x^k without constant term, and each coefficient has absolute value less than unity. From (2), (4), and (5) we have

$$\| f(x) - [p_1](x^k) \| < \varepsilon,$$

which establishes Pál's result.

The case $\alpha = 1$ is interesting because here the criterion is not merely that $f(-1)$, $f(0)$, and $f(1)$ be integers but, in addition, that $(f(1) - f(-1))$ is even. As α tends to 2 more and more conditions of an algebraic nature must be satisfied by f. This can be seen most clearly from the results in Hewitt and Zuckerman [6].

Supposing now that X is any interval, $X = [\alpha, \beta]$, it is a surprising fact that for $\beta - \alpha \geqslant 4$ no function on X can be uniformly approximated by polynomials with integral coefficients (unless, of course, it is already such a polynomial). This would probably not have surprised Chebyshev since it can be easily proved as follows. Suppose $\{p_n\}$ is a sequence of polynomials with integral coefficients tending uniformly to f, and f is not a polynomial with integral coefficients. Then there exist n and m such that $\|p_n - f\| < 1$, $\|p_m - f\| < 1$, and $p_n \neq p_m$. It follows that

$$\|p_n - p_m\| < 2$$

and since $p_n - p_m$ is not zero it has a leading coefficient c, say, which is a non-zero integer, hence

$$\left\| \frac{p_n - p_m}{c} \right\| < 2.$$

However, $(p_n - p_m)/c$ is a monic polynomial and it is a well-known result of Chebyshev that on an interval of length 4 (or more) the norm of a monic polynomial is at least 2.

In the case where $(\beta - \alpha) < 4$ the problem has the following nontrivial solution (Hewitt and Zuckerman [6] and Ferguson [2]). Let $J = J(X)$ be the union of all complete sets of conjugate algebraic integers lying entirely in X. J is called the algebraic kernel of X by Fekete who proved that it is finite in the present case. A continuous (real-valued) function on X can be uniformly approximated by polynomials with integral coefficients if and only if the Lagrange interpolating polynomial for f on J has integral coefficients. Thus the problem is solved once we have determined J(X) but this last is usually difficult. See, however, Hewitt and Zuckerman [6] for intervals and Ferguson [4] for arcs of the unit circle.

The above theory has been extended to certain compact subsets of the complex plane; namely, those with void interior and connected complement. Here the role of the integers is played by any discrete subring A of the complex numbers with rank 2 and the functions to be approximated are complex valued. The transfinite diameter d(X) of X is the proper measure of the size of X. If $d(X) \geqslant 1$ then a complex valued function f on X can be uniformly approximated by polynomials with coefficients in A if and only if f coincides on X with such a polynomial. On the other hand, if $d(X) < 1$ and X is infinite, the last statement is false. See Fekete [1] and for proofs and extensions, Ferguson [2].

In the case of a compact X in the plane with $d(X) < 1$ and nonvoid interior little is known. This is the main subject of Ferguson [3]. Also, the following result fits into this category. Suppose that A as above is also a unique factorization domain. Let X be a compact subset of the open unit disk containing the origin in its interior and with a connected complement. Then a rational function f is uniformly approximable on X by polynomials with coefficients in A if and only if f can be represented in the form $f = p/g$ where p and g have coefficients in A, g(0) is a unit of A, and the roots of g lie outside of X (Ferguson [5]).

References

1. FEKETE, M. 'Approximations par polynomes avec conditions diophantienes, I et II'. C. R. Acad. Sci. Paris, 239 (1954), pp. 1337-1339 and 1445-1457.

2. FERGUSON, L. B. O. 'Uniform approximation by polynomials with integral coefficients I'. Pacific J. Math., 27 (1968), pp. 53-59.

3. FERGUSON, L. B. O. 'Uniform approximation by polynomials with integral coefficients II', Pacific J. Math., 26 (1968), pp. 273-281.

4. FERGUSON, L. B. O. 'Algebraic kernels of planar sets'. Duke Math. J., 36 (Dec. 1969).

5. FERGUSON, L. B. O. 'Uniform approximation of rational functions by polynomials with integral coefficients'. To appear, Duke Math. J.

6. HEWITT, E. and ZUCKERMAN, H. S. 'Approximation by polynomials with integral coefficients, a reformulation of the Stone-Weierstrass Theorem'. Duke Math. J., 26 (1959), pp. 305-324.

7. PÁL, J. 'Zwei kleine Bemerkungen'. Tôhoku Math. J., 6 (1914-1915), pp. 42-43.

CHARACTERIZATION OF BEST SPLINE APPROXIMATIONS WITH FREE KNOTS

D. C. Handscomb

(University of Oxford)

1. Introduction

If $a < \xi_1 < \xi_2 < \ldots < \xi_k < b$, and if x_+^n denotes the function

$$x_+^n = x^n (x \geq 0), \quad = 0 (x < 0), \tag{1}$$

then a spline function of degree $n (n \geq 1)$ with knots $\xi_1, \xi_2, \ldots, \xi_k$ is defined to be any function of the form

$$g(x) = \sum_{r=0}^{n} c_r x^r + \sum_{j=1}^{k} \beta_j (x - \xi_j)_+^n. \tag{2}$$

Characterization of minimax approximating splines with fixed knots has been very fully investigated by Rice [2]. Here we extend this investigation as far as we are able to the case of free knots. For brevity we omit almost everything in the way of proof, which can, by and large, be reconstructed by reference to Rice's paper.

We shall deal also with the closely-related problem of optimal quadrature. Suppose that we have a function f such that

$$f^{(n+1)}(x) = n!\, w(x) > 0. \tag{3}$$

Then

$$\begin{aligned} &\int_a^b [f(x) - g(x)] \phi^{(n+1)}(x)dx \\ &= \sum_{r=0}^{n} (-)^r \left\{ [f^{(r)}(b) - g^{(r)}(b)] \phi^{(n-r)}(b) - [f^{(r)}(a) - g^{(r)}(a)] \phi^{(n-r)}(a) \right\} + \\ &\quad + (-)^{n+1} n! \left\{ \int_a^b w(x)\, \phi(x)dx - \sum_{j=1}^{k} \beta_j \phi(\xi_j) \right\}, \end{aligned} \tag{4}$$

where g is a spline of the form (2). Therefore, provided that

$$g^{(r)}(a) = f^{(r)}(a), \quad g^{(r)}(b) = f^{(r)}(b) \quad (r=0 \text{ to } n), \tag{5}$$

we can assert that

$$n! \left| \int_a^b w(x)\, \phi(x)dx - \sum_{j=1}^{k} \beta_j\, \phi(\xi_j) \right| \leqslant \|f - g\|_{p'} \|\phi^{(n+1)}\|_p, \tag{6}$$

where $1/p' + 1/p = 1$. Thus a spline of the form (2) giving a best $L_{p'}$ approximation to f subject to the conditions (5) yields a formula for quadrature with weight $w(x) = f^{(n+1)}(x)/n!$, which is optimal with respect to $\|\phi^{(n+1)}\|_p$.

2. Characterization of minimax spline approximations with coincident knots

We first examine the simpler problem without the additional condition (5). As a first step the characterization theorem must be extended to the case of fixed but possibly coincident knots. This is not difficult.

Supposing that $\xi_j = \xi_{j+1} = \ldots = \xi_{j+\mu-1}$ (where $\mu \leqslant n$), but that either $j+\mu = k+1$ or $\xi_{j+\mu} > \xi_j$, define

$$\pi_j^n(x,\xi) = \frac{n!}{(n - \mu + 1)!} (x - \xi_j)_+^{n-\mu+1}. \tag{7}$$

Then if $a \leqslant \xi_1 \leqslant \xi_2 \leqslant \ldots \leqslant \xi_k \leqslant b$, not more than n knots coinciding at any one point, we replace the definition (2) by

$$g(x) = \sum_{r=0}^{n} c_r x^r + \sum_{j=1}^{k} \beta_j \pi_j^n (x,\xi). \tag{8}$$

If for $x_0 < x_1 < \ldots < x_N$ and $\xi_1 \leqslant \xi_2 \leqslant \ldots \leqslant \xi_k$ we define the $(N+1) \times (n+1)$ matrix

$$P_N^n(x) = \{x_i^r (i = 0 \text{ to } N,\ r = 0 \text{ to } n)\} \tag{9}$$

and the $(N+1) \times k$ matrix

$$Q_{Nk}^n(x,\xi) = \{\pi_j^n(x_i,\xi) \quad (i = 0 \text{ to } N,\ j = 1 \text{ to } k)\}, \tag{10}$$

it is possible to prove a lemma similar to that used by Rice:

Lemma 1

$$\det \left[P_{n+k}^n(x) \middle| Q_{n+k,k}^n(x,\xi) \right] \geqslant 0, \tag{11}$$

with strict inequality if and only if either $k = 0$ (i.e. Q is empty) or

$$x_{j-1} < \xi_j < x_{j+n} \quad (j = 1 \text{ to } k). \tag{12}$$

Rice's arguments then extend to prove:

Theorem 1

If $a = \xi_0 \leq \xi_1 \leq \dots \leq \xi_{k+1} = b$, then the spline g_0 of degree n with knots $\xi_1, \xi_2, \dots, \xi_k$ (not more than n of which coincide at any point) is a minimax approximation, among all splines of degree n with the same knots, to the real continuous function f on [a,b] if and only if there exist n+p+2 alternating extrema of $e_0 = f - g_0$ (i.e. points $x_0 < x_1 < \dots < x_{n+p+1}$ such that $|e_0(x_i)| = \max_x |e_0(x)|$ and $e_0(x_{i+1}) = - e_0(x_i)$) in the interval $[\xi_m, \xi_{m+p+1}]$, for some $m \geq 0$, $p \geq 0$, $m+p \leq k$. If this condition can be satisfied only when p=k then the minimax approximation is unique.

3. Conditions for minimax spline approximations with free knots

When we come to consider splines with free knots, complication arises from the possibility that a knot disappears through the vanishing of β_j, when its position ξ_j becomes indeterminate. To allow for this possibility, define a genuine knot to be one at which $\beta_j \neq 0$.

Theorem 2

A necessary condition that, among splines of degree $n (n \geq 2)$ with k free knots in [a,b], the spline g_0 with γ genuine knots $\zeta_1 \leq \zeta_2 \leq \dots \leq \zeta_j$ in (a,b) is a minimax approximation to the real continuous function f is that there exist $n+2p+k-\gamma+2$ alternating extrema of $e_0 = f-g_0$ in $[\zeta_1, \zeta_{m+p+1}]$ for some $m \geq 0$, $p \geq 0$, $m+p \leq \gamma$, where $\zeta_0 = a$, $\zeta_{\gamma+1} = b$.

Outline of proof. Let g_1 be a spline of degree n with double knots at $\zeta_1, \zeta_2, \dots, \zeta_\gamma$ and some $k-\gamma$ further simple knots $\eta_1, \eta_2, \dots, \eta_{k-\gamma}$ (none necessarily genuine). Let $\beta_j \neq 0$ and δ_j be the respective discontinuities in $g_0^{(n)}$ and $g_1^{(n-1)}$ at ζ_j. Then

$$(1-\theta)g_0(x) + \theta g_1(x) = g_2(x) + o(\theta), \tag{13}$$

where g_2 is a spline with k single knots at $(\zeta_j - \theta\delta_j/\beta_j)$ and at η_j.

If g_0 is minimax among splines with k free knots, we have, for all θ in [0,1],

$$\begin{aligned} \|e_0\| &\leq \|e_2\| = \|f - g_2\| \\ &= \|f - (1-\theta)g_0 - \theta g_1 + o(\theta)\| = \|(1-\theta)e_0 + \theta e_1 + o(\theta)\| \\ &\leq (1-\theta)\,\|e_0\| + \theta\,\|e_1\| + o(\theta), \end{aligned} \tag{14}$$

so that $\theta\,\|e_0\| \leq \theta\,\|e_1\| + o(\theta)$, and $\|e_0\| \leq \|e_1\|$. Therefore g_0 is minimax among splines with double knots at $\zeta_1,\zeta_2,\ldots,\zeta_\gamma$ and single knots at any $k-\gamma$ points $\eta_1,\eta_2,\ldots,\eta_{k-\gamma}$. The conclusion now follows from Theorem 1. (Slight modifications are required if ζ_j are not distinct.)

The nearest that we can get to a converse is:

Theorem 3

A sufficient condition for the spline g_0 of Theorem 2 to be a minimax approximation is that these exist $n + p + k + 2$ alternating extrema of e_0 in $[\zeta_m,\zeta_{m+p+1}]$ for some $m \geq 0$, $p \geq 0$, $m+p \leq \gamma$. If this condition can be satisfied only when $p=k$ then the minimax approximation is unique.

4. Special case with free knots

There is one special case in which the necessary and sufficient conditions coincide:

Theorem 4

If $f^{(n-1)}$ exists and is strictly convex in [a,b], then the minimax approximation to f on [a,b] by a spline of degree $n (n \geq 2)$ with k free knots is unique, all of its knots are genuine and distinct, and all its coefficients β_j are positive.

Proof. If g is any spline of degree n with genuine knots ζ_j then $g^{(n-1)}$ is piecewise linear with discontinuities of $n!\,\beta_j$ in the gradient at ζ_j, so that $e^{(n-1)}$ vanishes at most $2p+2$ times in $[\zeta_m,\zeta_{m+p+1}]$ (this number being attained only if $\zeta_{m+1},\ldots,\zeta_{m+p}$ are distinct and $\beta_{m+1},\ldots,\beta_{m+p}$ are positive), so that e' vanishes at most $n+2p$ times in this interval. Apart from points at which e' vanishes, e can have extrema only at a and b. Therefore the necessary condition of Theorem 2 can hold only with $m = 0$, $p = \gamma = k$, all knots genuine and distinct, and all $\beta_j > 0$. The sufficient condition of Theorem 3 also can hold only with $m = 0$ and $p = \gamma = k$, so that the minimax approximation is unique.

5. Minimax approximation with end conditions and coincident knots

We now add in the further condition (5). Define a further $(n+1)\times k$ matrix

$$R_k^n(\xi) = \{\pi_j^{n-r}(b,\xi) \quad (r = 0 \text{ to } n,\ j = 1 \text{ to } k)\}. \tag{15}$$

Then we can prove:

Lemma 2

$$\det \begin{bmatrix} Q_{k-n-2,k}^n(x,\xi) \\ R_k^n(\xi) \end{bmatrix} \geq 0 \quad (k > n), \tag{16}$$

with strict inequality if and only if either $k = n+1$ or

$$\xi_{j+1} < x_j < \xi_{j+n+2} \quad (j = 0 \text{ to } k-n-2). \tag{17}$$

This leads to:

Theorem 5

Under the conditions of Theorem 1 with the addition of (5), and provided that $k \geq n+1$ (without which (5) can not in general be satisfied), g_0 is a minimax approximation to f if and only if e_0 has

either $n+p+2$ alternating extrema in $[\xi_m,\xi_{m+p+1}]$, for some $m > 1$, $m+p+1 < k$, $p \geq 0$, $n+p+2 < k-n$,

or $p + 1$ alternating extrema in $(a,\xi_{p+1}]$ or $[\xi_{k-p},b)$ for some $p \geq 0$, $p+1 < k-n$,

or $k - n$ alternating extrema in (ξ_1,ξ_k).

If only the last of these alternatives is satisfied the minimax approximation is unique.

6. Minimax approximation with end conditions and free knots; optimal quadrature

From Theorem 5 we derive necessary and sufficient conditions for minimax approximations by splines with free knots subject to (5). Provided now that $k + \gamma \geq n + 1$, the necessary condition is the existence of

either $n + 2p + k - \gamma + 2$ alternating extrema in $[\zeta_m,\zeta_{m+p+1}]$ for some $m > 1$, $m+p+1 < \gamma$, $p \geq 0$, $n+2p+k-\gamma + 2 < k + \gamma - n$,

or $2p + k - \gamma + 1$ alternating extrema in $(a,\zeta_{p+1}]$ or $[\zeta_{\gamma-p},b)$ for some $p \geq 0$, $2p + k - \gamma + 1 < k + \gamma - n$,

<u>or</u> $k + \gamma - n$ alternating extrema in (ζ_1, ζ_γ),

and the sufficient condition is the existence of

<u>either</u> $n + p + k + 2$ alternating extrema in $[\zeta_m, \zeta_{m+p+1}]$ for some $m > 1$, $m+p+1 < \gamma$, $p \geq 0$, $n+p+k+2 < k+\gamma-n$,

<u>or</u> $p+k+1$ alternating extrema in $(a, \zeta_{p+1}]$ or $[\zeta_{\gamma-p}, b)$ for some $p \geq 0$, $p+k+1 < k+\gamma-n$,

<u>or</u> $k+\gamma-n$ alternating extrema in (ζ_1, ζ_γ),

with uniqueness if only the last of the sufficient conditions can be satisfied.

We can now give the analogue of Theorem 4 (the proof is on similar lines and is omitted).

Theorem 6

If $f^{(n)}$ exists and is strictly increasing in $[a,b]$, then the minimax approximation to f on $[a,b]$ by a spline of degree n ($n \geq 2$, $n + 1 \leq 2k$), subject to condition (5), exists and is unique, all of its knots are genuine and distinct, and all of its coefficients β_j are positive.

This theorem has the important

<u>Corollary</u>

If $2k \geq n+1$, then the k-point quadrature formula for $\int_a^b w(x)\, \phi(x) dx$ (where $w(x) > 0$) with free abscissae, optimal with respect to $\int_a^b |\phi^{(n+1)}(x)| dx$, is unique, having all of its abscissae distinct and all of its coefficients positive.

7. L_1 approximation

Turning briefly to the conjugate problem of L_1 approximation, we shall content ourselves with necessary conditions only. We assume for simplicity that there is no interval over which $f^{(n+1)}(x) = 0$, so that the zeros of $e(x)$ are discrete.

If for $a = z_0 < z_1 < \ldots < z_{N+1} = b$ we define a further $(N+1) \times (n+1)$ matrix

$$I_N^n(z) = \{ \int_{z_i}^{z_{i+1}} x^r dx \quad (i = 0 \text{ to } N,\ r = 0 \text{ to } n)\} \tag{17}$$

and an $(N+1) \times k$ matrix

$$J^n_{Nk}(z,\xi) = \{\int_{z_i}^{z_{i+1}} \pi^n_j(x,\xi)dx \quad (i = 0 \text{ to } N,\ j = 1 \text{ to } k)\}, \tag{18}$$

then by integration of Lemmas 1 and 2 we get:

Lemma 3

$$\det \left[I^n_{n+k}(z) \middle| J^n_{n+k,k}(z,\xi) \right] \geq 0, \tag{19}$$

with strict inequality if and only if either k=0 or

$$z_{j-1} < \xi_j < z_{j+n+1} \quad (j = 1 \text{ to } k); \tag{20}$$

Lemma 4

$$\det \begin{bmatrix} J^n_{k-n-2,k}(z,\xi) \\ R^n_k(\xi) \end{bmatrix} \geq 0 \quad (k > n+1), \tag{21}$$

with strict inequality if and only if either $k = n+2$ or

$$\xi_j < z_j < \xi_{j+n+2} \quad (j = 1 \text{ to } k-n-2). \tag{22}$$

8. Conditions for best L_1 spline approximations with fixed or free knots

From Lemma 3 we deduce that a necessary condition for a spline g_0 of degree n with k knots to be a best L_1 approximation to the continuous function f on [a,b] is the existence of n+p+3 changes of sign of $e_0 = f-g_0$ in $[\xi_m,\xi_{m+p+1}]$, for some $m \geq 0$, $p \geq 0$, $m+p \leq k$, if the knots are fixed, or $n+2p+k-\gamma+3$ changes of sign in $[\zeta_m,\zeta_{m+p+1}]$, for some $m \geq 0$, $p \geq 0$, $m+p \leq \gamma$, if they are free, where the points a and b are counted among the changes of sign in each case.

Similarly from Lemma 4 we deduce necessary conditions under the additional condition (5), which are the existence of

<u>either</u> $n+p+3$ changes of sign in $[\xi_m,\xi_{m+p+1}]$
for some $m > 1$, $m+p+1 < k$, $p \geq 0$, $n+p+3 < k-n-1$,
<u>or</u> $p+1$ changes of sign on $(a,\xi_{p+1}]$ or $[\xi_{k-p},b)$
for some $p \geq 0$, $p+1 < k-n-1$,
<u>or</u> $k-n-1$ changes of sign on (ξ_1,ξ_k),

if the knots are fixed, and

<u>either</u> $n + 2p + k - \gamma + 3$ changes of sign in $[\zeta_m,\zeta_{m+p+1}]$
for some $m > 1$, $m+p+1 < \gamma$, $p \geq 0$, $n+2p+k-\gamma+3 < k + \gamma - n - 1$,
<u>or</u> $2p+k-\gamma+1$ changes of sign in $(a,\zeta_{p+1}]$ or $[\zeta_{\gamma-p},b)$

for some $p \geq 0$, $2p + k - \gamma + 1 < k + \gamma - n - 1$,

or $k + \gamma - n - 1$ changes of sign in (ζ_1, ζ_γ),

if they are free.

9. Further special case; another form of optimal quadrature

Finally the following may be proved, corresponding to Theorems 4 and 6 (but notice that uniqueness is not mentioned).

Theorem 7

If $f^{(n-1)}$ exists and is strictly convex in $[a,b]$, then a best L_1 approximation to f on $[a,b]$ by a spline of degree $n (n \geq 2)$ with k free knots has all of its knots genuine and distinct and all of its coefficients β_j are positive.

The same holds, if $f^{(n)}$ exists also, for a best L_1 approximation subject to condition (5), provided that $n+1 \leq 2k$.

Corollary

If $2k \geq n+1$, then a k-point quadrature formula for $\int_a^b w(x)\, \phi(x) dx$ $(w(x) > 0)$ with free abscissae, optimal with respect to the upper bound of $|\phi^{(n+1)}(x)|$ on $[a,b]$, has all of its abscissae distinct and all of its coefficients positive.

10. Concluding remarks

Results similar to Theorems 4, 6, and 7 have been proved for L_2 spline approximation by Powell [1]; we conjecture that they hold good in any norm, the Corollaries perhaps even extending to higher dimensions.

Some of the results given here can also be derived from the theory of Chebyshevian splines; see Schumaker [3].

References

1. POWELL, M. J. D. 'On best L_2 spline approximations' AERE report T.P. 264., 1966.

2. RICE, J. R. 'Characterization of Chebyshev approximation by splines'. SIAM J.Numer.Anal., 4 (1967), pp. 557-565.

3. SCHUMAKER, L. 'Uniform approximation by Chebyshev spline functions II: free knots'. SIAM J. Numer.Anal., 5 (1968), pp. 647-656.

A NOTE ON INTERPOLATING PERIODIC QUINTIC SPLINE FUNCTIONS

F. Schurer

(Technological University Eindhoven)

1. Introduction and summary

The Banach space (with supremum norm) of real-valued, continuous periodic functions with period 1 will be denoted by C. To each division of the interval $[0,1]$ into n subintervals $\{0 = x_0 < x_1 < \dots < x_{n-1} < x_n = 1\}$, there corresponds an n-dimensional subspace $S(x_0,x_1,\dots,x_n)$ of C, whose members are the periodic quintic spline functions. So, $s \in S(x_0,x_1,\dots,x_n)$ if and only if

1) $s \in C^4[0,1]$ and $s^{(i)}(0) = s^{(i)}(1)$, $\quad (i = 0,1,2,3,4)$;

2) the restriction of s to an arbitrary subinterval $[x_{i-1},x_i]$ is an ordinary polynomial of degree at most five.

Throughout the paper we assume that the nodes x_i are equally spaced on $[0,1]$, i.e. $x_i = i/n$ $(i = 0,1,\dots,n)$. Section 2 of this note presents a number of preliminaries about quintic splines; much of this material can be found in Schurer [3]. In section 3 we establish two theorems which improve similar results in [3]. The main part of this paper deals with the computation of the norm of the interpolating periodic quintic spline operator. For this purpose various assertions about cardinal quintic spline functions are required.

Except in a few cases no proofs of the asserted statements are given. In particular, the calculations involved are too lengthy and tedious to be reproduced here. The reader is referred to Schurer [4] for a more elaborate exposition. The results in this note are comparable to those in Cheney and Schurer [2], where similar theorems for interpolating periodic cubic splines are derived.

2. Preliminaries on quintic splines

It is known (Ahlberg et al. [1], p. 135; Schurer [3]) that to each $f \in C$ there corresponds a uniquely determined element $s \in S(x_0,x_1,\ldots,x_n)$ which interpolates the function f at the nodes x_i $(i = 0,1,\ldots,n)$. If we put

$$f_i = f(x_i),\ \overline{\lambda}_i = s'(x_i),\ \overline{\mu}_i = s''(x_i),\ \overline{m}_i = s'''(x_i),$$

then on the interval $[x_{i-1},x_i]$ the quintic spline function s can be given explicitly in the following form:

$$s(x) = f_{i-1}A_i(x)+f_iB_i(x)+\overline{\lambda}_{i-1}C_i(x)+\overline{\lambda}_iD_i(x)+\overline{m}_{i-1}E_i(x)+\overline{m}_iF_i(x). \tag{1}$$

In this formula $A_i(x),\ldots,F_i(x)$ are certain quintic polynomials. If we denote these polynomials by $A(t),\ldots,F(t)$ when $[x_{i-1},x_i]$ is replaced by $[0,1]$, then

$$A(t) = \tfrac{1}{2}(1 - t)^2(-2t^3 + t^2 + 4t + 2), \quad B(t) = A(1 - t),$$

$$C(t) = \tfrac{1}{4}t(1 - t)^2(-2t^2 + t + 4), \quad D(t) = -C(1 - t),$$

$$E(t) = \tfrac{1}{48}t^2(1 - t)^2(2t - 3), \quad F(t) = -E(1 - t).$$

The expressions for $A_i(x),\ldots,F_i(x)$ are now obtained by setting $t = n(x - x_{i-1})$, multiplying $C_i(x)$, $D_i(x)$ by n^{-1} and $E_i(x)$ $F_i(x)$ by n^{-3}. We note that $A_i(x)$, $B_i(x)$, $C_i(x)$, $F_i(x) \geq 0$ on $[x_{i-1},x_i]$, whereas $D_i(x)$, $E_i(x) \leq 0$ on this interval. Moreover,

$$A_i(x) + B_i(x) = 1, \tag{2}$$

$$C_i(x) - D_i(x) = (x - x_{i-1})(1 - n(x - x_{i-1})) \leq \frac{1}{4n} \tag{3}$$

$$F_i(x) - E_i(x) = \frac{1}{12n}(x - x_{i-1})^2(1 - n(x - x_{i-1})) \leq \frac{1}{192n^3}. \tag{4}$$

Because of $s \in C^4[0,1]$ and $s^{(i)}(0) = s^{(i)}(1)$ $(i = 0,1,\ldots,4)$, the parameters $\overline{\lambda}_i$, $\overline{\mu}_i$ and $\overline{m}_i$ have to satisfy particular relations for $i = 1,2,\ldots,n$ (cf. [3]). Assuming that all occurring indices are interpreted modulo n, we have

$$\overline{\lambda}_{i-2}+26\overline{\lambda}_{i-1}+66\overline{\lambda}_i+26\overline{\lambda}_{i+1}+\overline{\lambda}_{i+2} = 5n(f_{i+2}+10f_{i+1}-10f_{i-1}-f_{i-2}), \tag{5}$$

$$\overline{\mu}_{i-2}+26\overline{\mu}_{i-1}+66\overline{\mu}_i+26\overline{\mu}_{i+1}+\overline{\mu}_{i+2} = 20n^2(f_{i+2}+2f_{i+1}-6f_i+2f_{i-1}+f_{i-2}),$$

$$\bar{m}_{i-2}+26\bar{m}_{i-1}+66\bar{m}_i+26\bar{m}_{i+1}+\bar{m}_{i+2} = 60n^3(f_{i+2}-2f_{i+1}+2f_{i-1}-f_{i-2}). \quad (6)$$

Due to the fact that the matrix associated with the two systems of equations (5) and (6) is diagonally dominant, it follows by a standard procedure (cf. [3]) that

$$\max_i|\bar{\lambda}_i| \leq \frac{25}{6}\, n\omega(f;1/n), \quad (7)$$

$$\max_i|\bar{m}_i| \leq 20n^3\, \omega(f;1/n). \quad (8)$$

Let $s^i(x) \in S(x_0,x_1,\ldots,x_n)$ denote the i-th cardinal spline - this function is defined by the equations $s^i(x_j) = \delta^i_j$ for $i,j = 1,2,\ldots,n$ - then in terms of these functions we have

$$s \equiv L_n f = \sum_{i=1}^{n} f(x_i)s^i(x). \quad (9)$$

If, as usual, the norm of the interpolating periodic quintic spline operator is defined as

$$\| L_n\| = \sup\{ \|L_n f\| \ :\ f \in C,\ \|f\| = 1 ,$$

it is not difficult to prove that

$$\|L_n\| = \| \sum_{i=1}^{n} |s^i(x)| \| . \quad (10)$$

3. Improving some results of [3]

Using the contents of section 2 we will now show how theorems 3 and 4 of [3] can be improved upon.

Theorem 1

Let $f \in C$ and let s be the interpolating periodic quintic spline function associated with f. Then

$$\|s - f\| \leq 2\,\frac{7}{48}\,\omega(f;1/n).$$

Proof. Let x be an arbitrary point of [0,1] and assume that $x \in [x_{i-1},x_i]$. In view of (1) and (2) we have

$$s(x) - f(x) = (f_{i-1} - f(x))A_i(x) + (f_i - f(x))B_i(x) + \\ + \bar{\lambda}_{i-1}C_i(x)+\bar{\lambda}_iD(x)+\bar{m}_{i-1}E_i(x)+\bar{m}_iF_i(x).$$

Now recall that in the interval $[x_{i-1},x_i]$ the functions $A_i(x)$, $B_i(x)$ $C_i(x)$

and $F_i(x)$ are nonnegative, whereas $D_i(x)$, $E_i(x) \leq 0$ there. Hence,

$$|s(x)-f(x)| \leq \omega(f;1/n)+ \max_j|\bar{\lambda}_j|.(C_i(x)-D_i(x))+ \max_j|\bar{m}_j|.(F_i(x)-E_i(x)).$$

From this inequality we obtain the result of theorem 1 by a simple calculation using (3), (4), (7) and (8).

Theorem 2

A uniform upper bound for the norm of the interpolating periodic quintic spline operator L_n, as defined in (9), is given by

$$\|L_n\| \leq 3\tfrac{7}{24}.$$

Proof. As we remarked in (10), the norm of the quintic spline operator is equal to the Chebyshev norm of the function $\sum_{i=1}^{n}|s^i(x)|$. Let ξ be chosen so that $\sum_{i=1}^{n}|s^i(\xi)| = \|\sum_{i=1}^{n}|s^i(x)|\|$. Furthermore, let f be a continuous function which is linear in each interval $[x_{i-1},x_i]$ and takes values $f_i = \text{sgn}\, s^i(\xi)$. If s is the spline function which interpolates to f at the nodes, then $\|L_n\| = \|L_nf\| = \|s\|$. To determine an upper bound for $\|L_n\|$ we consider the spline function s on an arbitrary subinterval, say $[x_{i-1},x_i]$. Because of (1) we have

$$s(x) = f_{i-1}A_i(x)+f_iB_i(x)+\bar{\lambda}_{i-1}C_i(x)+\bar{\lambda}_iD_i(x)+\bar{m}_{i-1}E_i(x)+\bar{m}_iF_i(x),$$

whence by (2), (3), (4), (7), (8)

$$|s(x)| \leq \|f\|(A_i(x)+B_i(x))+ \max_j|\bar{\lambda}_j|.(C_i(x)-D_i(x)) + \max_j|\bar{m}_j|.(F_i(x)-E_i(x))$$

$$\leq \|f\| + \frac{25}{6}n\,\omega(f;1/n).\frac{1}{4n} + 20n^3\,\omega(f;1/n).\frac{1}{192n^3} = 1 + \frac{55}{48}\,\omega(f;1/n).$$

Theorem 2 follows by observing that $\omega(f;1/n) \leq 2$.

4. On the cardinal spline function s^k

In view of formulae (9), (10), it will be clear that knowledge about the cardinal spline functions would be useful. This is the subject of this section. Depending on whether n is even or odd we put n = 2k, n = 2k+1, respectively. Furthermore, we write $\lambda_i = (s^k)'(x_i)$ and $m_i = (s^k)'''(x_i)$. Since the functions s^i are periodic and the nodes are equally spaced, we have $s^i(x) = s^k(x - x_{i-k})$. So it is sufficient to compute one cardinal quintic spline function, for instance s^k. Then

$$(s^i)'(x_j) = (s^k)'(x_j - x_{i-k}) = (s^k)'(x_{j-i+k}) = \lambda_{j-i+k}.$$

Consequently, taking into account (1), we get on the interval $[x_{j-1}, x_j]$

$$\left.\begin{aligned} s^i(x) &= \delta^i_{j-1}A_j(x)+\delta^i_jB_j(x)+(s^i)'(x_{j-1})C_j(x)+(s^i)'(x_j)D_j(x) + \\ &\qquad +(s^i)'''(x_{j-1})E_j(x)+(s^i)'''(x_j)F_j(x) \\ &= \delta^i_{j-1}A_j(x)+\delta^i_jB_j(x)+\lambda_{j-i+k-1}C_j(x)+\lambda_{j-i+k}D_j(x) + \\ &\qquad +m_{j-i+k-1}E_j(x)+m_{j-i+k}F_j(x). \end{aligned}\right\} \quad (11)$$

Obviously the parameters λ_i and m_i $(i = 1,2,\ldots,n)$ will have to be computed. To this end we rewrite equations (5) and (6) in their appropriate form. For $i = 1,2,\ldots,n$ we get

$$\lambda_{i-2}+26\lambda_{i-1}+66\lambda_i+26\lambda_{i+1}+\lambda_{i+2} = 5n(\delta^k_{i+2}+10\delta^k_{i+1}-10\delta^k_{i-1}-\delta^k_{i-2}),$$

$$m_{i-2}+26m_{i-1}+66m_i+26m_{i+1}+m_{i+2} = 60n^3(\delta^k_{i+2}-2\delta^k_{i+1}+2\delta^k_{i+1}-\delta^k_{i-2}).$$

The main result of this section is a lemma which contains the solution of these two systems of equations. As a consequence of (11), all cardinal spline functions then can be determined completely. In order to state the lemma we proceed as follows.

Let

$$\begin{aligned} Q(z) &= z^3 - 26z^2 + z, \\ R(z) &= -z^2 + z, \\ S(z) &= -z^3 + 26z^2 - 26z + 1, \\ P(z) &= z^4 - 26z^3 + 66z^2 - 26z + 1 = (z - z_1)(z - z_2)(z - z_3)(z - z_4), \end{aligned} \quad (12)$$

where $z_3 = z_2^{-1}$, $z_4 = z_1^{-1}$ and the numbers z_1, z_2 are given by

$$z_1 = \tfrac{1}{2}(13+\sqrt{105}-\sqrt{270+26\sqrt{105}}) = 0.04309\ldots, \quad (13)$$

$$z_2 = \tfrac{1}{2}(13-\sqrt{105}-\sqrt{270-26\sqrt{105}}) = 0.43057\ldots \,. \quad (14)$$

Let

$$C_j = \frac{z_j^2}{P'(z_j)}, \quad C_j^* = \frac{Q(z_j)}{P'(z_j)}, \quad D_j = \frac{R(z_j)}{P'(z_j)}, \quad D_j^* = \frac{S(z_j)}{P'(z_j)}, \quad (j=1,2,3,4). \quad (15)$$

Furthermore, we introduce the sequences $\{\rho_i^{(1)}\}$, $\{\rho_i^{(2)}\}$, $\{\rho_i^{(3)}\}$, $\{\rho_i^{(4)}\}$ $(i = 0,1,2,\dots)$ determined by

$$\rho_i^{(1)} = -C_1(z_1)^{-i-1} - C_2(z_2)^{-i-1} - C_3(z_3)^{-i-1} - C_4(z_4)^{-i-1}, \tag{16}$$

$$\rho_i^{(2)} = -C_1^*(z_1)^{-i-1} - C_2^*(z_2)^{-i-1} - C_3^*(z_3)^{-i-1} - C_4^*(z_4)^{-i-1}, \tag{17}$$

$$\rho_i^{(3)} = -D_1(z_1)^{-i-1} - D_2(z_2)^{-i-1} - D_3(z_3)^{-i-1} - D_4(z_4)^{-i-1}, \tag{18}$$

$$\rho_i^{(4)} = -D_1^*(z_1)^{-i-1} - D_2^*(z_2)^{-i-1} - D_3^*(z_3)^{-i-1} - D_4^*(z_4)^{-i-1}, \tag{19}$$

Now the lemma for the computation of the parameters λ_i and m_i reads as follows.

Lemma 1

The first and third derivatives λ_i and m_i $(i = 0,1,\dots,n)$ of the cardinal quintic spline function s^{i_k} are given by the formulae

$$\begin{cases} \lambda_i = (-1)^{k+i+1}\, 5n\, a_k^{-1} a_i & , (n=2k,\ k=1,2,\dots;\ i=0,1,\dots,k-1), \\ \lambda_i = -\lambda_{2k-i} & , (i=k,k+1,\dots,2k), \end{cases}$$

$$\begin{cases} \lambda_i = (-1)^{k+i+1}\, 5n\, b_k^{-1} b_i & , (n=2k+1,\ k=1,2,\dots;\ i=0,1,\dots,k-1), \\ \lambda_i = -\lambda_{2k-i} & , (i=k,k+1,\dots,2k), \end{cases}$$

$$\begin{cases} m_i = (-1)^{k+i+1}\, 60n^3 a_k^{*-1} a_i^*, & (n=2k,\ k=1,2,\dots;\ i=0,1,\dots,k-1), \\ m_i = -m_{2k-i} & , (i=k,k+1,\dots,2k), \end{cases}$$

$$\begin{cases} m_i = (-1)^{k+i+1}\, 60n^3 b_k^{*-1} b_i^*, & (n=2k+1,\ k=1,2,\dots;\ i=0,1,\dots,k-1), \\ m_i = -m_{2k-i} & , (i=k,k+1,\dots,2k), \end{cases}$$

where

$$a_i = \rho_i^{(1)} \frac{(16\rho_k^{(2)} - \rho_{k+1}^{(2)} - \rho_{k-1}^{(2)})}{(-16\rho_k^{(1)} + \rho_{k+1}^{(1)} + \rho_{k-1}^{(1)})} + \rho_i^{(2)}, \tag{20}$$

$$b_i = \rho_i^{(3)} \frac{(16\rho_k^{(4)} - \rho_{k+1}^{(4)} - \rho_{k-1}^{(4)})}{(-16\rho_k^{(3)} + \rho_{k+1}^{(3)} + \rho_{k-1}^{(3)})} + \rho_i^{(4)}, \quad (i=0,1,\dots,k) \tag{21}$$

$$a_i^* = \rho_i^{(1)} \frac{(28\rho_k^{(2)} - \rho_{k+1}^{(2)} - \rho_{k-1}^{(2)})}{(-28\rho_k^{(1)} + \rho_{k+1}^{(1)} + \rho_{k-1}^{(1)})} + \rho_i^{(2)}, \tag{22}$$

$$b_i^* = \rho_i^{(3)} \frac{(28\rho_k^{(4)} - \rho_{k+1}^{(4)} - \rho_{k-1}^{(4)})}{(-28\rho_k^{(3)} + \rho_{k+1}^{(3)} + \rho_{k-1}^{(3)})} + \rho_i^{(4)}. \tag{23}$$

Remark. The formulae appearing in the lemma are rather complicated and in view of (12),...,(19) they do not seem suitable for the computation of the λ_i and m_i. Fortunately, this is not the case. In fact, the sequences $\{\rho_i^{(1)}\}$, $\{\rho_i^{(2)}\}$, $\{\rho_i^{(3)}\}$ and $\{\rho_i^{(4)}\}$ are all solutions of the difference equation

$$\rho_{i+1} - 26\rho_i + 66\rho_{i-1} - 26\rho_{i-2} + \rho_{i-3} = 0, \quad (i = 3,4,\ldots).$$

Once the first four elements of every sequence are known, they can be generated in an easy way. It turns out that

$$(\rho_0^{(1)},\rho_1^{(1)},\rho_2^{(1)},\rho_3^{(1)}) = (0,0,1,26),$$

$$(\rho_0^{(2)},\rho_1^{(2)},\rho_2^{(2)},\rho_3^{(2)}) = (0,1,0,-65),$$

$$(\rho_0^{(3)},\rho_1^{(3)},\rho_2^{(3)},\rho_3^{(3)}) = (0,1,25,584),$$

$$(\rho_0^{(4)},\rho_1^{(4)},\rho_2^{(4)},\rho_3^{(4)}) = (1,0,-40,-1015).$$

Using lemma 1 the calculation of the first and third derivatives λ_i and m_i $(i = 0,1,\ldots,n)$ then becomes a simple matter.

5. Consequences of lemma 1

In the sequel we will use lemma 1 for the computation of the norm of L_n. To this end additional information on the behaviour of the first and third derivatives of the spline function s^k is required. The following assertions are all consequences of lemma 1; a sketch of their proofs can be found in Schurer [4].

The form of the expressions for λ_i and m_i $(i = 0,1,\ldots,k-1)$ as given in lemma 1, suggests that the first and third derivatives of the cardinal spline function s^k alternate in sign. This indeed is true, as follows from

Assertion 1

Let k be an arbitrary, but fixed, positive integer. Then

$$a_i,\ b_i \geqslant 0, \quad (i = 0,1,\ldots,k),$$

$$a_i^*,\ b_i^* \geqslant 0, \quad (i = 0,1,\ldots,k-1),$$

$$a_k^*,\ b_k^* < 0,$$

where a_i, b_i, a_i^*, b_i^* are given by (20), (21), (22), (23).

The next assertion states that the absolute values of the first and third derivatives λ_i and m_i $(i = 0,1,\ldots,k-1)$ are decreasing if we move from the node x_k on the left. There is only one exception to this rule and this occurs for the third derivative in case n=5; indeed, $|m_0| > |m_1|$, as can be verified by a simple calculation. Moreover, $\lambda_0 = m_0 = 0$ in case n is even.

Assertion 2

Let n be an arbitrary positive integer > 1 and let n=2k, n=2k+1, respectively. Then

$$|\lambda_0| < |\lambda_1| < \ldots < |\lambda_{k-1}|$$

and

$$|m_0| < |m_1| < \ldots < |m_{k-1}|, \quad (n \neq 5).$$

We conclude this section by stating a result about the sign and magnitude of the second cardinal spline derivative μ_k.

Assertion 3

If μ_i denotes the second derivative of the spline function s^k at the node x_i, then

$$|\mu_k| > |\mu_i|, \quad (i \neq k)$$

and

$$\mu_k < 0.$$

6. On the norm of the quintic spline operator

In this section we first give some expressions for the norm of the interpolating periodic quintic spline operator, which involve the values of the various cardinal spline derivatives at the nodes. The contents of lemma 2, together with lemma 1, then enable us to write down a formula by which it is possible to compute the exact value of $\|L_n\|$ for each positive integer n. Because of the complexity of this formula we refrain from giving it here; it can be found in [4]. Instead we state the least upper bound for the sequence $\{\|L_n\|\}$ $(n = 2,3,\ldots)$, together with some other properties of these numbers. The paper is concluded with a table containing the numerical values of the first elements of $\{\|L_n\|\}$.

Lemma 2

If the numbers λ_i and m_i $(i = 0,1,\ldots,n)$ are defined as in lemma 1, the norm of the interpolating periodic quintic spline operator L_n is given by

$$\|L_n\| = 1 + \frac{1}{4n} \sum_{i=1}^{n} |\lambda_i| + \frac{1}{192n^3} \sum_{i=1}^{n} |m_i|.$$

Proof. By (10) we know that the norm of L_n is equal to the Chebyshev norm of the function $\sum_{i=1}^{n} |s^i|$. Select x so that $\|L_n\| = \sum_{i=1}^{n} |s^i(x)|$ and select j such that $x_{j-1} \leq x \leq x_j$. Hence by (11) we have

$$\begin{aligned}
&\sum_{i=1}^{n} |s^i(x)| \\
&= \sum_{i=1}^{n} |\delta^i_{j-1}A_j(x)+\delta^i_jB_j(x)+\lambda_{j-1+k-1}C_j(x)+\lambda_{j-i+k}D_j(x)+m_{j-i+k-1}E_j(x)+m_{j-i+k}F_j(x)| \\
&= |A_j(x)+\lambda_kC_j(x)+\lambda_{k+1}D_j(x)+m_kE_j(x)+m_{k+1}F_j(x)| + \\
&\quad + |B_j(x)+\lambda_{k-1}C_j(x)+\lambda_kD_j(x)+m_{k-1}E_j(x)+m_kF_j(x)| + \\
&\quad + \left(\sum_{i=1}^{k-1} + \sum_{i=k+2}^{n}\right) |\lambda_{i-1}C_j(x)+\lambda_iD_j(x)+m_{i-1}E_j(x)+m_iF_j(x)|.
\end{aligned}$$

By assertion 1 the coefficients λ_i alternate in sign as the index i runs through the sets $\{0,1,\ldots,k-1\}$ and $\{k+1,\ldots,n\}$. Assertion 1 also establishes the alternation of the parameters m_i when i runs through these sets. Furthermore, $\lambda_k = m_k = 0$, $\lambda_{k-1} > 0$, $m_{k-1} < 0$ and $\lambda_{k+1} < 0$, $m_{k+1} > 0$. The way in which the numbers λ_i and m_i alternate, together with the properties of the polynomials $A_j(x),\ldots,F_j(x)$, completely determine the shape of the cardinal spline functions. Between two adjacent nodes they do not have zeros and the sign of the function changes when a node is passed. Moreover, $s^k > 0$ on (x_{k-1}, x_{k+1}) and this function is symmetric with respect to x_k. These facts imply that

$$\sum_{i=1}^{n} |s^i(x)| = 1+\{C_j(x)-D_j(x)\}\sum_{i=1}^{n} |\lambda_i|+\{F_j(x)-E_j(x)\}\sum_{i=1}^{n} |m_i|.$$

Since x was chosen to make $\sum_{i=1}^{n} |s^i|$ a maximum, it is apparent from formulae (3) and (4) that $x = \frac{1}{2}(x_{j-1} + x_j)$. Then $C_j(x) - D_j(x)$ and $F_j(x) - E_j(x)$ both attain their maximal value. In view of (3), (4) we obtain

$$|| \sum_{i=1}^{n} |s^i| \, || = 1 + \frac{1}{4n} \sum_{i=1}^{n} |\lambda_i| + \frac{1}{192n^3} \sum_{i=1}^{n} |m_i|,$$

which is equivalent to the lemma.

The next lemma gives an expression for $\|L_n\|$ in which the first and second cardinal spline derivatives of s^k are involved.

Lemma 3

Let μ_j denote the second derivative of the cardinal spline function s^k at the node x_j. Then

$$||L_n|| = 1 + \frac{5}{16n} \sum_{i=1}^{n} |\lambda_i| + \frac{\mu_k}{32n^2}, \quad (n=2k+1),$$

$$||L_n|| = 1 + \frac{5}{16n} \sum_{i=1}^{n} |\lambda_i| + \frac{(\mu_k+|\mu_0|)}{32n^2}, \quad (n=2k).$$

Lemmas 2 and 3, together with assertion 3, imply the following simple

Corollary

$$1 + \frac{1}{4n} \sum_{i=1}^{n} |\lambda_i| < ||L_n|| < 1 + \frac{5}{16n} \sum_{i=1}^{n} |\lambda_i|.$$

Using lemmas 1 and 2, the next step would be to state the formula by which it is possible to compute the norm of L_n for n=2,3,... . Because of the intricateness of the expression it is omitted here. One of the consequences which can be drawn from it is the following theorem; the exhibited upper bound for $\|L_n\|$ is best possible.

Theorem 3

Let the numbers z_1, z_2 be given by (13), (14) and let

$$K = 1 + \frac{15}{8} \frac{(z_1 + z_2 - 13z_1z_2 + (z_1z_2)^2)}{(1 - z_1)(1 - z_2)(1 - z_1z_2)} = 1.8161\ldots .$$

Then the norms $||L_n||$ are ordered as follows:

(i) $||L_2|| < ||L_4|| < ||L_6|| < \ldots < K$,

(ii) $||L_3|| < ||L_5|| < ||L_7|| < \ldots < K$,

(iii) $||L_3|| = ||L_6||,\ ||L_5|| = ||L_{10}||,\ ||L_7|| = ||L_{14}||, \ldots .$

We remark that similar results hold for the norm of the interpolating periodic cubic spline operator, the nodes being equally spaced (cf. theorem 2 in [2]).

In the following table we have collected some numerical results. They clearly show that already for small values of n the norm of $||L_n||$ is very close to the least upper bound 1.8161... .

$\|\|L_2\|\| = 1$	$\|\|L_3\|\| = 1\frac{5}{8} = 1.625$
$\|\|L_4\|\| = 1\frac{105}{256} = 1.4101\ldots$	$\|\|L_5\|\| = 1\frac{123}{158} = 1.7784\ldots$
$\|\|L_6\|\| = 1\frac{5}{8} = 1.625$	$\|\|L_7\|\| = 1\frac{680745}{841352} = 1.8091\ldots$
$\|\|L_8\|\| = 1\frac{8775}{12016} = 1.7302\ldots$	$\|\|L_9\|\| = 1\frac{39385}{48333} = 1.8148\ldots$
$\|\|L_{10}\|\| = 1\frac{123}{158} = 1.7784\ldots$	$\|\|L_{11}\|\| = 1\frac{1988418655}{2436972728} = 1.8158\ldots$

Acknowledgement. The author wishes to thank J. H. van Lint of this university and F. W. Steuel, Technological University Twente, for some valuable suggestions.

References

1. AHLBERG, J. H., NILSON, E. N. and WALSH, J. L. The theory of splines and their applications. Academic Press, 1967.

2. CHENEY, E. W. and SCHURER, F. 'On interpolating cubic splines with equally spaced nodes'. Indag. Math. 30 (1968), pp. 517-524.

3. SCHURER, F. 'A note on interpolating periodic quintic splines with equally spaced nodes'. J. Approx. Theory 1 (4) (1968), pp. 493-500.

4. SCHURER, F. 'On interpolating periodic quintic spline functions with equally spaced nodes'. Report 69-WSK-01, Technological University Eindhoven, 1969.

NON-NEGATIVE INTERPOLATION FORMULAS FOR HARMONIC AND ANALYTIC FUNCTIONS*

P. J. Davis

(Brown University, Providence, R.I.)

1. Non-negative interpolation formulas

Let T be a compact set in R^q the space of q real variables or in K^q the space of q complex variables. Let $C_N(T)$ be the N+1-dimensional linear space spanned by the N+1 linearly independent continuous functions $\phi_0(t),\phi_1(t),\ldots,\phi_N(t)$ defined on T. By an interpolation formula for $C_N(T)$, we shall mean a formula of the type

$$p(t^*) = \sum_{k=0}^{n} a_k p(t_k) \tag{1}$$

valid for all $p \in C_N(T)$. The points $t^*,t_0,\ldots,t_n$ are assumed to be distinct points in T and $n \geq N$. If, in addition, we have

$$a_k \geq 0, \ k=0,1,\ldots,n \tag{2}$$

or

$$a_k > 0, \ k=0,1,\ldots,n \tag{2'}$$

then formula (1) is said to be a non-negative or a positive interpolation formula respectively.

Depending upon the selection of T and $C_N(T)$, non-negative interpolation formulas may or may not exist.

Example 1. Let $T = [a,b]$, $-\infty < a \leq t^* \leq b < \infty$, and let $C_1(T)$ be the space spanned by the functions 1,t. That is, C_1 comprises the linear function on T. Then, "ordinary" linear interpolation

* The results of this report were obtained under the support of the Office of Naval Research Contract Nonr 562 (36) with Brown University.

$$p(t^*) = \frac{b-t^*}{b-a}\, p(a) + \frac{t^*-a}{b-a}\, p(b) \tag{3}$$

is a non-negative interpolation formula for C_1.

Example 2. On the other hand, if $T = [a,b]$, if $a < t_0 < t_1 < \dots < t_n < b$, $a < t^* < b$, and if $C(T)$ contains at least 3 functions, say ϕ_0,ϕ_1,ϕ_2 which form a Tschebyscheff system on $[a,b]$, (the functions $1,t,t^2$ will do, for example), then it is impossible to have a non-negative interpolation formula for $C(T)$. This implies, in particular that if $n \geq 2$, there are no non-negative interpolation formulas for the class P_n of (algebraic) polynomials of degree $\leq n$.

Proof. By definition, ϕ_0,ϕ_1,ϕ_2 comprise a Tschebyscheff system on $[a,b]$ if for any three distinct points t_0,t_1,t_2 in $[a,b]$, the determinant

$$|\phi_i(t_j)| \neq 0. \tag{4}$$

Equivalently, we may say that 0 is the only function of the form $a_0\phi_0 + a_1\phi_1 + a_2\phi_2$ which has 3 or more roots on $[a,b]$.

Case 1. Let $t_0 < t^* < t_n$. Designate by t_j and t_{j+1} the two nearest neighbors of t^* on the right and left: $t_j < t^* < t_{j+1}$. In view of (4) we can find a linear combination $\Phi = a_0\phi_0 + a_1\phi_1 + a_2\phi_2$ such that $\Phi(t_j) = 1$, $\Phi(t^*) = -1$, $\Phi(t_{j+1}) = 1$. Since Φ is continuous, it must have a zero in (t_j,t^*) and in (t^*,t_{j+1}). Since Φ can have at most 2 zeros on $[a,b]$, it follows that Φ is positive at $t_0,t_1,\dots,t_n$. If we assume there is a non-negative interpolation formula, then $-1 = \Phi(t^*) = \sum_{k=0}^{n} a_k\Phi(t_k) \geq 0$, a contradiction.

Case 2. $a < t^* < t_0 < t_1 < \dots < t_n < b$. Select a point a' with $a < a' < t^*$. As before we can find $\Phi = a_0\phi_0 + a_1\phi_1 + a_2\phi_2$ such that $\phi(a') = 1$, $\phi(t^*) = -1$, $\phi(t_1) = 1$. Hence, as before, $\Phi(t_k) \geq 0$, $k=0,1,\dots,n$ and this leads to a contradiction. Similarly if $a < t_0 < t_1 < \dots < t_n < t^*$.

Example 3. Let T be the square $0 \leq x,y \leq 1$ in R^2. Let $C_7(T)$ be the space spanned by the harmonic functions $1,x,y,xy,x^2-y^2,x^3-3xy^2,3x^2y-y^3$. Then,

$$p(\tfrac{1}{2},\tfrac{1}{2}) = \tfrac{1}{4}[p(0,0) + p(0,1) + p(1,0) + p(1,1)] \tag{5}$$

is valid for all $p \in C_7(T)$ and hence is a positive interpolation formula.

Example 4. Let T be the square $-1 \leq x,y \leq 1$. Then the formula developed from the nine-point approximation to the Laplacian

$$p(0,0) = \frac{1}{20}\{p(1,1)+p(1,-1)+p(-1,1)+p(-1,-1)\} + \frac{1}{5}\{p(0,1)+p(1,0)+p(-1,0)+p(0,-1)\} \tag{6}$$

is a positive interpolation formula, valid for all harmonic functions p in T for which $\partial^8 p/\partial x^4 \partial y^4 \equiv 0$. This formula is commonly employed in the numerical solution of Laplace's equation by finite difference methods. See, e.g. Forsythe and Wasow [11] p. 194. On non-negative descrete approximations to elliptic differential operators see Motzkin and Wasow [4].

On the other hand, if we can move into the complex plane, then positive interpolation formulas exist for classes of polynomials.

Example 5. Let T be the unit disc $|z| \leq 1$ in the complex plane. Let $C_N(T)$ designate the space of complex polynomials of degree $\leq N$. Then, if

$$z_k = w^k, \quad w = \exp(2\pi i/(N+1)), \tag{7}$$

$$p(0) = \frac{1}{N+1}\sum_{k=1}^{N+1} p(z_k) \tag{8}$$

valid for all $p \in C_N(T)$. See, e.g. J. L. Walsh [8] p. 179, Eq. (48) with $z=0$.

Nor, in the complex plane, are the points limited to the vertices of regular polygons as in Ex. 5.

Example 6. Let j,k be arbitrary positive constants. Set

$$\sigma^2 = jk+j+k, \quad w_1 = j/\sigma^2, \quad w_2 = k/\sigma^2, \quad w_3 = jk/\sigma^2, \tag{9}$$

and

$$\begin{aligned} a &= [-\sigma^2 j+j^2+i(-\sigma j+\sigma^3)]/(\sigma^2+j^2), \\ b &= [-\sigma^2 j+j^2-i(\sigma j+\sigma j^2)]/(\sigma^2+j^2), \\ i &= \sqrt{-1}. \end{aligned} \tag{10}$$

Then

$$p(0) = w_1 p(a)+w_2 p(b)+w_3 p(1) \tag{11}$$

is a positive interpolation formula valid for all complex polynomials of degree ≤ 2.

It would be interesting to have a comprehensive theory of positive interpolation for complex polynomials of arbitrary degree.

Example 7. Here is an unusal positive interpolation formula of a slightly different type. Let the discs $|z-z_i| \leq r_i$, $i=1,2,3$, constitute a complete packing of the unit disc $|z| \leq 1$. Then, for <u>all</u> functions $p(z)$ analytic in $|z| < 1$ and continuous in $|z| \leq 1$, we have

$$p(0) = \pi \sum_{i=1}^{\infty} r_i p(z_i). \tag{12}$$

See P. J. Davis [4].

A quite useful general criterion for the existence of a non-negative interpolation formula may be arrived at by an application of Farkas' Lemma. For reference, we state this in a matrix formulation.

For arbitrary positive integers m and n, let D, x, c, and w be $m \times n$, $n \times 1$, $n \times 1$, $m \times 1$ matrices. The prime will designate transposes. If M is a matrix, we write $M \geq 0$ iff all the elements of M are ≥ 0.

Farkas' Lemma

> For real matrices, $Dx \geq 0$ implies $c'x \geq 0$ iff $c = D'w$ where $w \geq 0$.

We shall need to extend this to matrices with complex elements m_{ij}. Write $\text{Re } M = (\text{Re } m_{ij})$.

Lemma 1.1

> $\text{Re } Dx \geq 0$ implies $\text{Re } c'x \geq 0$ iff $c = D'w$ where $w \geq 0$, i.e. w is a matrix with real and non-negative elements.

<u>Proof</u>. Let $c = D'w$ with $w \geq 0$. Then, $c' = w'D$. Hence $c'x = w'Dx$. Now $\text{Re } Dx \geq 0$ implies

$$\text{Re } c'x = \text{Re } w'Dx = w' \text{Re } Dx \geq 0.$$

Conversely, let $\text{Re } Dx \geq 0$ imply $\text{Re } c'x \geq 0$. Write $D = E + iF$, $c = r + is$, $x = y + iz$ where E, F, r, s, y, z are real matrices and $i = \sqrt{-1}$. Then,

$$\text{Re } Dx = \text{Re}(E+iF)(y+iz) = Ey - Fz = (E|-F)\left(\frac{y}{z}\right)$$

$$\text{Re } c'x = \text{Re}(r'+is')(y+iz) = r'y - s'z = (r'|-s')\left(\frac{y}{z}\right).$$

In the last expression the horizontal and vertical bars are used to set off matrix blocks. The conditions now read that

$$(E|-F)\left(\frac{y}{z}\right) \geq 0 \text{ implies } (r'|-s')\left(\frac{y}{z}\right) \geq 0.$$

Since all is now real, we may apply the Farkas Lemma and obtain that

$$\left(\frac{r}{-s}\right) = \left(\frac{E'}{-F'}\right)w \text{ where } w \geq 0.$$

Hence $r = E'w$, $-s = -F'w$ and therefore

$$c = r+is = (E'+iF')w = D'w.$$

Theorem 1.2

There is a non-negative interpolation formula

$$p(t^*) = \sum_{k=0}^{n} w_k p(t_k), \quad w_k \geq 0, \; k=0,1,\ldots,n \tag{13}$$

valid for all $p \in C_N(T)$ iff

$$\text{Re } p(t_k) \geq 0 \quad k=0,1,\ldots,n \quad p \in C_N(T) \tag{14}$$

implies

$$\text{Re } p(t^*) \geq 0 \tag{15}$$

(Compare also Davis [8] on p. 241.)

Proof. In the previous Lemma 1.1, set

$$D = \begin{pmatrix} \phi_0(t_1),\ldots,\phi_N(t_1) \\ \vdots \quad\quad \vdots \\ \phi_0(t_n),\ldots,\phi_N(t_n) \end{pmatrix}, \; x = \begin{pmatrix} a_0 \\ \vdots \\ a_N \end{pmatrix}, \; c = \begin{pmatrix} \phi_0(t^*) \\ \vdots \\ \phi_N(t^*) \end{pmatrix}, \; w = \begin{pmatrix} w_0 \\ \vdots \\ w_n \end{pmatrix}. \quad //$$

2. Non-negative interpolation formulas for harmonic and analytic functions

We turn next to a situation in which the point evaluation functional $L(f) = f(t^*)$ is strictly positive. This has been studied to some extent in Davis and Wilson [7]. We begin with a slightly less general theorem than is proved in [7].

Let D be a bounded, open, connected set in R^q, with boundary ∂D and closure $\overline{D}$. We are not interested in pathological situations, so we shall assume that ∂D is composed of a finite number of rectifiable Jordan curves in the case $q=2$ or is "sufficiently smooth" in the case $q > 2$. Let $u_0,u_1,\ldots,u_N$ be $N+1$ linearly independent functions which are harmonic in D and continuous in $\overline{D}$. Designate the linear span of the u's by $H_N(=H_N(D))$ and assume that H_N contains a function that is positive on ∂D. (For example, assume that H_N contains the function 1.)

Theorem 2.1

Let t^* be a fixed point of D. Under the above conditions there exist points $t_0, t_1, \ldots, t_N \in \partial D$ and constants a_k with

$$a_k \geq 0 \quad k=0,1,\ldots,N \tag{16}$$

such that

$$u(t^*) = \sum_{k=0}^{N} a_k u(t_k), \quad \text{for all } u \in H_N \tag{17}$$

In other words, there exists a non-negative interpolation formula valid for harmonic "polynomials" which involves at most as many points as the dimension of the polynomial space.

The move to analytic functions of a single complex variable is now immediate.

Theorem 2.2

Let P_N designate the complex linear space of polynomials of the complex variable t and of degree $\leq N$. Let t^* be a fixed point in D. Then we can find points $t_0, t_1, \ldots, t_{2N}$ on ∂D and constants a_k with

$$a_k \geq 0 \tag{18}$$

such that

$$p(t^*) = \sum_{k=0}^{2N} a_k p(t_k), \quad \text{for all } p \in P_N. \tag{19}$$

Proof. Consider the harmonic functions $u_0 = 1$, $u_1 = \text{Re } t$, $u_2 = \text{Re } t^2, \ldots,$ $u_N = \text{Re } t^N$, $u_{N+1} = \text{Im } t$, $u_{N+2} = \text{Im } t^2, \ldots, u_{2N} = \text{Im } t^N$. Given $t^* \in D$, we can, by the previous theorem, find points $t_0, t_1, \ldots, t_{2N} \in \partial D$ and non-negative constants $a_0, a_1, \ldots, a_{2N}$ such that

$$u_j(t^*) = \sum_{k=0}^{2N} a_k u_j(t_k), \quad j=0,1,\ldots,2N. \tag{20}$$

Hence, for $j=1,2,\ldots,N$,

$$i\, u_{N+j}(t^*) = i \sum_{k=0}^{2N} a_k u_{N+j}(t_k), \quad i = \sqrt{-1}. \tag{21}$$

Adding,

$$u_j(t^*) + i\, u_{N+j}(t^*) = \sum_{k=0}^{2N} a_k(u_j(t_k) + iu_{N+j}(t_k)), \qquad j=1,2,\ldots,N \quad (22)$$

or

$$(t^*)^j = \sum_{k=0}^{2N} a_k t_k^j, \quad j=1,2,\ldots,N. \quad (23)$$

From j=0 in (20) we have $1 = \sum_{k=0}^{2N} a_k$ so that (23) holds for $j=0,1,\ldots,N$. By linear combinations it holds for all $p \in P_N$.

Remarks

1. Comparing this with Ex. 2 of §1, we see that non-negative interpolation formulas for polynomials of degree > 1 are possible when the abscissas t_k can take positions in the complex plane, but are impossible when they are confined to the real line.

2. If D is the unit circle and $t^* = 0$, Ex. 5, §1 shows that formulas exist with fewer than 2N+1 points.

3. If $t_1,\ldots,t_p$ are p complex points and if $a_1,a_2,\ldots,a_p$ are p non-negative numbers then the point $\sum_{i=1}^{p} a_i t_i$ must lie in the convex hull of $t_1,\ldots,t_p$. It follows that the points $t_0,t_1,\ldots,t_{2N}$ whose existence is guaranteed by Theorem 2.2 cannot accumulate on "one side" of ∂D; they must spread out. The point t^* must lie in the convex hull of $t_0,\ldots,t_{2N}$ and more generally, for each $j=1,2,\ldots,N$, the point $(t^*)^j$ must lie in the convex hull of $\{t_k^j\}$. It would be of interest to work out the equidistribution properties of the sequences $t_0,t_1,\ldots,t_{2N}$.

4. Nor are we confined to algebraic polynomials. If we take functions $\phi_0(t),\phi_1(t),\ldots,\phi_N(t)$ which are analytic in D and continuous in $\overline{D}$ and such that the real or imaginary part of at least one of them is non-negative on ∂D, then a similar theorem is valid for the linear span of the ϕ's.

5. A similar theorem holds for analytic functions of several complex variables. For the real and imaginary parts of such functions are pluriharmonic and hence satisfy a maximum principle. The point evaluation functional is accordingly strictly positive and the theory goes through. (See Davis and Wilson [7].)

We next reproduce a particular version of Theorem 3.3 of [7]. Refer to the notation for Theorem 2.1.

Theorem 2.3

Let G be a compact set contained in D. Then we can find points $t_0, t_1, \ldots, t_n \in \partial D$ and functions $a_0(t), \ldots, a_n(t)$ such that

$$a_i(t) \geq 0, \ t \text{ in } G, \quad i=0,1,\ldots,n \tag{24}$$

and

$$p(t) = \sum_{k=0}^{n} a_k(t) p(t_k) \tag{25}$$

for all $p \in H_N$ and all $t \in D$.

(In general $n >> N$ and n will depend upon G.)

Extending this to functions of a complex variable in the same way as Theorem 2.2 was obtained from Theorem 2.1, we obtain

Theorem 2.4

Let $\phi_0, \ldots, \phi_N$ be analytic in D and continuous in $\overline{D}$. Let P_N designate the (complex) linear span of the ϕ's and assume that P_N contains at least one function whose real or imaginary part is positive on ∂D. Let G be a compact set contained in D, then we can find points $t_0, t_1, \ldots, t_n$ on ∂D and functions $a_0(t), \ldots, a_n(t)$ satisfying (24) such that (25) holds for all $p \in P_N$ and all $t \in D$.

Note that what we are dealing with here is an expansion of an analytic function in terms of non-negative (and hence generally non-analytic) functions of a complex variable.

Theorem 2.5

Let D be a bounded region of the complex plane and P_N the set of all polynomials in t of degree $\leq N$. (P_N may also be a set of generalized polynomials providing that the constant 1 is also in the set.) Then, there exist points $t_0, t_1, \ldots, t_n \in \partial D$ such that

$$p(t_k) = \text{real}, \quad k=0,1,\ldots,n; \ p \in P_N \tag{26}$$

implies that $p \equiv$ a real constant.

Proof. Let G be any closed disc of positive radius contained in D. According to Theorem 2.4, there exist points $t_0, t_1, \ldots, t_n$ and functions $a_0(t), \ldots, a_n(t)$ such that (24) holds and (25) holds for all $p \in P_N$ and $t \in D$.

Suppose now that a $p \in P_N$ is selected and $p(t_k)$ = real, $k=0,1,\ldots,n$. Select $c = \min_{k=0,\ldots,n} p(t_k)$. Set $q(t) = p(t) - c$. Then $q(t_k) = p(t_k) - c \geq \min_k p(t_k) - c \geq 0$. Since $q \in P_N$, it follows directly from (24) and (25) that $q(t) \geq 0$ in G. Therefore $\text{Im } q(t) = 0$ in G. This implies (see e.g. Ahlfors [1]) that $q \equiv$ constant and hence $p \equiv$ constant.

This theorem may be regarded as a kind of uniqueness theorem for polynomials.

It should be observed that if an open arc is specified in advance, it will in general be impossible to find points $t_0,\ldots,t_n$ on it with this property.

3. Truncation error; rates of convergence

Let $u_0, u_1, \ldots$ be a sequence of functions each of which is harmonic in D and continuous in $\overline{D}$. Assume that $u_0 \geq \sigma > 0$ on $\overline{D}$. Assume further that the "boundary functions" of the u's: $u_0(s), u_1(s), \ldots, s \in \partial D$ are closed in the space $C(\partial D)$ of continuous functions defined on ∂D in the sup norm. This means that given an $h(s) \in C(\partial D)$ and an $\varepsilon > 0$, we can find constants $b_0, b_1, \ldots, b_p$ such that

$$\max_{s \in \partial D} \left|h(s) - \sum_{i=0}^{p} b_i u_i(s)\right| \leq \varepsilon. \tag{27}$$

For a fixed function $h(s) \in C(\partial D)$, set

$$\varepsilon_p(h) = \min_{b_i} \max_{s \in \partial D} \left|h(s) - \sum_{i=0}^{p} b_i u_i(s)\right|. \tag{28}$$

The quantity $\varepsilon_p(h)$ is the measure of best approximation of h by $u_0, \ldots, u_p$; and for each p, this measure is achieved by some linear combination $\sum_{i=0}^{p} b_i^* u_i(s)$. The closure hypothesis is equivalent to

$$\lim_{p \to \infty} \varepsilon_p(h) = 0 \quad \text{for all } h \in C(\partial D). \tag{29}$$

(See J. L. Walsh [18], p. 169.)

Let G be a compact set contained in D and for each integer $N=0,1,\ldots$, let $n=n(N), t_{0N}, t_{1N}, \ldots, t_{nN}$, and $a_{0N}(t), a_{1N}(t), \ldots, a_{nN}(t)$ be defined as in Theorem 2.3.

Let $h(s) \in C(\partial D)$ be given and let u be the unique solution of the

Dirichlet Problem on D with boundary data h(s). From Theorem 2.3 we have

$$u_j(t) = \sum_{k=0}^{n} a_{kN}(t)u_j(t_{kN}), \quad N=0,1,\ldots, \quad j=0,1,\ldots,N, \; t \in D. \tag{30}$$

Hence, if $p_N(t)$ designates any linear combination

$$p_N(t) = b_0u_0(t) + \ldots + b_Nu_N(t), \tag{31}$$

it follows that

$$p_N(t) = \sum_{k=0}^{n} a_{kN}(t)p_N(t_{kN}), \quad N=0,1,\ldots, \quad t \in D \tag{32}$$

Now

$$|u(t) - \sum_{k=0}^{n} a_{kN}(t)h(t_{kN})| \leq |u(t) - p_N(t)| + |p_N(t) - \sum_{k=0}^{n} a_{kN}(t)h(t_{kN})|$$

$$= |u(t) - p_N(t)| + |\sum_{k=0}^{n} a_{kN}(t)(p_N(t_{kN})-h(t_{kN}))|.$$

By the maximum principle,

$$\max_{t\in G} |u(t) - p_N(t)| \leq \max_{t\in\partial D} |h(t) - p_N(t)|.$$

Furthermore, since $a_{kN}(t) \geq 0$ for $t \in G$,

$$|\sum_{k=0}^{n} a_{kN}(t)(p_N(t_{kN}) - h(t_{kN}))| \leq \sum_{k=0}^{n} a_{kN}(t)|p_N(t_{kN}) - h(t_{kN}))|.$$

Now select $p_N(s)$ as the best approximation to h(s), then $|h(s) - p_N(s)| \leq \varepsilon_N(h)$, $s \in \partial D$. Hence,

$$\max_{t\in G} |u(t) - \sum_{k=0}^{n} a_{kN}(t)h(t_{kN})| \leq \varepsilon_N(h) + \varepsilon_N(h) \sum_{k=0}^{n} a_{kN}(t).$$

From (30) with j=0, $u_0(t) = \sum_{k=0}^{n} a_{kN}(t)u_0(t_{kN})$, $t \in G$. Now $u_0(t_{kN}) \geq \sigma > 0$. Hence, $u_0(t) \geq \sigma \sum_{k=0}^{n} a_{kN}(t)$.

If we set

$$M = \max_{t\in G} u_0(t) > 0 \tag{33}$$

it follows that

$$\sum_{k=0}^{n} a_{kN}(t) \leq \frac{M}{\sigma} \quad \text{for all } t \in G, \text{ independently of } N. \tag{34}$$

Thus, finally,

$$\max_{t\in G} \left|u(t) - \sum_{k=0}^{n} a_{kN}(t)h(t_{kN})\right| \leq \left(1 + \frac{M}{\sigma}\right)\varepsilon_N(h) . \tag{35}$$

This leads us to the following theorem.

Theorem 3.1

If the Dirichlet Problem is solved by interpolation as described, then under the above conditions, the truncation error does not exceed $(1 + \frac{M}{\sigma})\varepsilon_N(h)$ uniformly on G. The convergence of the interpolant $\sum_{k=0}^{n} a_{kN}(t)h(t_{kN})$ to u as $N \to \infty$ is uniform in G.

The asymptotics of $\varepsilon_N(h)$ as $N \to \infty$ has been the object of extensive investigations by J. L. Walsh and others and these results may be applied directly to the present situation.

4. On the asymptotics of n(N)

Working in R^2, let D be simply connected and $P_1,\ldots,P_n$ designate n points on ∂D. Let H_N designate the linear span of the harmonic functions $u_0,u_1,\ldots,u_N$. Let P be a fixed point in D. Under what circumstances do

$$u(P_i) \geq 0 \quad i=1,2,\ldots,n \tag{36}$$

imply

$$u(P) \geq 0 \text{ for all } u \in H_N? \tag{37}$$

This, following Theorem 1.1, is a necessary and sufficient condition for the existence of a non-negative interpolation formula at $P,P_1,\ldots,P_n$.

In this section we shall take $P_1,\ldots,P_n$ to be equi-distributed on ∂D with respect to arc length. We shall obtain asymptotic information on the integer n(N) which makes (36) and (37) true.

Let D have perimeter p and parametrize ∂D by its arc length s from some initial point: $0 \leq s \leq p < \infty$. The solution to the Dirichlet problem for D can be written in the form

$$u(P) = \frac{1}{2\pi}\int_0^p \frac{\partial g(P,s)}{\partial n}\, u(s)ds \tag{38}$$

where g(P,Q) is the harmonic Green's function for D.

It is well known that

$$\frac{\partial g(P,s)}{\partial n} > 0, \quad 0 \leq s \leq p. \tag{39}$$

Write

$$h_i(s) = \frac{1}{2\pi}\frac{\partial g(P,s)}{\partial n} u_i(s) \quad i=0,1,\ldots,N \tag{40}$$

Assume that $u_i(s)$ and hence $h_i(s)$ are N+1 independent functions and set $\tilde{H}_N$ = linear span of $h_0(s), h_1(s), \ldots, h_N(s)$. The functions $h_i(s)$ are periodic functions with period p. We shall furthermore assume that the $h_i(s)$ are sufficiently smooth functions and that the derivatives which occur subsequently exist. (This depends ultimately upon the smoothness of ∂B. If, e.g., ∂D is an analytic curve and the u_i are harmonic in $\overline{D}$, then the h_i will be periodic analytic functions.)

We shall require the Euler-Maclaurin Formula and write it in the following form. (See, e.g., Davis and Rabinowitz [9], pp. 54-56.)

Let $f(x) \in C^{2k+1}[0,p]$. Then

$$\frac{p}{n}[\tfrac{1}{2}f(0) + f(h) + f(2h) + \ldots + f((n-1)h) + \tfrac{1}{2}f(p)] =$$
$$\int_0^p f(x)dx + \frac{B_2}{2!} h^2[f'(p)-f'(0)]+\ldots+ \frac{B_{2k}}{(2k)!} h^{2k}[f^{(2k-1)}(p)-f^{(2k-1)}(0)]$$
$$+ h^{2k+1}\int_0^p P_{2k+1}(nx/p)f^{(2k+1)}(x)dx. \tag{41}$$

Here $k=0,1,\ldots$; $n=1,2,\ldots$; $h = p/n$, B_{2k} are the Bernoulli numbers while $P_{2k+1}(x)$ are the (periodic) Bernoulli polynomials given by

$$P_{2k+1}(x) = (-1)^{k-1}\sum_{n=1}^{\infty}\frac{2\sin 2\pi nx}{(2\pi n)^{2k+1}}. \tag{42}$$

In the case k=0, no bracketed derivative terms appear on the right hand of (41). The functions to which we shall apply (41) are all sufficiently many times differentiable and periodic with period p. The formula therefore reduces to

$$\frac{p}{n}\sum_{j=1}^{n} f(jh) = \int_0^p f(x)dx + h^{2k+1}\int_0^p P_{2k+1}(nx/p)f^{(2k+1)}(x)dx. \tag{43}$$

We abbreviate this formula further to

$$T_n(f) = \int_0^p f(x)dx + E_{n,k}(f) \tag{44}$$

using an obvious notation.

We shall make $\tilde{H}_N$ into an inner product space by writing

$$(f_1,f_2) = \int_0^p f_1(s)f_2(s)ds, \quad \|f\|^2 = \int_0^p f^2(s)ds. \tag{45}$$

Orthonormalize the independent functions $h_0(s),\ldots,h_N(s)$ yielding the orthonormal basis for $\tilde{H}_N$, $h_0^*(s),\ldots,h_N^*(s)$:

$$\begin{aligned} h_0^*(s) &= c_{00}h_0(s) \\ h_1^*(s) &= c_{10}h_0(s) + c_{11}h_1(s) \\ &\vdots \end{aligned} \qquad (c_{ii} > 0). \tag{46}$$

That is, we have $(h_i^*,h_j^*) = \delta_{ij}$ $i,j=0,1,\ldots,N$.

In the work that follows N is kept fixed. k is kept fixed and has been selected to reflect the amount of differentiability of the elements of $\tilde{H}_N$. However $n \to \infty$.

Lemma 1

For each integer $j=0,1,\ldots$ we can find a positive constant K_{Nj} depending only on j and N such that for all $f \in \tilde{H}_N$,

$$|f^{(j)}(s)| \leq K_{Nj} \|f\|, \quad 0 \leq s \leq p, \; j=0,1,2,\ldots \tag{47}$$

<u>Proof</u>. For any $f \in \tilde{H}_N$, write

$$f(s) = \sum_{r=0}^{N} a_r h_r^*(s), \quad a_r = (f,h_r^*), \quad \|f\|^2 = \sum_{r=1}^{N} a_r^2.$$

Hence,

$$f^{(j)}(s) = \sum_{r=0}^{N} a_r h_r^{*(j)}(s), \quad j=0,1,\ldots$$

By the Schwarz inequality,

$$(f^{(j)}(s))^2 \leq \sum_{r=0}^{N} a_r^2 \sum_{r=0}^{N} (h_r^{*(j)}(s))^2.$$

We can therefore take

$$K_{Nj} = \max_{0\leq s\leq p} \left[\sum_{r=0}^{N} (h_r^{*(j)}(s))^2\right]^{1/2} \tag{48}$$

as the appropriate constants. //

Note that $\sum_{r=0}^{N} (h_r^{*(j)}(s))^2$ are the derivatives of the finite kernel of the orthonormal system $h_i^*(s)$.

Lemma 2

Let $E_{n,k}(s) = h^{2k+1} \int_0^p P_{2k+1}(nx/p) f^{(2k+1)}(x)dx$, $h = p/n$. Then, we can find positive constants $\Gamma_{N,n,k}$ such that for all $f \in \tilde{H}_N$, we have

$$|E_{n,k}(f)| \leq \Gamma_{N,n,k} ||f|| \ . \tag{49}$$

Proof.

$$|E_{n,k}(f)| \leq h^{2k+1} \int_0^p |P_{2k+1}(nx/p)| |f^{(2k+1)}(x)| dx.$$

From (42),

$$|P_{2k+1}(x)| \leq \sum_{n=1}^{\infty} \frac{2}{2^{2k+1} n^{2k+1} \pi^{2k+1}} = 2^{-2k} \pi^{-2k-1} \sum_{n=1}^{\infty} \frac{1}{n^{2k+1}} \ .$$

Write $\zeta(V) = \sum_{n=1}^{\infty} \frac{1}{n^v}$, then we have

$$|P_{2k+1}(x)| \leq 2^{-2k} \pi^{-2k-1} \zeta(2k+1), \quad \text{all } x. \tag{50}$$

Using (50) and (47),

$$|E_{n,k}(f)| \leq h^{2k+1} p . 2^{-2k} \pi^{-2k-1} \zeta(2k+1) K_{N,2k+1} ||f|| \ .$$

Hence, we may take $\Gamma_{N,n,k}$ as

$$\Gamma_{N,n,k} = \frac{p^{2k+2}}{(n\pi)^{2k+1} 2^{2k}} \zeta(2k+1) K_{N,2k+1} \ . \quad // \tag{51}$$

Lemma 3

For each integer $j=0,1,\ldots$ we can find positive constants $M_{N,j}$ such that for all $f \in \tilde{H}_N$,

$$\max_{0 \leq s \leq p} |(f^2(s))^{(j)}| \leq M_{N,j} ||f||^2. \tag{52}$$

Proof. By Leibniz' Rule, we have

$$(f^2(s))^{(j)} = \sum_{r=0}^{j} \binom{j}{r} f^{(j-r)}(s) f^{(r)}(s).$$

Hence,

$$|(f^2(s))^{(j)}| \leq \sum_{r=0}^{j} \binom{j}{r} |f^{(j-r)}(s)| \; |f^{(r)}(s)|$$
$$\leq \sum_{r=0}^{j} \binom{j}{r} K_{N,j-r} \, ||f|| \, K_{N,r} \, ||f|| \, .$$

(the last inequality being derived from (47).) Hence, we may take $M_{N,j}$ as

$$M_{N,j} = \sum_{r=0}^{j} \binom{j}{r} K_{N,j-r} K_{N,r} . \quad // \tag{53}$$

Lemma 4

Let

$$E_{n,k}(f^2) = h^{2k+1} \int_0^p P_{2k+1}(nx/p)(f^2(x))^{(2k+1)} dx. \tag{54}$$

Then we can find positive constants $\Delta_{N,n,k}$ such that for all $f \in \tilde{H}_N$, we have

$$|E_{n,k}(f^2)| \leq \Delta_{N,n,k} \, ||f|| \; . \tag{55}$$

Proof. Estimating the integral in the usual way and using Lemma 3, we have

$$|E_{n,k}(f^2)| \leq (\tfrac{p}{n})^{2k+1} \, p.2^{-2k}\pi^{-2k-1} \, \zeta(2k+1) M_{N,2k+1} \, ||f||^{\,2}.$$

Hence we may take $\Delta_{N,n,k}$ as

$$\Delta_{N,n,k} = \frac{p^{2k+2}}{(\pi n)^{2k+1} 2^{2k}} \zeta(2k+1) M_{N,2k+1} . \quad // \tag{56}$$

In the next lemma, keeping N and k fixed, we allow n the privilege of becoming large. Note that $\lim_{n\to\infty} \Delta_{N,n,k} = 0$.

Lemma 5

Let $f \in \tilde{H}_N$ and suppose that

$$f(jh) \geq 0 \quad j=1,2,\ldots,n; \; h = p/n \tag{57}$$

Then, for all n sufficiently large,

$$T_n(f) \geq ||f|| \; \sqrt{p(1 - \Delta_{N,n,k})/n}. \tag{58}$$

<u>Proof</u>. $T_n(f) = \frac{p}{n} \sum_{j=1}^{n} f(jh)$. Since $f(jh) \geq 0$, $j=1,\ldots,n$, it follows that

$$(T_n(f))^2 \geq \frac{p^2}{n^2} \sum_{i=1}^{n} f^2(jh) = \frac{p}{n} \left(\frac{p}{n} \sum_{j=1}^{n} f^2(jh)\right) = \frac{p}{n} T_n(f^2). \tag{59}$$

Now the function f is in $\tilde{H}_N$ and is p-periodic and sufficiently many times differentiable. The function f^2 (though not necessarily in $\tilde{H}_N$) is also p-periodic and sufficiently differentiable. Hence, from (43), (44),

$$T_n(f^2) = \int_0^p f^2(s)ds + E_{n,k}(f^2).$$

Therefore from (59),

$$(T_n(f))^2 \geq \frac{p}{n} \left(\int_0^p f^2(s)ds + E_{n,k}(f^2)\right) . \tag{60}$$

From Lemma 4, (55), $|E_{n,k}(f^2)| \leq \Delta_{N,n,k} \|f\|^2$. For n sufficiently large, $\Delta_{N,n,k} < 1$ and hence $|E_{n,k}(f^2)| < \|f\|^2$. Therefore, for n sufficiently large,

$$(T_n(f))^2 \geq \frac{p}{n} [\|f\|^2 - \Delta_{N,n,k} \|f\|^2], \tag{61}$$

and (58) follows.

Lemma 6

Let $f \in \tilde{H}_N$. Then, if n is sufficiently large and if $f(jh) \geq 0$, $j=1,2,\ldots,n$, $h = p/n$, we have

$$\int_0^p f(s)ds \geq \left(\sqrt{p(1 - \Delta_{N,n,k})/n} - \Gamma_{N,n,k}\right) \|f\| . \tag{62}$$

<u>Proof</u>. From (44), $\int_0^p f(s)ds = T_n(f) - E_{n,k}(f)$. For n sufficiently large, we have Lemma 5, $T_n(f) \geq \|f\| \sqrt{p(1 - \Delta_{N,n,k})/n}$. From Lemma 2, (49), we have $|E_{n,k}(f)| \leq \Gamma_{N,n,k} \|f\|$. Note that from (51) with N and k fixed, $\Gamma_{N,n,k} \to 0$ as $1/n^{2k+1}$. Since $\sqrt{1 - \Delta_{N,n,k}} \to 1$ as $n \to \infty$, it follows that for n sufficiently large, $\Gamma_{N,n,k} \leq \sqrt{p(1 - \Delta_{N,n,k})/n}$. Therefore at that stage

$$\int_0^p f(s)ds \geq \sqrt{p(1 - \Delta_{N,n,k})/n}\, \|f\| - \Gamma_{N,n,k} \|f\| . \quad //$$

Lemma 7

Let N,k be fixed. Let (as was shown possible in Lemma 6) n be selected so large that

$$\Gamma_{N,n,k} < \sqrt{p(1 - \Delta_{N,n,k})/n} \tag{63}$$

Then for any $f \in \tilde{H}_N$, if $f(jh) \geq 0$, $j=1,2,\ldots n$, $h = p/n$, it follows that $\int_0^p f(s)ds \geq 0$.

Proof. This follows immediately from Lemma 6.

Theorem

Let N,k be fixed. Let n be selected so large that (63) holds. Then if $u \in H_N$ and if $u(jh) \geq 0$, $j=1,2,\ldots,n$, $h = \frac{p}{n}$, it follows that $u(P) \geq 0$.

Proof. If $u \in H_N$, then $f(s) = \frac{1}{2\pi} \frac{\partial g(P,s)}{\partial n} u(s) \in \tilde{H}_N$, and $f(jh) \geq 0$, $j=1,2,\ldots,n$. Now $u(P) = \int_0^p f(s)ds$. The theorem now follows from Lemma 7.

Remarks. The integers k that may be used are governed by the continuity class of the functions $h_i(s) = \frac{1}{2\pi} \frac{\partial g(P,s)}{\partial n} u_i(s)$.

In view of the structure of the constant $\Gamma_{N,n,k}$, (51), a lower value of n satisfying (63) will presumably result from using a higher value of k. In the case where the functions $h_i(s)$ are analytic, one should probably forego the use of the Euler-Maclaurin formula in favor of estimates for the trapezoidal rule obtained in Davis [5].

Computational experiments that reflect some of the theory of this paper are under way.

It would be of considerable interest to work out the asymptotics more precisely in certain simple cases of D and also to obtain results for harmonic functions in three or more variables.

References

1. AHLFORS, L. Complex Analysis, 2nd ed. McGraw-Hill, 1966.

2. BRAMBLE, J. J. and HUBBARD, B. E. 'New monotone type approximations for elliptic problems'. Math. Comp., 18 (1964), pp. 349-367.

3. CURTISS, J. H. 'Interpolation with harmonic and complex polynomials to boundary values'. J. Math. Mech., 9 (1960), pp. 167-192.

4. DAVIS, P. J. 'Additional simple quadratures in the complex plane'. Aequationes Mathematicae. To appear.

5. DAVIS, P. J. 'On the numerical integration of periodic analytic functions', in Langer, R.E. (Ed.), On Numerical Approximation, pp. 45-49. University of Wisconsin Press, 1959.

6. DAVIS, P. J. 'A construction of non-negative approximate quadratures'. Math. Comp., 21 (1967), pp. 578-582.

7. DAVIS, P. J. and WILSON, M. W. 'Non-negative interpolation formulas for uniformly elliptic equations'. J. Approx. Theory, 1 (1968), pp. 374-380.

8. DAVIS, P. J. 'Approximate integration rules with non-negative weights', in Aziz, A.K. (Ed.), Lecture Series in Differential Equations, Vol. II. Van Nostrand Math. Studies no. 19, Van Nostrand Reinhold, 1969.

9. DAVIS, P. J. and RABINOWITZ, P. Numerical Integration. Blaisdell, 1967.

10. FAN, K. 'Convex sets and their applications', Argonne National Laboratory, 1959.

11. FORSYTHE, G. E. and WASOW, W. R. Finite Difference Methods for Partial Differential Equations. Wiley, 1960.

12. GREENSPAN, D. and JAIN, P. C. 'On non-negative difference analogs of elliptic differential equations'. J. Franklin Inst. 279 (1965), pp. 360-365.

13. KARLIN, S. and STUDDEN, W. J. Tchebycheff Systems. Interscience, 1966.

14. MOTZKIN, T. S. and WASOW, W. 'On the approximation of linear elliptic differential equations by difference equations with positive coefficients'. J. Math. and Phys., 31 (1952), pp. 253-259.

15. WALSH, J. L., SEWELL, W. E. and ELLIOT, H. M. 'On the degree of polynomial approximation to harmonic and analytic functions'. Trans. Amer. Math. Soc., 67 (1949), pp. 381-420.

16. WALSH, J. L. and ELLIOTT, H. M. 'Polynomial approximation to harmonic and analytic functions: generalized continuity conditions'. Trans. Amer. Math. Soc., 68 (1950), pp. 183-203.

17. WALSH, J. L. 'Solution of the Dirichlet problem for the ellipse by interpolating harmonic polynomials'. J. Math. Mech., 9 (1960), pp. 193-196.

18. WALSH, J. L. Interpolation and Approximation, 3rd ed. Amer. Math. Soc., 1960.

19. WILSON, M. W. 'Uniform approximation of non-negative continuous linear functionals'. J. Approx. Theory. To appear.

APPROXIMATION RELATIVE TO HAUSDORFF DISTANCE

B. Sendov

(Bulgarian Academy of Sciences, Sofia)

1. Introduction

This communication aims at giving a survey of some of the results obtained in the theory of approximation relative to Hausdorff distance (Sendov [1]).

Let $f(x)$ be a function defined on an interval Δ. By completed graph $\bar{f}$ of the function $f(x)$ we mean the intersection of all closed point sets in the plane, convex relative to the y axis, which contain the graph of the function $f(x)$. By the Hausdorff distance $r(f,g)$ between $f(x)$ and $g(x)$ we mean the deviation between point sets $\bar{f}$ and $\bar{g}$ in Hausdorff sense.

The Hausdorff distance in the set of continuous functions determines the same topology as a uniform distance does. But $r(f,g)$ can be used in broader sets of functions, including discontinuous functions.

The distance $r(f,g)$ does not depend on the coordinate system. The ε-neighbourhood of a function relative to uniform distance is obtained by varying the points of its graph only in the y-axis direction, while the ε-neighbourhood of this function relative to Hausdorff distance is obtained by varying the points of its graph in all directions of the plane. Since in numerical computations not only the values of a given function but also their respective arguments are found with a certain error, the application of Hausdorff distance seems to be appropriate.

2. Hausdorff distance

Let $\rho(A,B)$ be an arbitrary Minkowski distance in the plane and F and G two closed point sets in the plane. The Hausdorff distance $r(F,G)$ between F and G determined by means of $\rho(A,B)$ is

$$r(F,G) = \max\left\{\max_{A\in F}\min_{B\in G}\rho(A,B),\ \max_{A\in G}\min_{B\in F}\rho(A,B)\right\}.$$

For simplicity we shall use only Minkowski distance

$$\rho(A,B) = \rho(A(x,y),B(\xi,\eta)) = \max[|x - \xi|,|y - \eta|].$$

Let F_Δ be the set of all closed and bounded point sets in the plane, convex relative to the y axis, whose projections on the x axis coincide with the interval $\Delta = [a,b]$. Let $f(x)$ be a bounded function defined on the interval Δ. By the completed graph $\bar{f}$ of the function $f(x)$ we mean the intersection of all elements of F_Δ which contain the graph of $f(x)$. The completed graph of every bounded function defined in Δ is an element of F_Δ, but the converse is not true. The completed graph of every continuous function coincides with the graph of this function.

By a Hausdorff distance $r(f,g)$ between two bounded functions $f(x)$ and $g(x)$ we mean the Hausdorff distance between their completed graphs, i.e. $r(f,g) = r(\bar{f},\bar{g})$.

The relation between Hausdorff and uniform distance is represented as follows.

Theorem 1

Let $f(x)$ and $g(x)$ be two functions defined on the interval $\Delta = [a,b]$ with moduli of continuity $\omega_f(\delta)$ and $\omega_g(\delta)$ respectively. If $R(f,g)$ is the uniform distance between $f(x)$ and $g(x)$,

$$R(f,g) = \sup_{x\in\Delta} |f(x) - g(x)|$$

and

$$\omega(\delta) = \min [\omega_f(\delta),\omega_g(\delta)],$$

then

$$r(f,g) \leqslant R(f,g) \leqslant r(f,g) + \omega(r(f,g)).$$

Immediately from Theorem 1 follows

Theorem 2

Let $\{f_n(x)\}$ be a sequence of functions defined on the interval Δ and $f(x)$ be a continuous function defined on the same interval. The sequence $\{f_n(x)\}$ converges uniformly to $f(x)$ in Δ if and only if $\lim_{n\to\infty} r(f_n,f) = 0$.

3. Best approximation by means of polynomials

Let H_n be the set of algebraic polynomials with degree $\leqslant n$. If

$P(x) \in H_n$, then P will be the graph of $P(x)$ on the interval Δ.

Let F be an arbitrary bounded and closed point set in the plane. We call

$$E_{n,r}(F;\Delta) = \inf_{P \in H_n} r(F,P)$$

the best approximation of F relative to Hausdorff distance by means of algebraic polynomials in the interval Δ. $P^*(x) \in H_n$ is a polynomial of best approximation for F in Δ if $z(F,P^*) = E_{n,r}(F;\Delta)$.

It is easy to show that for every bounded and closed point set F in the plane and every interval Δ, there exists a polynomial $P(x) \in H_n$ of best approximation for F, but it may not be unique. If F is the completed graph of a monotone function, then the polynomial of best approximation in H_n for F is unique.

Let us state the analogue of Bernstein's theorem.

Theorem 3

Let F be a bounded and closed point set in the plane. $F \in F_\Delta$ if and only if

$$\lim_{n\to\infty} E_{n,r}(F;\Delta) = 0.$$

One of the most interesting results of this theory is the following:

Theorem 4

If $F \in F_\Delta$, then

$$E_{n,r}(F;\Delta) \leq 7|\Delta| \frac{\log 2Mn}{n} + C(\Delta,M) \left(\frac{\log n}{n}\right)^2,$$

where $M = \max_{(x,y)\in F} y$, $C(\Delta,M)$ is a function of the constants $|\Delta|$ and M.

In the periodic case, the best approximation $E^T_{n,r}(F)$ obtained by means of trigonometrical polynomials satisfies the inequality

$$E^T_{n,r}(F) \leq 14 \frac{\log 2Mn}{n} + C(M) \left(\frac{\log n}{n}\right)^2 .$$

We do not consider $E_{n,r}(f;\Delta)$ if $f(x)$ is a "good" function, say a Lipschitz function, because in this case according to Theorem 1 the problem is reduced to uniform approximation.

Let us state two inverse theorems for $E_{n,r}(f;\Delta)$.

Theorem 5

If $F \in F_\Delta$ and $E_{n,r}(F;\Delta) = o(n^{-1})$, then the point set F in the open interval (a,b) is a graph of a continuous function.

Theorem 6

If $F \in F_\Delta$ and $E_{n,r}(F;\Delta) = o(n^{-2})$, then F is a graph of a continuous function in the closed interval Δ.

It is easy to see that for the square

$$G = \{(x,y) : |x| \leq 1, |y| \leq 1\}, \; E_{n,r}(G;[-1,1]) \leq \frac{\pi}{n} .$$

This means that Theorem 5 cannot be improved.

4. Approximation by means of step-wise functions

Let us denote

$$\xi_n = \frac{2n+1}{2} 2^{-[\log_2 n]} - 1; \; n = 1,2,3,...$$

and let

$$0 < \xi_{n,1} < \xi_{n,2} < ... < \xi_{n,n} < 1 \tag{1}$$

where the numbers in (1) are the numbers

$$0,\xi_1,\xi_2,...,\xi_n,1$$

put in ascending order.

Let us denote also

$$\xi_{n,0} = 0, \xi_{n,n+1} = 1,$$

$$\phi_0(x) = 1, \; \phi_n(x) = \begin{cases} 0 & \text{for } 0 \leq x < \xi_n, \\ 1/2 & \text{for } x = \xi_n, \\ 1 & \text{for } \xi_n < x \leq 1, \end{cases}$$

$$n = 1,2,3,...$$

and similarly

$$\phi_{n,0}(x) = 1, \; \phi_{n,i}(x) = \begin{cases} 0 & \text{for } 0 \leq x < \xi_{n,i}, \\ 1/2 & \text{for } x = \xi_{n,i}, \\ 1 & \text{for } \xi_{n,i} < x \leq 1, \end{cases}$$

$$i = 1,2,3,...,n; \; n = 1,2,3,...$$

It is easy to see that

$$\frac{1}{n-1} \leqslant |\xi_{n,i} - \xi_{n,i+1}| \leqslant \frac{2}{n+1}, \quad i = 0,1,2,\ldots,n.$$

Let S_n be the n-dimensional linear space which contains all the linear ombinations of the functions

$$\phi_0(x),\phi_1(x),\ldots,\phi_n(x)$$

nd let

$$E^S_{n,r}(F;[0,1]) = \inf_{p\in S_n} r(F,p)$$

here F is an arbitrary bounded and closed point set in the plane.

Obviously for every bounded and closed point set F there exists $*(x) \in S_n$ with

$$r(F,p^*) = E^S_{n,r}(F;[0,1]),$$

ut $p^*(x)$ is not necessarily unique.

For the best approximation $E^S_{n,r}(F;[0,1])$ obtained by means of elements f S_n we have

heorem 7

If $F \in F_{[0,1]}$, then $E^S_{n,r}(F;[0,1]) \leqslant \frac{4}{n}$.

Let us give an example of a set of functions which can be characterized y means of $E^S_{n,r}(F;[0,1])$. Let us denote by $A_\alpha C$ the set of functions f(x) efined on the interval [0,1] and representable in the form

$$f(x) = \sum_{k=0}^{\infty} a_k\phi_k(x) \tag{2}$$

here

$$|a_k| \leqslant \frac{c}{k^\alpha}\ ;\ k = 0,1,2,\ldots,\ c = \text{const}.$$

It is easy to see that for the coefficients in (2) when $\alpha > 1$ we ave

$$a_k = f(\xi_k + 0) - f(\xi_k - 0),$$

nd for every $x \in (0,1)$

$$f(x) = \tfrac{1}{2}(f(x+0) + f(x-0)).$$

heorem 8

For $\alpha > 1$ the function $f(x) \in A_\alpha C$ if and only if $E^S_{n,r}(f;[0,1]) = O(n^{-\alpha})$.

5. Linear approximation

Let f(x) be a 2π-periodic function. By modulus of non-monotonicity $\mu_f(\delta)$ of the function f(x) we mean

$$\mu_f(\delta) = \sup_{|x_1-x_2|\leq\delta} \left\{ \sup_{x_1\leq x\leq x_2} \{|f(x_1)-f(x)| + |f(x_2)-f(x)|\} - |f(x_1)-f(x_2)|\right\}$$

If $\omega_f(\delta)$ is the modulus of continuity of the function f(x), i.e.

$$\omega_f(\delta) = \sup_{|x_1-x_2|\leq\delta} |f(x_1)-f(x_2)|,$$

then obviously $\mu_f(\delta) \leq \omega_f(\delta)$.

We shall call the function f(x) a locally monotonic one if its modulus of non-monotonicity satisfies the condition

$$\lim_{\delta\to 0} \mu_f(\delta) = \mu_f(0) = 0 .$$

Theorem 9

The 2π-periodic function f(x) is locally monotonic if and only if for every x there exists f(x - 0) and f(x + 0), and

$$[f(x) - f(x - 0)][f(x) - f(x + 0)] \leq 0.$$

Let $B^{\mu}_{2\pi}$ be the set of 2π-periodic and locally monotonic functions f(x) for which

$$\sup_x |f(x)| \leq B \text{ and } \mu_f(\delta) \leq \mu(\delta),$$

where $\mu(\delta)$ is non-decreasing function with $\lim_{\delta\to 0} \mu(\delta) = \mu(0) = 0$.

Let K(t) be a positive and symmetric kernel with

$$\int_{-\pi}^{\pi} K(t)\,dt = 1.$$

We denote by k(f;x) the linear operator

$$k(f;x) = \int_{-\pi}^{\pi} f(x+t)K(t)dt,$$

defined for every $f(x) \in B^{\mu}_{2\pi}$.

Theorem 10

If $f(x) \in B^{\mu}_{2\pi}$, then $r(f,k(f)) \leq \max(\delta,\mu(4\delta) + 4B\int_{\delta}^{\pi} K(t)dt)$ for every $\delta > 0$.

Using Theorem 10, one can obtain estimates for the speed of convergence of different linear methods of approximation relative to Hausdorff distance.

If one considers Fejer's operator

$$\sigma_n(f;x) = \frac{1}{2\pi n}\int_{-\pi}^{\pi} f(x+t)\left(\frac{\sin\frac{nt}{2}}{\sin\frac{t}{2}}\right)^2 dt$$

then we have

Corollary 1

If $f(x) \in B_{2\pi}^{\mu}$, then $r(f,\sigma_n(f)) \leqslant \mu(8\sqrt{B}n^{-\frac{1}{2}}) + 2\sqrt{B}n^{-\frac{1}{2}}$.

Let $B_{2\pi}^{\alpha}$ be the set $B_{2\pi}^{\mu}$ if $\mu(\delta) \leqslant \delta^{\alpha}$; $\alpha > 0$.

Corollary 2

If $f(x) \in B_{2\pi}^{\alpha}$, then $r(f,\sigma_n(f)) \leqslant 8(\frac{B}{n})^{\alpha/(1+\alpha)}$.

The estimate given in Corollary 2 is exact in respect to order.

Theorem 11

If $f(x)$ is a 2π-periodic function and

$$f(x) = \begin{cases} \pi^{\alpha} & \text{for } -\pi \leqslant x < 0 \\ x^{\alpha} & \text{for } 0 \leqslant x < \pi;\ 0 < \alpha \leqslant 1 \end{cases}$$

then $f(x) \in B_{2\pi}^{\alpha}$ (for $B = \pi^{\alpha}$) and

$$r(f,\sigma_n(f)) \geqslant c\, n^{-\frac{\alpha}{1+\alpha}}\ ;\ c = \text{const.}\ .$$

Let us give some estimates for the speed of convergence in case of some other positive linear methods of approximation relative to Hausdorff distance. We use the notations

$$U_{m,r}(f;x) = C_{m,r}\int_{-\pi}^{\pi} f(t)\left(\frac{\sin\frac{1}{2}m(t-x)}{\sin\frac{1}{2}(t-x)}\right)^{2r} dt,$$

$$C_{m,r}^{-1} = \int_{-\pi}^{\pi}\left(\frac{\sin\frac{mt}{2}}{\sin\frac{t}{2}}\right)^{2r} dt;$$

$$V_n(f;x) = \frac{(2n)!!}{2\pi(2n-1)!!}\int_{-\pi}^{\pi} f(x+t)\cos^{2n}\frac{t}{2}\, dt;$$

$$U_n^*(f;x) = U_{m,r}(f;x) : m = [2n/\log n],\ r = n/m.$$

The estimates are given in the following table.

$k_{m,r}(f;x)$	$r(f;k(f))$	
	$f \in B_{2\pi}^{\mu}$	$f \in B_{2\pi}^{\alpha}; 0 < \alpha \leq 1$
$U_{m,2}(f;x)$	$\mu(8\sqrt{B}\, n^{-\frac{1}{2}}) + 2\sqrt{B}\, n^{-\frac{1}{2}}$	$8(\frac{B}{n})^{\frac{\alpha}{1+\alpha}}$
$U_{m,4}(f;x)$	$\mu(16\sqrt[4]{B}\, n^{-\frac{3}{4}}) + 4\sqrt[4]{B}\, n^{-\frac{3}{4}}$	$8\left(\frac{3\sqrt[3]{B}}{n}\right)^{\frac{3\alpha}{3+\alpha}}$
$U_{m,r}(f;x)$	$\mu(m^{-\frac{2r-1}{2r}}) + O(m^{-\frac{2r-1}{2r}})$	$O(m^{-\frac{(2r-1)\alpha}{2r-1+\alpha}})$
$V_n(f;x)$	$\mu\left(\left(\frac{\log n}{n}\right)^{\frac{1}{2}}\right) + O\left(\left(\frac{\log n}{n}\right)^{\frac{1}{2}}\right)$	$O\left(\left(\frac{\log n}{n}\right)^{\alpha/2}\right)$
$U_n^*(f;x)$	$\mu\left(\frac{\log n}{n}\right) + O\left(\frac{\log n}{n}\right)$	$O\left(\left(\frac{\log n}{n}\right)^{\alpha}\right)$

References

1. SENDOV, B. Nekotorye voprosy teorii priblizhenii funktsii i mnozhestv v khausdorfovoi metrike. (Some problems in the theory of approximation of functions and sets in the Hausdorff metric.) Uspekhi Mat. Nauk., 24, 5 (1969), pp. 143-180.

TSCHEBYSCHEFF-APPROXIMATION WITH SUMS OF EXPONENTIALS

H. Werner

(University of Münster)

Dedicated to Professor Lothar Collatz on the occasion of his 60th birthday.

1. Introduction

The advent of high speed computers caused the need of representations for transcendental functions $f(x)$ that can easily be evaluated and that are uniformly good on a prescribed interval I, i.e. with respect to the norm

$$\|g\|_I := \max_{x \in I} |g(x)|, \quad g(x) \text{ continuous in } I. \tag{1}$$

(We dispense with the insertion of a weight function $w(x)$ in this definition.)

At first linear combinations of n given functions $z_1, \dots, z_n$ were used as approximating families of functions ("linear T-approximation"). The theory is well exploited and constructive solutions to the approximation problem are known. The concept of the alternant is fundamental:

Let $\varepsilon(x)$ be a continuous function on I. Then $x_0, \dots, x_n \in I$ form an alternant, if $x_0 < x_1 < \dots < x_n$ and

$$\varepsilon(x_j) = -\varepsilon(x_{j-1}), \quad j=1,\dots,n, \tag{2}$$

$$|\varepsilon(x_j)| = \|\varepsilon(x)\| . \tag{3}$$

If the basis $z_1, \dots, z_n$ of the above family is a Tschebyscheff-System, then the linear combination $h(x)$ is the best approximation to $f(x)$ iff the error curve

$$\varepsilon(x) := f(x) - h(x) \tag{4}$$

possesses an alternant of n+1 points, written "length of alternant" alt $(f,h) = n+1$.

In the next step rational functions served as approximating families. A remarkable difference to the linear case is the possibility that alt (f,h), h the best rational approximation of prescribed degrees, may be less than one would expect according to the number of parameters available. This type of "degeneracy" is, however, exceptional and usually one has an analogy to the linear case if the approximated function $f(x)$ is "normal" (Werner [8]).

John Rice, in 1960-1969, was the first mathematician to attack approximation with sums of exponentials, at least in the verbal sense. The essential tools, as will be pointed out, date already back to the work of Polya-Szegö, several decades ago.

In 1963-1964 G. Meinardus developed the theory of asymptotic-convex families. He applied this theory to approximation with sums of exponentials to obtain unicity statements.

At Münster University we started in 1966 to thoroughly investigate this type of approximation. Our group was joined by D. Braess in 1967. He introduced the concept of "sign classes", while I stressed the idea that this family can easily be described by means of differential equations. He followed the advice to generalize the descent algorithm from rational approximation to exponentials in his Habilitationsschrift [1]. It will be submitted in revised form for publication in several parts in mathematical journals. At the same time E. Schmidt investigated the continuity properties of the approximation with exponentials, along the lines worked out in [1], in his dissertation [6]. His papers are also to appear, as is my own, [9], presented at Oberwolfach in 1967.

This paper gives a survey of this work and contains also new proofs and methods that considerably shorten the investigations. For the longer proofs I have to refer the reader to the quoted papers. The question of existence, uniqueness, characterisation and continuity with respect to several classes of approximating functions will be discussed. As the example at the end of section 4 shows one cannot employ the theory of varisolvent functions without adaptation. We give therefore an independent representation. The variety of phenomena will be larger than for rational T-approximation.

The methods used here allow also generalisations to other classes of functions as will be shown in a forthcoming dissertation at Münster

University.

2. Definitions and basic theorems

Primarily the following families of functions will be considered:

$$E_n^+ := \{y(x) \mid y(x) = \sum_{j=1}^{n} c_j e^{\lambda_j x}, \lambda_j \text{ real}, c_j \geq 0\}, \quad (5)$$

$$E_n^o := \{y(x) \mid y(x) = \sum_{j=1}^{n} c_j e^{\lambda_j x}, \lambda_j \text{ real}\}, \quad (6)$$

$$E_n := \{y(x) \mid y(x) = \sum_{j=1}^{\ell} P_j(x) e^{\lambda_j x}, \lambda_j \text{ real}, P_j \text{ polynomial of degree } \partial P_j \text{ with real coefficients}, k := \Sigma \partial P_j + \ell \leq n\} \quad (7)$$

Sometimes the c_j are called coefficients, the λ_j frequencies, ℓ the length of the sum, k the degree of the function y. We will always assume $\lambda_1 < \lambda_2 < \ldots < \lambda_\ell$. A function $y \in E_{n-1}$ may be called n-degenerate, $y \in E_n - E_{n-1}$ n-non-degenerate.

To motivate these definitions, we may consider a physical example. Given an empirical curve that represents the activities of a decaying material one will ask for a decomposition into a sum of type (6) at first glance. This class, however, is shown not to be closed under the T-norm; a best approximation does not always exist.

Example: Let $\lambda_1 < \lambda_2 < \ldots < \lambda_m$ and take the (m-1)st difference quotient (highest coefficient of Lagrange interpolation polynomial) of $e^{\lambda x}$:

$$\Delta_\lambda^{m-1}(\lambda_1,\ldots,\lambda_m)e^{\lambda x} := \sum_{j=1}^{m} w_j e^{\lambda_j x} \in E_n^o \text{ for } m \leq n,$$

$$\text{where } w_j = 1/\prod_{\substack{i=1\\i\neq j}}^{m} (\lambda_j - \lambda_i). \quad (8)$$

For $\lambda_1 \to \lambda_0,\ldots,\lambda_m \to \lambda_0$ we get

$$\lim_{(\lambda_1,\ldots,\lambda_m)\to(\lambda_0,\ldots,\lambda_0)} \Delta^{m-1} e^{\lambda x} = \frac{1}{(m-1)!} x^{m-1} e^{\lambda_0 x} \notin E_n^o. \quad (9)$$

Hence $x^{m-1}e^{\lambda_0 x}$ may be approximated arbitrarily closely by functions of E_n^0 although it is not contained in it.

To overcome this difficulty the class E_n is introduced.

Physically this does not make sense. What significance shall a term

$xe^{\lambda x}$ have? A better answer is found by a closer look at the physical requirements. The coefficients c_r usually represent masses, hence are non-negative. Narrowing the class E_n^o yields E_n^+, which will be found to be closed.

In the sequel it is more convenient to use the following obviously equivalent definition of E_n, based on the observation, that each $y \in E_n$ satisfies a linear homogeneous differential equation of order n. Therefore

$$E_n := \{y(x) \mid y \in C^n[I], \text{ there are \underline{real} numbers } \lambda_1,\dots,\lambda_n \text{ depending upon } y \text{ such that } \prod_{j=1}^{n} (D - \lambda_j)y = 0\}. \tag{10}$$

(Here $C^n[I]$ denotes the functions with continuous derivatives in I up to the n-th order, and $D := d/dx$.)

Instead of the given differential equation one also uses

$$Ly := a_n y^{(n)} + \dots + a_1 y' + a_o y = c\Pi(D - \lambda_j)y = 0 \tag{11}$$

normalised by $\Sigma a_i^2 = 1$; for $\lambda_j = \pm\infty$ the factor $(D - \lambda_j)$ is to be replaced by 1.

An immediate consequence of (10) is

Theorem 2.1 (Polya-Szegö)

Every $y \in E_n$ has at most n-1 zeros, or vanishes identically.

<u>Proof</u>. The theorem is true for n=1. Suppose it is true for n-1. Let $y \in E_n$, $y \neq 0$ have m zeros. Then

$$z := (D - \lambda_n)y = e^{\lambda_n x} D(ye^{-\lambda_n x}) \in E_{n-1}, \tag{12}$$

since $(D - \lambda_1)\dots(D - \lambda_{n-1})z = 0$. By Rolle's theorem z has at least m-1 zeros. The assumption of the induction insures $m - 1 \leq n - 2 \Rightarrow m < n$. //

Since $E_n^+ \subset E_n^o \subset E_n$ we have

Corollary 2.1a

Every $y \in E_n^+$ or E_n^o has at most n-1 zeros, or vanishes identically.

A further consequence of (10) is

Lemma 2.1

If $y \in E_n$, then it belongs to $C^\infty(-\infty,+\infty)$, and $D^r y \in E_n$ for r=1,2,... .

The proof follows from the fact that every solution of $Ly = 0$ is holomorphic and

$$0 = D(Ly) = L(Dy).$$

Hence

Corollary 2.1b

If $y \in E_n$, each derivative $D^r y$ has at most n-1 zeros, or vanishes identically.

The closedness, compactness, etc. of E_n depend upon certain a priori estimates for the derivatives of $y \in E_n$, given an estimate for $\|y\|$.

Theorem 2.2*

Let $I := [a,b]$ and $I_1 := [a_1,b_1] \subset (a,b)$. There are factors $K^r(I,I_1)$ depending only on these two intervals, such that for every $y \in E_n$ we have

$$\|D^r y\|_{I_1} \leq K^r(I,I_1) \|y\|_I. \tag{13}$$

Proof. We use [9] together with an idea of E. Schmidt [6].

A) Let $J_r := \{x \mid |x-x_o| \leq (m-r).d\} \subset I.$, where x_o,m,d are fixed quantities, $d > 0$.

Assume $D^r y(x) \neq 0$ in J_0 for $r = 0,1,\ldots,m+1$. Then

$$|D^r y(x)| \leq d^{-r} \|y\|_I \text{ for } x \in J_r, \quad r=0,1,\ldots,m. \tag{14}$$

The proof is by induction. For r=0 nothing is to be proved. In J_0 all functions $D^r y$ (r=0,...,m) are monotonic, and $|D^r y|$ attains its maximum at the boundary.

Assume (14) to hold for fixed $r < m$. Let $x \in J_{r+1}$ and z be that boundary point of J_r, where $|D_y^{r+1}|$ is maximal.

$$D^r(y(z) - y(x)) = \int_x^z D^{r+1}y(t)dt, \tag{15}$$

hence

$$|D^r y(z)| \geq |z-x| \min |D^{r+1}y(t)| = |z-x|.|D^{r+1}y(x)|. \tag{16}$$

Therefore

* The subscript with the norm indicates the interval used for determination of the norm. As the proof shows, $\|y\|_I$ could be replaced by norms over smaller point sets.

$$\|D^r y\|_{J_r} \geq d \, \|D^{r+1} y\|_{J_{r+1}}, \tag{17}$$

thus (14) is true for r+1, if it is true for r. This concludes step A).

B) Given a positive integer m, the functions $y, Dy, \dots, D^{m+1}y$ have at most $N = (m+2)(n-1)$ zeros in I. Hence we conclude: to every $y \in E_n$ there are two intervals J_0, one in $[a, a_1]$, the other in $[b_1, b]$ such that the said functions do not vanish on J_0 and the length of the intervals is at least $(a_1-a)/(N+1)$ and $(b-b_1)/(N+1)$ respectively, this lower bound being independent of y. In the said intervals we have points a^*, b^*, where we know bounds for $|y|, |Dy|, \dots, |D^m y|$, say K, independent of y by step A).

C) For a fixed positive integer k, we proceed to give a bound for $|D^k y|$ on $J := [a^*, b^*]$, which also holds on I_1 because $I_1 \subset J$. By A), we may assume that

$$|D^r y(a^*)| \leq K, \quad |D^r y(b^*)| \leq K \quad (r=k, k+1, \dots, k+n). \tag{18}$$

We claim - and this is the device of E. Schmidt - that

$$\|D^k y\|_J \leq K \sum_{r=0}^{n-1} c^r = K_{n-1} \text{ where } c=b-a. \tag{19}$$

Assume the contrary, i.e. that there is $x_1^1 \in J$ with

$$|D^k y(x_1^1)| = \|D^k y\|_J > K_{n-1} \text{ and } D^{k+1} y(x_1^1) = 0; \tag{20}$$

then $D^{k+1}y$ has at least <u>one</u> zero in J. (Compare Fig. 1, where k=0.) Furthermore, in $[a^*, x_1]$ the function $|D^{k+1}y|$ attains a maximum at x_2^1 that can be estimated:

$$|D^{k+1} y(x_2^1)| \geq \frac{|D^k y(x_2^1) - D^k y(a^*)|}{x_1^1 - a^*} > \frac{K \sum_0^{n-1} c^r - K}{c} = K \sum_0^{n-2} c^r =: K_{n-2}. \tag{21}$$

Hence $D^{k+1}y$ attains its maximum in the interior and not at the boundary of J. Therefore

$$D^{k+2} y(x_2^1) = 0. \tag{22}$$

Analogously there is $x_2^2 \in (x_1^1, b^*)$ where

$$|D^{k+1} y(x_2^2)| > K_{n-2} \text{ and } D^{k+2} y(x_2^2) = 0.$$

Thus $D^{k+2}y$ has <u>two</u> zeros in J.

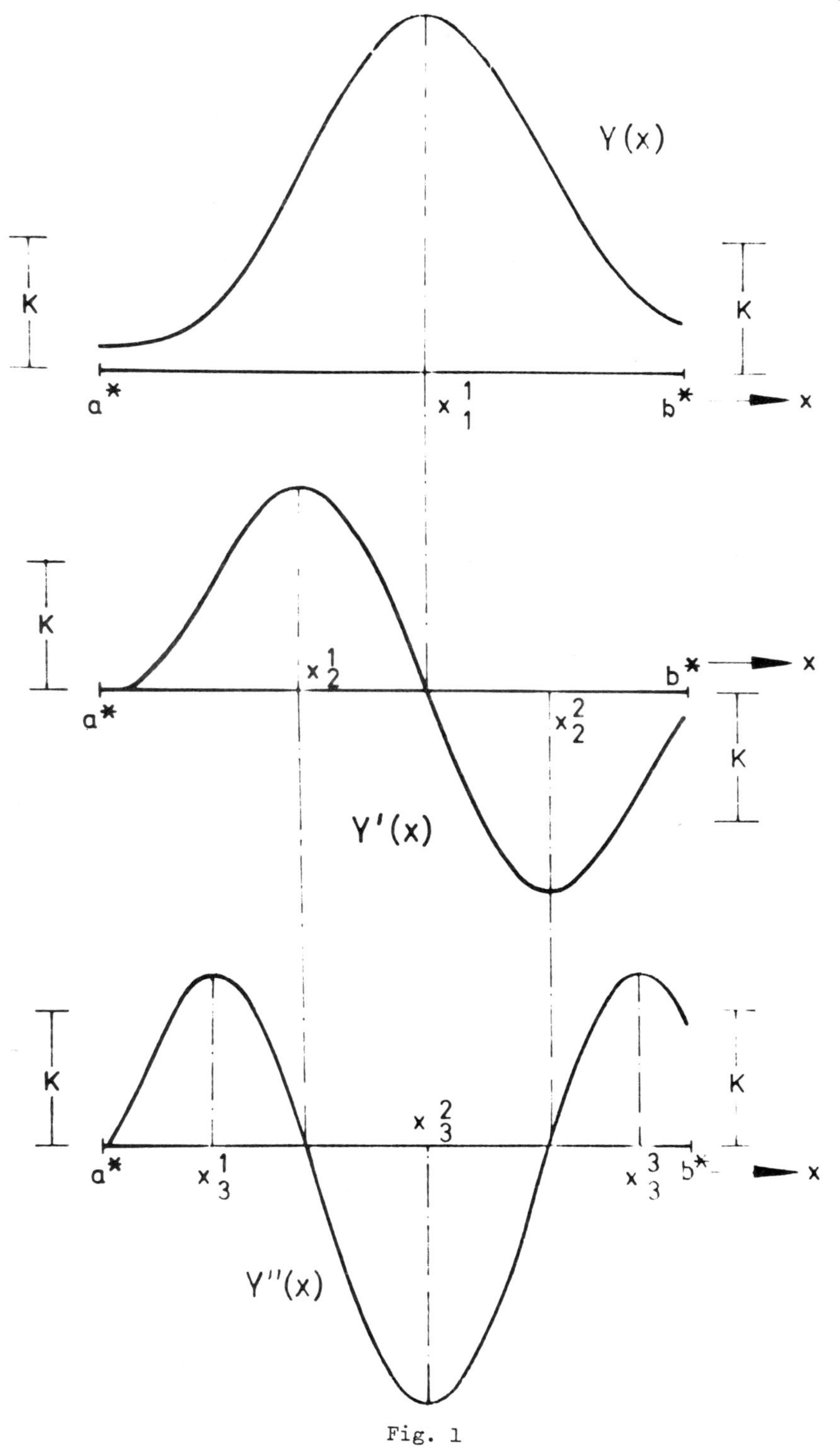

Fig. 1

This construction may be generalized by induction to $D^{k+3}y,\dots,D^{k+\mu}y$ to show that there are $\mu-2$ zeros by Rolle's theorem and two extra zeros because of maxima of $D^{k+\mu-1}y$ in the neighborhood of a^* and b^*. $D^{k+n}y$ then has n zeros in J, contradicting corollary 2.1b.

Thus Theorem 2.2 is proved.

3. Existence theorems

We are now in a position to give compactness and existence theorems. One cannot expect every bounded sequence of E_n to contain a uniformly converging subsequence, as is shown by the example (Rice [4]):

$$y_r = e^{-rx} \text{ for } r=0,1,\dots \text{ in } I = [0,1], \text{ with the limit } \tilde{y} = \begin{cases} 1 & x=0 \\ 0 & x\neq 0 \end{cases} .$$

We may, however, do so for <u>uniform convergence in the interior</u>, i.e. pointwise convergence in the interior of I, which is uniform in every closed subinterval.

Theorem 3.1

Every infinite sequence $\{y_r\}_{r=1,2,\dots}$ of elements of E_n with $\|y_r\|_I \leq c$ contains a subsequence for which the functions and their derivatives up to a prescribed order m converge uniformly in the interior to an element $\tilde{y}$ of E_n and its derivatives.

<u>Proof</u>. By Theorem 2.2 it is easy to extract a subsequence which, together with the derivatives of order up to m, converges uniformly in every closed interval to a limit function $\tilde{y}$ and its derivatives. (We may employ the method of diagonal sequences.)

To show $\tilde{y} \in E_n$ we assume $m \geq n$ and associate with each y_r the (n+1)-dim. unit vector $\underline{a}_r$ defined by the differential equation (11), i.e. $L_r y_r = 0$. Assume the $\underline{a}_r$ (and the associated frequencies on the projective line) converge with limit $\underline{a}$. Then $\tilde{y}$ satisfies the differential equation given by $\underline{a}$ in the interior of I. At the boundary points of I we may define $\tilde{y}$ by continuation of this solution. The limits of the frequencies that are finite may be frequencies of $\tilde{y}$, those limits which are infinite will make no contribution to $\tilde{y}$, as in the above example. If k limits are infinite then $\tilde{y}$ belongs to E_{n-k}, because one easily sees that $L\tilde{y} = 0$ is a differential equation of order n-k as the k highest order coefficients a_j have become zero and the finite limits are the characteristic roots of this differential equation, which are real.

orollary 3.1

If $\{y_r\}$ is an infinite sequence of elements of E_n that converges uniformly in the interior of I to $\tilde{y} \in E_n - E_{n-1}$ then the convergence is uniform in all of I.

roof. We may take $y_r - \tilde{y} \in E_{2n}$ and apply Theorem 2.2 to see that the erivatives also converge uniformly in the interior. Looking at the equences of frequencies of the previous proof we see that none of the imits is infinite. Hence we may use the differential equations in the form $\Pi(D-\lambda_j^{(r)})y_r = 0$. The data $y_r^{(0)}(x_o),\ldots,y_r^{(n-1)}(x_o)$ for fixed $x_o \in (a,b)$ onverge uniformly for $r \to \infty$. Hence the theorem on the continuous ependence of the solution of an initial value problem of ordinary ifferential equations may be applied.

A further consequence of Theorem 3.1 is

heorem 3.2

Every function $f(x) \in C[I]$ has a best approximation (in the T-norm) in E_n.

roof. Take a sequence $\{y_r\}$ of E_n minimizing $\|y - f\|$, i.e.

$$\lim \|y_r - f\| = \eta(f) := \min\{ \|y-f\| \mid y \in E_n\}. \tag{23}$$

he sequence $\{y_r\}$ is obviously bounded and by Theorem 3.1 we may assume niform convergence in the interior to $\tilde{y}(x)$, extending as above the efinition of $\tilde{y}(x)$ to all of I. Then

$$\max_I |\tilde{y}(x)-f(x)| = \sup_{(a,b)} |\tilde{y}(x)-f(x)| = \sup (\lim |y_r(x)-f(x)|) \tag{24}$$
$$\leq \lim \|y_r - f\| = \eta(f). \quad //$$

For the sake of completeness we may state

heorem 3.3

The family E_n is the closure of E_n^o with respect to uniform convergence.

or the proof we need only summarise what we already know:

If $\{y_n\}$ is a uniformly converging sequence of E_n^o, then its limit belongs o E_n by Theorem 3.1.

On the other hand, if $y \in E_n - E_n^o$ it contains terms of the form $(a_r x^r + a_{r-1}x^{r-1} + \ldots + a_0)e^{\lambda_0 x}$ which may be approximated arbitrarily closely by

$$r!.a_r\Delta^r(\lambda_0,\ldots,\lambda_r)e^{\lambda x}+(r-1)!a_{r-1}\Delta^{r-1}(\lambda_0,\ldots,\lambda_{r-1})e^{\lambda x}+\ldots+a_0e^{\lambda_0 x}, \quad (25)$$

$\lambda_0 < \lambda_1 < \lambda_2 < \ldots < \lambda_r$ being sufficiently close together. Hence $y \in \overline{E_n^o}$. //

For the family E_n^+ Theorems 3.1, 3.2, 3.3 hold with E_n replaced by E_n^+. To see this it is not even necessary to use all of Theorem 2.2. Instead one may observe that

$$|\sum c_j e^{\lambda_j x}| \leqslant c \text{ with } c_j > 0 \text{ in } x \in I \quad (26)$$

implies

$$|c_j e^{\lambda_j x}| \leqslant c \text{ in } I. \quad (27)$$

Hence one may restrict the attention to E_1^+, i.e. $y_r = c_r e^{\lambda_r x}$. There are two cases to be considered.

(i) $|\lambda_r|$ is bounded; $|\lambda_r| \leqslant M$. Then the coefficients

$$|c_r| \leqslant ce^{M(|a|+|b|)}$$

are also bounded, hence one can extract a uniformly converging subsequence of such a sequence in E_n^+.

(ii) $|\lambda_r| \to \infty$, say $\lambda_r \to +\infty$. Then for $x \in (a,b)$ we have, using (27),

$$|y_r(x)| = |c_r e^{\lambda_r x}| \leqslant e^{\lambda_r(x-b)}|c_r e^{\lambda_r b}| \quad (28)$$
$$\leqslant e^{\lambda_r(x-b)} . c \to 0 \text{ for } r \to \infty,$$

uniformly in every closed subinterval of (a,b).

The limit functions belong to E_1^+ in both cases. We have therefore

Theorem 3.4

In E_n^+ every uniformly bounded sequence contains a subsequence uniformly converging in the interior of I. The family E_n^+ is closed under uniform convergence. Finally, to every $f(x) \in C[I]$ there is a best approximation in E_n^+.

4. Unicity and characterisation for the T-approximation with respect to E_n and E_n^o

The ideas of these investigations go back to Meinardus [2], details are given in the Habilitationsschrift of Braess.

To motivate the situation we write

$$y(x;c,\lambda) = \sum_{j=1}^{\ell} c_j e^{\lambda_j x} \quad \text{where} \quad \begin{matrix} c = (c_1,\ldots,c_\ell), \\ \lambda = (\lambda_1,\ldots,\lambda_\ell). \end{matrix} \tag{29}$$

Clearly we may derive the gradients

$$\mathrm{grad}_c y := (e^{\lambda_1 x},\ldots,e^{\lambda_\ell x})^T, \ \mathrm{grad}_\lambda y := (xc_1 e^{\lambda_1 x},\ldots,xc_\ell e^{\lambda_\ell x})^T. \tag{30}$$

If $\Delta c,\Delta\lambda$ denote small changes of the vectors c and λ we find for the error curve (4) the expansion

$$\varepsilon(x;c+\Delta c,\lambda+\Delta\lambda) = \varepsilon(x;c,\lambda)-(\Delta c,\mathrm{grad}_c y)-(\Delta\lambda,\mathrm{grad}_\lambda y)+O(\|\Delta c\|^2+\|\Delta\lambda\|^2) \tag{31}$$

with the scalar products $(\Delta c,\mathrm{grad}_c y)$, $(\Delta\lambda,\mathrm{grad}_\lambda y)$ and any norm for Δc and $\Delta\lambda$.

Whether the norm $\|\varepsilon(x;c+\Delta c,\lambda+\Delta\lambda)\|$ may be decreased depends essentially on these two scalar products, i.e. linear combinations of the 2ℓ scalar functions written down in (30). The Theorem 2.1 of Polya-Szegö states that these functions are a Tschebyscheff-System of 2ℓ functions. One may look at this locally as a linear problem, namely that of approximating $\varepsilon(x;c,\lambda)$ up to second order terms by the linear term $(\Delta c,\mathrm{grad}_c y)$ + $(\Delta\lambda,\mathrm{grad}_\lambda y)$.

In varying the parameters c_j,λ_j to find the best approximation in E_n^0, we could add $n-\ell$ terms with coefficients $c_j = 0$, hence we have available the Tschebyscheff-system

$$\underbrace{e^{\lambda_1 x},\ldots,e^{\lambda_\ell x},e^{\lambda_{\ell+1} x},\ldots,e^{\lambda_n x},xe^{\lambda_1 x},\ldots,xe^{\lambda_\ell x}}_{\substack{n+\ell \text{ functions.} \\ \lambda_i \neq \lambda_j \text{ for } i \neq j.}} \ \Big| \ \underbrace{0xe^{\lambda_{\ell+1} x},\ldots,0xe^{\lambda_n x}}_{\substack{\text{no significant} \\ \text{contribution}}} \tag{32}$$

Thus the following theorem is plausible: we omit the proof.

Theorem 4.1

The function $y(x) \in E_n^0$ is the best approximation of a given function $f(x)$, iff the error curve has an alternant of length $\mathrm{alt}(f,y)=n+\ell+1$, where ℓ denotes the length of y.

These considerations can be generalised to the functions of $E_n-E_n^0$. If k is the degree of y defined in Section 2, there are available k coefficients, i.e. parameters entering linearly into the sum

$$y = \sum_{j=1}^{\ell} P_j(x).e^{\lambda_j x}.$$

If y is to be the best approximation of f(x) in E_n, it is locally the best approximation. We have available a Tschebyscheff-System of $n+\ell$ functions, namely

$$\left.\begin{array}{ll} e^{\lambda_1 x},\ xe^{\lambda_1 x},\ldots,x^{r_1}e^{\lambda_1 x}, & \text{if the degree } \partial P_1 = r_1 \\ e^{\lambda_2 x},\ldots,\ \ x^{r_2}e^{\lambda_2 x} & (\partial P_2 = r_2) \\ \ldots\ldots & \\ e^{\lambda_\ell x},\ldots,\ \ x^{r_\ell}e^{\lambda_\ell x} & (\partial P_\ell = r_\ell) \end{array}\right\} \text{k functions, from } \mathrm{grad}_c y. \tag{33}$$

- - - - - - -

$$\left.\begin{array}{l} e^{\lambda_{\ell+1}x}, \\ \vdots \\ e^{\lambda_n x} \end{array}\right\} \begin{array}{l}\text{n-k functions, formally added with } c_j=0, \\ \text{which also arise from } \mathrm{grad}_c y, \\ \text{but do not appear in } \mathrm{grad}_\lambda y.\end{array} \tag{34}$$

- - - - -

$$\left.\begin{array}{l} e^{\lambda_1 x}\cdot x^{r_1+1} \\ \vdots \\ e^{\lambda_\ell x}\cdot x^{r_\ell+1} \end{array}\right\} \begin{array}{l}\ell \text{ functions from } \mathrm{grad}_\lambda y, \text{ supplementing the functions} \\ \text{already noted under (33).}\end{array} \tag{35}$$

Altogether there are $n+\ell$ functions. This motivates the first part of

Theorem 4.2

(a) If the function y is a best approximation to f with respect to E_n then there exists an alternant of length alt $(f,y) = n+\ell+1$.

(b) If there is an alternant of length alt $(f,y) = n+k+1$, then y is a best approximation to f(x).

The second part may be proved by comparing y with any other function z of E_n. Then y-z belongs to E_{n+k}. The result is then obtained by counting zeros of this difference and using Theorem 2.1.

It is remarkable that necessary and sufficient conditions are different, hence sometimes additional information is needed when one wishes to determine that y is the best approximation of f(x). Both conditions coincide if $\ell = k$, i.e. y belongs to E_n^o.

From Theorems 4.1 and 4.2 we obtain

orollary 4.2

If y is a best approximation to $f(x)$ in E_n^o, it is also a best approximation to $f(x)$ in E_n.

Turning from characterisation to uniqueness we have the following act already to be found in the book of Meinardus [2].

heorem 4.3

If there is a best approximation of $f(x)$, with respect to E_n^o, then this approximation is uniquely determined.

raess generalised this and showed

heorem 4.4

If the best approximation to $f(x)$ with respect to E_n belongs to E_n^o then it is the unique best approximation in E_n.

t was conjectured in the literature that generally we would have niqueness in E_n. Braess probably was the first to see that this is alse. He gave the following <u>example</u>.

et $f(x) \in C[-1,+1]$, $f(x) = f(-x)$, positive in $[-1,+1]$ and strongly onotonically decreasing in $[0,1]$.

A unique best approximation of $f(x)$ in E_2 would have to be ymmetric and positive also, hence would be of the form $y = c_1 \cosh \lambda_1 x$ where $\lambda_1 = 0$ is possible). Then $\varepsilon(x) = f(x)-y(x)$ has at most one zero in 0,1) and is monotonically increasing in this interval, i.e. $|\varepsilon(x)|$ is xtremal at $0,+1$ (and therefore also at -1). Three points of alternation re, however, not enough to characterise a best approximation, by ondition (b) of Theorem 4.2.

Before considering the family E_n^+ we have to study further properties of ums of exponentials.

5. Sign classes

Braess discovered in his Habilitationsschrift [1] that some properties of approximation by sums of exponentials depend on the signs of the coefficients. We present his results giving a somewhat shorter derivation by means of the difference quotient and a modified definition.

In Section 2 we agreed on numbering the frequencies in ascending order $\lambda_1 < \lambda_2 < \dots$; this we keep in mind for the following definition.

<u>Definition 5.1</u> Let $y \in E_n^o - E_{n-1}^o$, say $y = \sum_{j=1}^{n} c_j \cdot e^{\lambda_j x}$, then we associate with

y an integer vector, its <u>signum</u>

$$s := \text{sgn } y := (\text{sgn } c_1, \text{sgn } c_2, \ldots, \text{sgn } c_n) \in R^n,$$

and we denote by $E_n^o(s)$ the set of all $y \in E_n^o$ with sgn $y = s$.

We wish to assign a signum to $y \in E_n - E_n^o$ in a "natural way". For instance, such that $\tilde{y} = \lim y_r : y_r \in E_n^o(s)$, $\tilde{y} \in E_n - E_{n-1}$, implies sgn $\tilde{y} = s$ We show that this is possible by the following definitions:

<u>Definition 5.2a</u>. If $y_1 \in E_{n_1} - E_{n_1-1}$ and $y_2 \in E_{n_2} - E_{n_2-1}$ and all frequencies of y_1 are smaller than the frequencies of y_2, then we define

$$\text{sgn } y = \text{sgn } y_1, \text{ sgn } y_2 \text{ where } y = y_1 + y_2 \tag{36}$$

<u>Definition 5.2b</u>. If $y = (a_r x^r + a_{r-1} x^{r-1} + \ldots + a_0) e^{\lambda x}$, $a_r \neq 0$, then we define

$$\text{sgn } y = ((-1)^r \text{sgn } a_r, (-1)^{r-1} \text{sgn } a_r, \ldots, (-1)^0 \text{sgn } a_r) \in R^{r+1}, \tag{37}$$

and we denote by $E_n(s)$ the set of all $y \in E_n - E_{n-1}$ with sgn $y = s$.

We remark that Def. 5.2a is consistent with Def. 5.1. The definition 5.2b is motivated by formulas (8) and (9). The coefficients w_r of (8) alternate in sign, hence $y = a_r x^r e^{\lambda x}$ is the limit of elements of E_{r+1}^o(sgn y)

Theorem 5.1

Let $y \in E_n(s)$. If $\{y_r\}$ converges uniformly to y, then almost all y_r belong to $E_n(s)$.

<u>Proof</u>. We observe that it is sufficient to prove the statement under the additional assumption $y_r \in E_n^o$. If this is shown, and $y_r \in E_n$, we may replace y_r by $\tilde{y}_r$, where sgn $\tilde{y}_r$ = sgn y_r and $\|\tilde{y}_r - y_r\| < 1/r$ to obtain the general result (r=1,2,3,...).

With each function y_r and y we may associate the set of its frequencies and the corresponding differential operator L_r,L. We saw in the proof of Theorem 3.1, that the frequencies converge. The coefficients of the differential equations converge also, properly normalized fundamental systems Y_r of L_r tending to a fundamental system Y of L. The coefficients of y_r with respect to the fundamental system Y_r will then tend to the coefficients of y with respect to Y.

a) If y has n distinct frequencies $\lambda_1 < \lambda_2 < \ldots < \lambda_n$, then these frequencies and, for almost all r, the frequencies $\lambda_1^{(r)} < \lambda_2^{(r)} < \ldots < \lambda_n^{(r)}$ of y_r yield respectively the fundamental systems

$$Y = (e^{\lambda_1 x}, e^{\lambda_2 x}, \ldots, e^{\lambda_n x}),\ Y_r = (e^{\lambda_1^{(r)} x}, e^{\lambda_2^{(r)} x}, \ldots, e^{\lambda_n^{(r)} x}). \tag{38}$$

he linear independence follows from Theorem 2.1. Since the coefficients $c_j^{(r)} \to c_j$, it is obvious that

$$\text{sgn } y_r = \text{sgn } y \text{ for } r \text{ sufficiently large.}$$

) If the frequencies of y form groups of equal frequencies, the system 38) no longer consists of linearly independent functions. We then ntroduce the terms

$$e^{\lambda x}, xe^{\lambda x}, \ldots, x^m e^{\lambda x}, \tag{39}$$

here λ stands for a frequency λ_j appearing m+1 times. With these unctions Y is again a fundamental system.

To generate Y_r we use the difference quotients

$$e^{\lambda_0 x}, 1!\,\Delta(\lambda_0,\lambda_1)e^{\lambda x}, \ldots, m!\,\Delta^m(\lambda_0,\ldots,\lambda_m)e^{\lambda x} \tag{40}$$

here $\lambda_0,\lambda_1,\ldots,\lambda_m$ denote those frequencies of y_r, in ascending order, hat tend to λ_j for $r \to \infty$. Again the coefficients with respect to these undamental systems converge. We check how this is reflected in the oefficients $c_j^{(r)}$ with respect to the original representation, $y_r = c_j^{(r)} e^{\lambda_j^{(r)} x}$.

We may restrict our attention to only one group of frequencies with the ame limit λ. Let

$$y = \sum_{j=0}^{m} d_j^{(r)} x^j e^{\lambda x},\quad d_m^{(r)} \neq 0, \tag{41}$$

hen

$$\begin{aligned} y_r &= \sum_{j=0}^{m} d_j^{(r)} j!\,\Delta_\lambda^j(\lambda_0^{(r)},\ldots,\lambda_j^{(r)})\ e^{\lambda x} \\ &= \sum_{j=0}^{m} d_j^{(r)} j! \sum_{k=0}^{j} e^{\lambda_k^{(r)} x} w_{jk}^{(r)},\ \text{where } w_{jk}^{(r)} = 1/\prod_{\substack{i=0 \\ i\neq k}}^{j} (\lambda_k^{(r)} - \lambda_i^{(r)}), \\ &= \sum_{k=0}^{m} e^{\lambda_k^{(r)} x} \sum_{j=k}^{m} w_{jk}^{(r)} j!\,d_j^{(r)}. \end{aligned} \tag{42}$$

Now we have expressions for the $c_k^{(r)}$ that can be analysed.

$$c_k^{(r)} = \sum_{j=k}^{m} w_{jk}^{(r)} j! d_j^{(r)}$$

$$= w_{mk}^{(r)} \{m! d_m^{(r)} + (m-1)!(\lambda_k^{(r)} - \lambda_m^{(r)}) d_{m-1}^{(r)} +$$

$$+ (m-2)!(\lambda_k^{(r)} - \lambda_m^{(r)})(\lambda_k^{(r)} - \lambda_{m-1}^{(r)}) d_{m-2}^{(r)} + \ldots\}. \qquad (43)$$

For $r \to \infty$ the factors $(\lambda_k^{(r)} - \lambda_m^{(r)}), \ldots$ tend to zero, hence sgn $c_k^{(r)}$ is given by sgn $(w_{mk}^{(r)} d_m^{(r)}) = (-1)^{m-k}$ sgn $d_m^{(r)}$ for almost all r. This shows that these y_r lie in the class $E_n(s)$. //

Having assigned a signum to proper and improper sums of $E_n - E_{n-1}$ we may formulate the sign-rule of Descartes. The proof of Polya-Szegö [3] written down for a proper sum, goes through without any difficulty.

Theorem 5.2

Let $y \in E_n(s)$, $n > 0$, have m zeros (multiple zeros counted according to multiplicity) on the real axis. Denote by W the sign changes of the vector s. Then

$$W \geq m \quad \text{and} \quad W \equiv m (\text{mod } 2). \qquad (44)$$

Proof. Observe that $y \not\equiv 0$, since $0 \notin E_n(s)$, $n > 0$, per definition. For $x \to +\infty$ the sign of y is given by the sign of the highest coefficient of the highest frequency of y, i.e. the last component of s = sgn y. For $x \to -\infty$ the sign of y is determined analogously by the first component of s. The odd multiplicity zeros of y divide the real line into m+1(mod 2) intervals of alternating signs of y. Denote by w the vector of the signs of y in these intervals. The first and last components of s and w have the same sign. Hence the number of sign changes of w (equal to m(mod 2)) is equal to the number of sign changes of s(mod 2). This proves the second relation.

The first relation is proved by induction with respect to n. For n=1 no function $y \in E_1(s)$ has a zero: $y = c_1 e^{\lambda_1 x}$, $c_1 \neq 0$, hence W=m=0. Now suppose $n > 1$ and let $y \in E_n(s)$ have m zeros, $m > 0$. Then s = sgn y must have at least one sign change, otherwise y could not vanish. Suppose that λ_j is the smallest frequency such that there is a change between s_j and s_{j+1}. Now

$$ye^{-\lambda_{j+1}x} \in E_n(s) \text{ and } D(ye^{-\lambda_{j+1}x}) \in E_{n-1},$$

because the degree of the polynomial associated as factor to $e^{\lambda_{j+1}x}$ is reduced by one, or that term drops out. If we look at the signum of y we find that s_j is cancelled by the differentiation, while all s_k with $k < j$ are associated with frequencies of constant coefficients, and hence are multiplied by $\mathrm{sgn}(\lambda_k - \lambda_j) = -1$, thus getting the sign of s_{j+1}.

For $k > j$, however,

$$D\{P(x)e^{(\lambda_k-\lambda_j x)}\} = \{(\lambda_k - \lambda_j)P(x) + P'(x)\} e^{(\lambda_k-\lambda_j)x} \tag{45}$$

and the sign of every highest coefficient and of all s_k with $k > j+1$ is unchanged.

Therefore the number of sign changes of $\mathrm{sgn}(D(y.e^{-\lambda_j x}))$ is W-1, while the number of zeros is at least m-1, so by the induction assumption we obtain $W-1 \geq m-1$, which proves our assertion. //

6. Uniqueness and characterisation of best approximation in E_n^+

It is now possible, and Braess does so, to estimate the number of positive and negative coefficients in a sum y by means of its zeros. It is clear that a term $x^m e^{\lambda x}$ stems from m+1 terms of sgn y, hence it accounts for m+1 coefficients. Since k(y), the degree of y, gives the total number of coefficients of y it is reasonable to make

<u>Definition 6.1</u>. Denote by $k^+(y)$ the number of positive, and by $k^-(y)$ the number of negative coefficients in sgn y.

If the number m of zeros of y is odd, say m=2r-1, then by Theorem 5.2

$$k^+(y) \geq r \quad \text{and} \quad k^-(y) \geq r, \tag{46}$$

while if m=2r, and y is positive for $x \to \infty$, then

$$k^+(y) \geq r+1, \quad k^-(y) \geq r. \tag{47}$$

We need in addition

<u>Definition 6.2</u>. The alternant of f and y is called <u>positive</u>, if $\varepsilon(x) = f(x)-y(x)$ is positive at the last (largest) point of the alternant. It is called <u>negative</u>, if the said value is negative.

Now we can state

Theorem 6.1

Let y be the best approximation to f(x) in E_n^o and suppose $z \in E_{n_1}$ $(n_1 > n)$ to be a better approximation.

If the difference $n - k(y)$ is odd ($= 2\rho + 1$) then

$$k^+(z) - k^+(y) \geq \rho+1, \quad k^-(z) - k^-(y) \geq \rho+1; \tag{48}$$

if the difference is even, $n-k(y) = 2\rho$, and the alternant is positive, then

$$k^+(z) - k^+(y) \geq \rho+1, \quad k^-(z) - k^-(y) \geq \rho. \tag{49}$$

Proof. If $y(x)$ is the best approximation in E_n^o, the alternant has length alt $(f,y) \geq n+k(y)+1$, by Theorem 4.1. Hence $z(x)-y(x) = (f-y)-(f-z)$ has at least $n+k(y)$ zeros, since $z(x)$ is a better approximation.

Obviously

$$k^+(z) + k^-(y) \geq k^+(z-y). \tag{50}$$

Now assume that $n-k(y) = 2\rho$, and the alternant is positive, then by (47) we find

$$k^+(z-y) \geq \frac{n+k(y)}{2} + 1 = \rho + 1 + k^+(y)+k^-(y). \tag{51}$$

From (50) and (51) the first of the relations (49) follows. The other cases are proved analogously.

The following criterion (Theorem 6.2) uses the

Corollary 6.1

If $y \in E_n^o$ is the best approximation to $f(x)$ and the alternant is positive then every better approximation $z \in E_{n_1}$ $(n_1 > n)$ has at least one more positive coefficient than y.

Theorem 6.2 (Characterisation theorem for E_n^+)

The function y is a best approximation to $f(x)$ with respect to E_n^+ iff one of the following conditions holds:

a) there is an alternant with alt $(f,y) \geq 2n+1$, or

b) there is a negative alternant with alt $(f,y) \geq 2k(y)+1$.

The best approximation is uniquely determined.

It is remarkable that n does enter into the condition of case b). If b) is to hold for a fixed n then y is also a best approximation with respect to E_{n_1} $(n_1 > n)$. In other words in this case it is not possible to improve the quality of the approximation by the addition of a positive exponential term. It may be puzzling that here even the sign of the error curve enters, but this is understandable, because the coefficients have fixed signs.

Proof. (Necessity). If $y \in E_n^+ - E_{n-1}^+$ is a best approximation to $f(x)$ the considerations of Section 4 apply. The gradient space $(\mathrm{grad}_c y)^T$, $(\mathrm{grad}_\lambda y)^T$ has dimension $2n$. A local minimum requires $\mathrm{alt}(f,y) \geq 2n+1$. Suppose $y \in E_k^+ - E_{k-1}^+$ $(k < n)$ is a best approximation in E_n^+. It is a best approximation with respect to E_k^+, hence has an alternant with $\mathrm{alt}(f,y) \geq 2k+1$. If this alternant is not negative its length is exactly equal to $2k+1$. Therefore there is a better approximation z in E_{k+1} to $f(x)$. By Corollary 6.1 z has at least one positive coefficient more than y, i.e. it has k+1 positive coefficients, thus $z \in E_{k+1}^+ \subset E_n^+$ and y was not the best approximation of $f(x)$ in E_n^+, a contradiction.

(Sufficiency). Assume that a) or b) is satisfied for $y \in E_k^+ - E_{k-1}^+$. Suppose $z \in E_n^+$ were an equally good or better approximation, but different from y. Then

$$z-y = (f-y) - (f-z), \quad (\|f-z\| \leq \|f-y\|) \tag{52}$$

is easily seen to have at least 2k zeros, counting double zeros twice.

If k=n then $z-y \in E_{2n}$. By Theorem 5.2 the difference z-y vanishes identically if it has 2n zeros. Contradiction.

Now let $k < n$. Consider the case $\|f-z\| < \|f-y\|$ first. Since all coefficients of z are positive, the negative coefficients of the sum z-y stem from y, i.e. there are exactly k, and the sequence of coefficients has at most 2k sign changes. Because of Theorem 5.2 and the above remark following (52) the function z-y has exactly 2k zeros, lying between the points of the alternant of y. Therefore the sign of (f-y) at the last point of the alternant is equal to the sign of (z-y) for $x \to +\infty$.

Due to the number of sign changes, namely 2k, each coefficient of y must account for two changes, hence z has one frequency larger than all frequencies of y. Therefore (z-y) is positive for large z. Consequently (f-y) was positive at the last point of the alternant. Hence the alternant could not be negative.

Next, suppose $\|f-z\| = \|f-y\|$, i.e. y and z are two different best approximations in E_n^+. Then we can find K, $n \geq K \geq k$, such that E_K^+ contains both functions and at least one of them, say $\tilde{y}$, is K-non-degenerate, in other words $y \in E_K^+ - E_{K-1}^+$ is a best approximation to $f(x)$ in E_K^+. Applying the reasoning of the sufficiency proof for k=n replacing n by K, we conclude that $\tilde{y}$ is the unique best approximation to $f(x)$ in E_K^+.

Hence y and z must coincide with it. This furnishes the contradiction $y \equiv z$, and concludes the reasoning of Braess for E_n^+.

7. Continuity properties of the approximation with sums of exponentials

Numerical experiments indicate that the calculation of fits in the classes under consideration are rather critical. It would be useful to have more details in this field. A qualitative analysis has been worked out in the Dissertation of E. Schmidt [6] at our department at Münster University.

For rational approximations it was possible to classify those functions for which the map $f \to T_{\ell,r}f$ (:= best rational approximation of a prescribed class $R_{\ell,r}$) is continuous. The considerations led to the concept of (ℓ,r)-Normality in Werner [8].

Is it possible to give an analogous definition of normality for our classes of approximating functions? The answer is not quite as satisfactory for this case as it is for rational functions. One obstacle is the fact that there may be more than one best approximation. To allow for this possibility we write $[T_n^\alpha f]$ to denote the set of all best approximations in E_n to f(x) on the interval I. Here and in the sequel α = +,o, or void. Schmidt introduces the following conventions.

<u>Definition 7.1.</u> T_n^α is called <u>continuous</u> at $f \in C[I]$, if

1) there exists a best approximation of f in the class E_n^α,
2) this approximation is unique,
3) there is a neighborhood of f in C[I]: $\|g-f\| < \delta$, $\delta > 0$,

such that for every such g the set $[T_n^\alpha g]$ is not empty and $\|g_r-f\| \to 0$ implies $\|y_r-T_n^\alpha f\| \to 0$ where $y_r \in [T_n^\alpha g_r]$.

On the other hand normality seems to be best defined by

<u>Definition 7.2.</u> The function $f \in C[I]$ is called <u>n^α-normal</u>, if

1) $[T_n^\alpha f]$ is not empty,
2) $[T_n^\alpha f]$ contains exactly one element (unicity of approximation)
2) $[T_n^\alpha f] \in E_n^\alpha - E_{n-1}^\alpha$: in words, the approximation is "not degenerate".

It is then comparatively easy to see

Theorem 7.1

At each n^α-normal function f(x) the operator T_n^α is continuous.

It is also not difficult to show that the normal functions form an open set in C[I].

If one looks for the converse of Theorem 7.1 things are more complicated than for rational approximation.

We get the expected result in E_n^o, namely discontinuity at every point $f \in C$ that is not n^o-normal.

In E_n the Operator $[T_n f]$ is discontinuous at non-normal points f, for example, if $[T_n f]$ contains more than one function or if $y = [T_n f]$ and $k(y) < n$ but $alt(f,y) \geq n+k(y)+1$. This, however, does not exhaust all possibilities, as can be seen from the quoted paper.

Interesting results are obtained for E_n^+: Continuity is found iff one of the following conditions is satisfied:

1) f is n^+-normal, or

2) The length of the alternant is exactly equal to $2k(y) + 1$, or

3) $\varepsilon(x) = f(x)-y(x)$ attains the value $-\|f-y\|$ at both endpoints of I, where $y = [T_n^+ f]$.

8. Constructive aspects*

Today we cannot claim the numerical treatment of approximation in the classes E_n to have reached a satisfactory state. As mentioned earlier, it is possible to simulate the descent method of Werner [7] to obtain best approximations, as has been done by Braess [1]. This is essentially a local search technique. One may carry things one step further by discussing in which sign class there may be a best approximation. Braess [1] demonstrated the possibility of local best approximations. But in certain cases one can see that there is at most one solution in a given sign class, e.g. in $E_2(+,-)$. If there were two different best approximations they would both belong to $E_2(+,-) - E_2^o(+,-)$, since a best local approximation in $E_2^o(+,-)$ would be the global best approximation in E_2^o and this is unique.

The difference of these two approximations would be of the form

$$(a_1+b_1x).e^{\lambda_1 x} - (a_2+b_2x)e^{\lambda_2 x} \in E_4(+,-,-,+) \text{ or } E_4(-,+,+,-),$$

since $b_1 > 0$, $b_2 > 0$. By Theorem 5.2 the difference should have at most 2 zeros. On the other hand considering the alternants the difference should have at least 3 zeros, and this is a contradiction.

The problem is however of global nature and we will comment on it. If

* This material is part of a paper presented at a meeting in Oberwolfach, June 1969.

The problem is however of a global nature and we will comment on it. If it happens that the best approximation $[T_n f]$ lies in E_n^o then by Section 4 it is known that there is only one solution - the local minimum furnishes the global solution. It cannot be said that "generally" this situation will be met. In contrast to the rational function case, where an arbitrarily small change of f(x) will alter a non-normal function into a normal one we really find balls in C[I] where the best solution lies in $E_n - E_n^o$.

To study the concrete cases numerically, it is advisable to separate the linear parameters from the (nonlinear) frequencies. Given frequencies $\lambda_1 \leq \lambda_2 \leq \ldots \leq \lambda_n$, the determination of the linear parameters, i.e. the coefficients of $e^{\lambda_j x}$ or $x^r e^{\lambda_j x}$ is a problem of linear approximation theory. In principle its solution by the Remes algorithm causes no difficulty.

If $y = T[f;\lambda_1,\ldots,\lambda_n]$ denotes the solution, write

$$\eta[f;\lambda_1,\ldots,\lambda_n] := \|f-y\| . \tag{53}$$

Our problem is therefore, to minimize $\eta[f;\lambda_1,\ldots,\lambda_n]$ on $\lambda_1 \leq \lambda_2 \leq \ldots \leq \lambda_n$. The function is not convex as is proven by the fact that there are functions where exactly two extreme points (with equal $\eta[f;\lambda_1,\ldots,\lambda_n]$) exist. We know that in this case some of the λ_j must coincide. It may also happen that there are local minima different from the global minimum. (Compare figures 3 and 4.) These points will always lie on the boundary, because interior points ($\lambda_1 < \lambda_2 < \ldots < \lambda_n$) give functions of E_n^o, where uniqueness persists and a local minimum is the global one.

The global search seems difficult, because the λ-domain is not compact. This difficulty we will remove by a proper definition.

We introduce for λ_j the values $\pm\infty$ in addition to the reals. We say that $\{\lambda_j^r\}_{r=1,2,\ldots}$ tends to $+\infty$ or $-\infty$, if the λ_j^r are larger or smaller respectively than any fixed real quantity for sufficiently large values of r.

We then agree to delete in the calculation of $\eta[f;\lambda_1,\ldots,\lambda_n]$ those terms with $\lambda_j = \pm\infty$, i.e. if m of the λ_j are infinite, we only consider sums of n-m terms, the frequencies being the finite λ_j. (These new values $\eta[f,\lambda_1,\ldots,\lambda_n]$ correspond to values already attained in the class E_{n-m}. This is of some advantage, if one ascends through $E_1, E_2, \ldots$ up to E_n.)

The domain B : $-\infty \leq \lambda_1 \leq \lambda_2 \leq \ldots \leq \lambda_n \leq \infty$ is compact and we have the useful fact given in

Theorem 8.1

$\eta[f;\lambda_1,\ldots,\lambda_n]$ is continuous on B.

Proof. Let $\lambda^r := (\lambda_1^r,\ldots,\lambda_n^r) \to \lambda = (\lambda_1,\ldots,\lambda_n)$ for $r \to \infty$.
We denote the associated solutions of the linear problems by y^r. Since $||f-y^r|| \leq ||f||$, the norms $||y^r||$ are bounded.

By Theorem 3.1 there is a subsequence $\{y^\mu\}$ uniformly converging in the interior of I to a function $\tilde{y}$, which is associated with the frequencies $(\lambda_1,\ldots,\lambda_n)$, such that $\eta[f,\lambda^\mu] \to \liminf \eta[f,\lambda^r]$. If some of the λ_j are infinite, then $\tilde{y}$ is degenerate, but this does not matter.

Denote by J_ν the interval $[a + \frac{1}{\nu}, b - \frac{1}{\nu}] \subset I$ for ν sufficiently large. Then

$$\|f-\tilde{y}\|_{J_\nu} = \lim_\mu \|f-y^\mu\|_{J_\nu} \leq \liminf \|f-y^\mu\|_I = \liminf \eta[f,\lambda^\mu] =: c_1. \quad (54)$$

For $\nu \to \infty$ we find

$$\eta[f,\lambda] \leq \|f-\tilde{y}\|_I \leq c_1. \quad (55)$$

On the other hand let $\hat{y} = T[f,\lambda]$ be the best approximation,

$$\hat{y} = \sum{}' d_j e^{\lambda_j x}, \quad (56)$$

where the dash indicates that we sum over the finite λ_j only.
The functions $\hat{y}^r = \sum' d_j e^{\lambda_j^r x}$ are admissible functions for the linear problem with the parameters $(\lambda_1^\mu,\ldots,\lambda_n^\mu)$. Therefore

$$\|f-\hat{y}^r\| \geq \eta[f;\lambda^r]. \quad (57)$$

Since $\lim \|\hat{y}-\hat{y}^r\| = 0$ we have

$$\eta[f,\lambda] = \|f-\hat{y}\|_I = \lim \|f-\hat{y}^r\|_I \geq \limsup \eta[f;\lambda^r]. \quad (58)$$

From (55) and (58) we conclude

$$\limsup \eta[f,\lambda^r] \leq \eta[f,\lambda] \leq \liminf \eta[f,\lambda^r], \quad (59)$$

which can be correct only if the equality signs hold. This proves our assertion.

We hope that this smoothes the way for the numerical treatment of our problem. Global and local methods have to be combined.

Examples

To illustrate, we give in Figures 2, 3, and 4 the level lines for functions $\eta[f,\lambda], \lambda = (\lambda_1,\lambda_2)$, where f(x) is equal to

$$\begin{array}{ll} 1 + e^{-0.4x} + e^{1.6x} & \text{in } I = [-1,+1], \\ \cos x & \text{"} \quad , \\ \cos (x + 0.2) & \text{"} \end{array}$$

respectively. In each case the various regions $E_2(s)$ are shaded as follows: $E_2(+,+)$ is left white, $E_2(-,+)$///, $E_2(+,-)$\\\. The boundaries are indicated by circles.

In the neighborhoods of local (or global) extrema the level lines form closed curves with corners. The corners lie on the curve indicated by -.-.-. . These curves contain also the minima.

In the first case (Fig. 2) there is one unique minimum located in $E_2(+,+)$.

In the second case (Fig. 3) we have two equally good minima, one in $E_2(+,-)$, the other in $E_2(-,+)$ as is clear by the example of Braess in Section 4.

In Fig. 4 the function is slightly modified and now there are two local minima, belonging to $E_2 - E_2^o$. While the one in $E_2(-,+)$ is only local, that in $E_2(+,-)$ is the global one. This decision could only be made by looking at the total domain of (λ_1,λ_2). The cases represented are typical.

If $y \in E_2^o$ is a best approximation, it is unique. If y belongs to $E_2 - E_2^o$ there may be one (local) minimum in $E_2(-,+)$ and a second one in $E_2(+,-)$, hence there are at most two solutions.

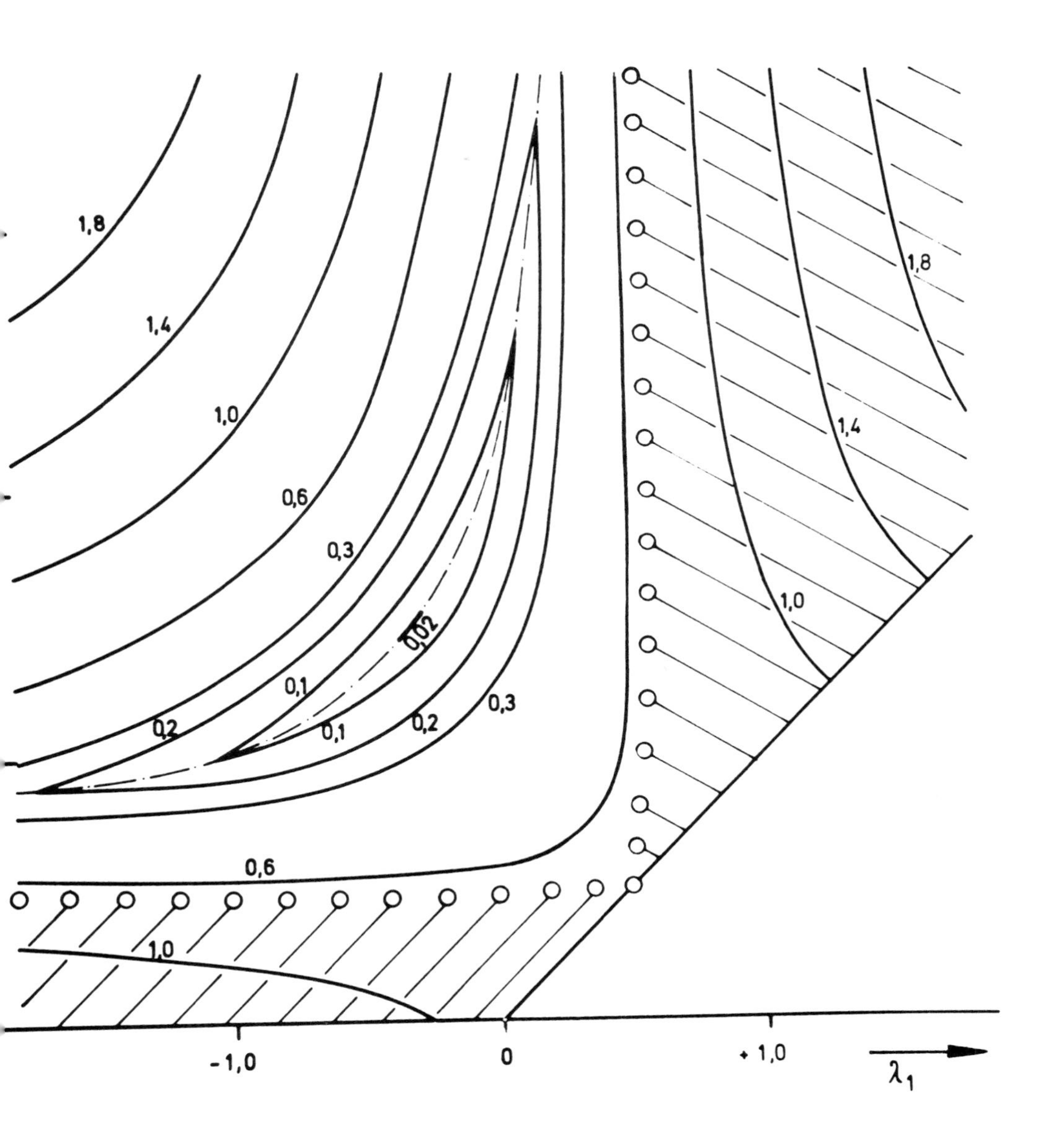

Fig. 2

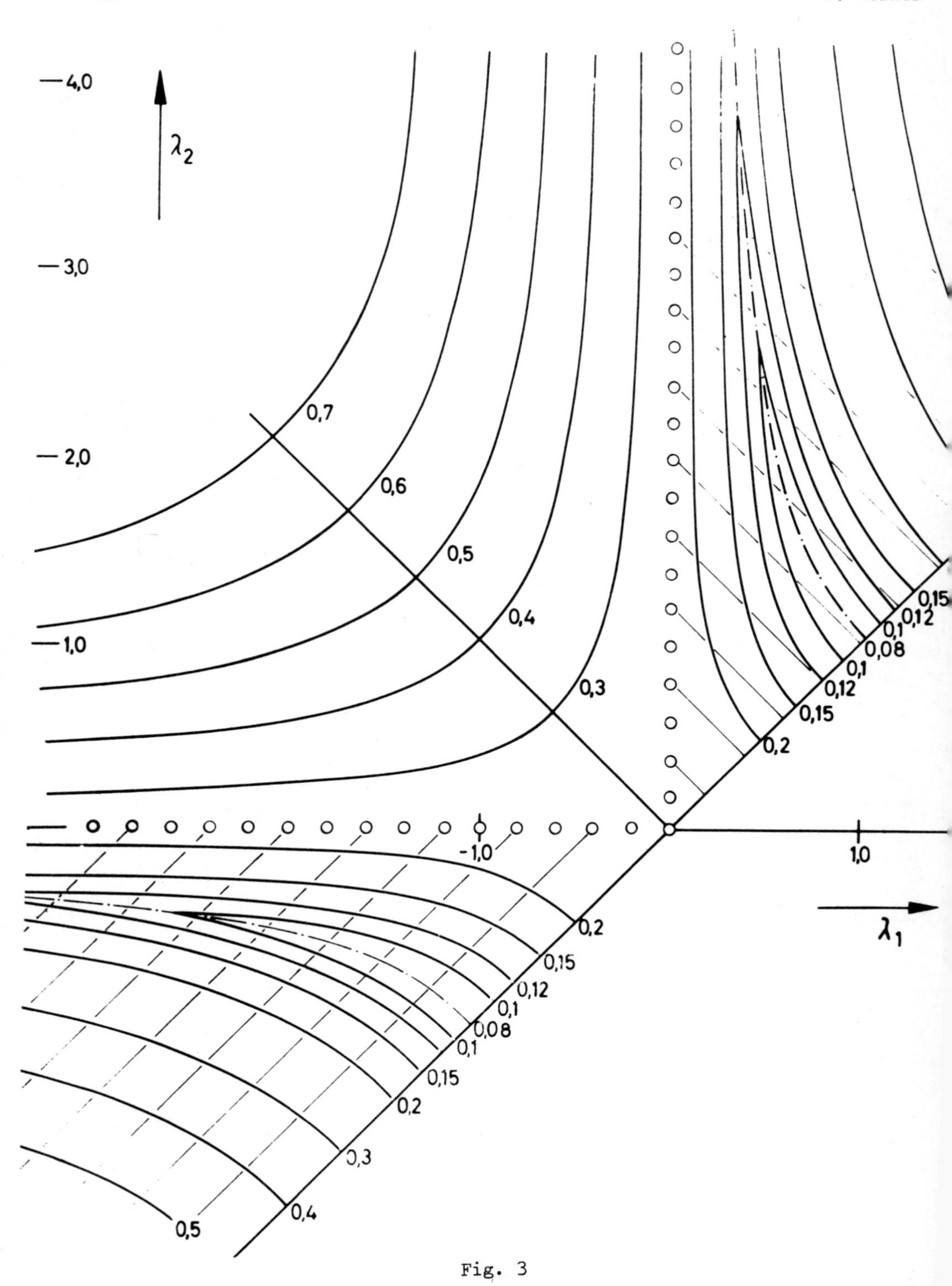

4,0
3,0
2,0
1,0
λ_2
0,7
0,6
0,5
0,4
0,3
0,2
0,15
0,12
0,1
0,08
-1,0
1,0
λ_1
0,5
0,4

Fig. 3

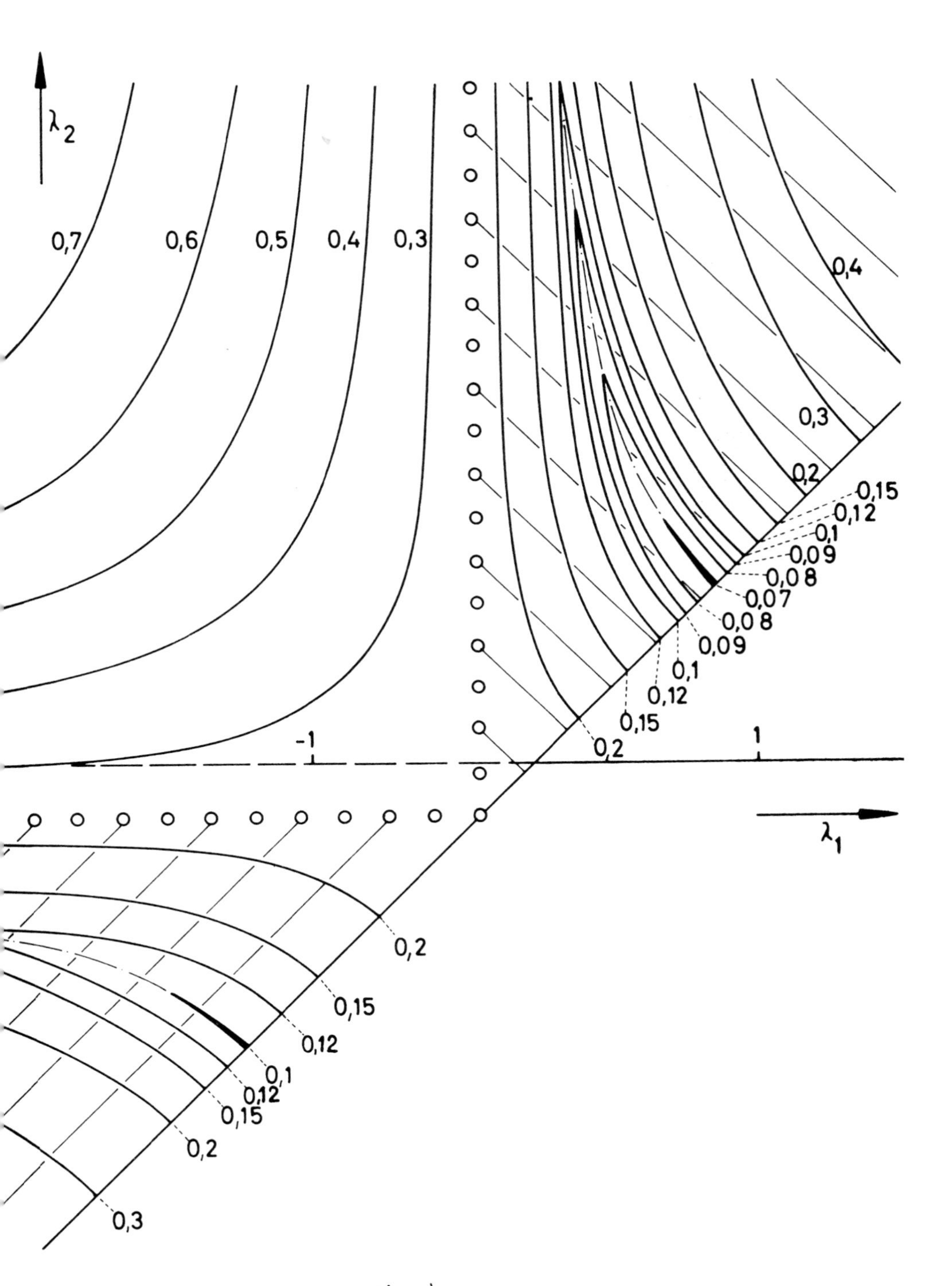

λ2
0,7
0,6
0,5
0,4
0,3
0,4
0,3
0,2
0,15
0,12
0,1
0,09
0,08
0,07
0,08
0,09
0,1
0,12
0,15
0,2
-1
1
λ1
0,2
0,15
0,12
0,1
0,12
0,15
0,2
0,3

Fig. 4

References

1. BRAESS, D. Habilitationsschrift Münster, Wintersemester 1967/68. Part I: 'Approximation mit Exponentialsummen'. Computing, 2, pp. 309-321. The other parts will appear in revised form.

2. MEINARDUS, G. Approximation of Functions: Theory and Numerical Methods. Springer 1967.

3. POLYA-SZEGÖ, G. Aufgaben und Lehrsätze aus der Analysis, vol 2, p. 49. Springer, 1964.

4. RICE, J. R. 'Chebyshev Approximation by Exponentials'. J. SIAM, 10 (1962), pp. 149-161.

5. RICE, J. R. The Approximation of Functions, vol. II - Advanced Topics. Addison-Wesley, 1969.

6. SCHMIDT, E. Normalität und Stetigkeit bei der Tschebyscheff-Approximation mit Exponentialsummen. Dissertation Münster, 1968. (To appear in several parts.)

7. WERNER, H. 'Die konstruktive Ermittlung der Tschebyscheff-Approximierenden im Bereich der rationalen Funktionen'. Arch. Rat. Mech. Anal., 11 (1962),pp. 368-384.

8. WERNER, H. 'Die Bedeutung der Normalität bei rationaler Tschebyscheff-Approximation'. Computing, 2 (1967),pp. 34-52.

9. WERNER, H. 'Das Tschebyscheff-Problem in der Klasse der Exponentialfunktionen'. Presented at the Tagung über Approximationstheorie, Oberwolfach Nov. 1967. To be published by Birkhauser Verlag.

ON THE SOLUBILITY OF THE CAUCHY INTERPOLATION PROBLEM

J. Meinguet

(University of Louvain, Belgium)

1. Introduction

As candidates for the efficient representation of mathematical functions by easily computed expressions, rational functions are often to be preferred to polynomials. Indeed it has been found empirically that, in general, rational approximations can achieve a smaller maximum error for the same amount of computation than polynomial approximations. Moreover, unlike polynomials, rational functions can still be used successfully to approximate singular or nearly singular functions, possibly over infinite intervals.

Notwithstanding these strong motivations and in spite of an apparent similarity to the classical subject of polynomial interpolation, the so-called Cauchy interpolation problem (i.e. the problem of pointwise interpolation by polynomial rational functions) has received comparatively little attention. The relevant literature itself does not seem to be widely known to numerical analysts and it can even be said that some of the most significant references are almost completely overlooked nowadays. A survey of the original works, most of which are only available in the German language, however shows that the subject is manifestly still worth while studying, if not for its own sake, at least because of its many (but often unsuspected) connections with a whole body of mathematical knowledge. Of particular importance are the connections with, for example, the theory of polynomials and of continued fractions (both from the algebraic and analytic standpoints), the theory of determinants and matrices, the calculus of finite differences, the moment problem, the quotient-difference algorithm. As announced in the title, and in spite of the constructive character of most of the arguments developed hereafter, this paper is concerned with theoretical aspects of the Cauchy interpolation problem rather than with related computational matters, its primary object being indeed to provide a unification that seems to be lacking in the existing literature.

It will be shown that the fundamental question of the existence of a (necessarily unique) solution can be answered in various ways, which lead to specific characterizations of the sets of nodes of interpolation for which the Cauchy problem is soluble and also lay bare interesting cross-connections between several earlier investigations. As explained in Sec. 2, on the basis of a general analysis due to Maehly and Witzgall (see [21], Sec. 3), the complete answer to the existence question is easy to formulate in terms of the (equivalent) ratios of polynomials which represent the always existing solution of a "modified" interpolation problem. In the remaining three sections, explicit expressions of that candidate for the solution of the Cauchy problem will be obtained and discussed in detail, with related topics. In Sec. 3, we shall be concerned with the Cauchy interpolation formula, which can be interpreted as the formal extension to the class of rational functions of the well known Lagrange interpolation formula. In Sec. 4, a continued-fraction approach will be elaborated in a systematic way from an elementary polynomial identity; the special determinants called bigradients or subresultants playing here the prominent role, there is hardly a resemblance to the direct (but artificial) exploitation of continued fractions that was briefly explained by Kronecker in [18]. Finally, in Sec. 5, we shall make use of the fact that the numerator can readily be eliminated, from the modified interpolation problem, by a suitable equivalence transformation; initiated by Jacobi (see [17]), this interesting approach was discussed in great detail by Kronecker in [18], rediscovered by Werner a few years ago (see e.g. [39], Sec. 3) and exploited repeatedly since; to simplify the general discussion we shall make use of an extension (stated recently by Householder, see e.g. [15], p. 61) of a nearly forgotten theorem by Netto, which establishes a fundamental cross-connection between bigradients and Hankel determinants.

It should be noticed that attention is here deliberately focused on the general case where the formal degrees of the numerator and denominator of the candidates for the solution of the Cauchy interpolation problem are specified independently; the case where these degrees must coincide is thus treated only as a special case. This explains why the most interesting but specific) approach which is based on the systematic use of Löwner atrices (see [20], Secs. 4,5, and [30]) is not considered here; in actual act, that approach proves specially useful under an additional assumption f "positivity" (which can be formulated in different ways, depending on the ontext), the matrices becoming then eventually of the Nevanlinna-Pick type see e.g. Akhiezer [2], p. 105). The Cauchy interpolation problem is known o have interesting applications to passive network synthesis, not only in heory (see e.g. Belevitch [3]) but just as well on the algorithmic level see Meinguet [23]).

. The problem of rational interpolation

Let $\mathbb{F}(\ell,m)$, where ℓ and m are nonnegative integers, denote the set of all real or complex) expressions of the form

$$F(x) = \frac{P(x)}{Q(x)} \equiv \frac{p_0+p_1x+\ldots+p_\ell x^\ell}{q_0+q_1x+\ldots+q_m x^m}, \quad Q \not\equiv 0. \tag{1}$$

The natural interpretation of polynomial ratios P/Q as representations of rational functions F suggests the partition of $\mathbb{F}(\ell,m)$ into mutually exclusive classes, any two of its elements (say P_1/Q_1 and P_2/Q_2) being clearly to be regarded as equivalent in this sense iff

$$P_1Q_2 \equiv P_2Q_1. \tag{2}$$

In particular, the multiplication of P and Q in (1) by the same nonzero scalar is always an equivalence transformation and the number of independent parameters actually involved is thus $n+1$ where

$$n = \ell+m. \tag{3}$$

The <u>Cauchy interpolation problem</u> can be formulated as follows: Given $n+1$ distinct (real or complex) points $x_0,x_1,\ldots,x_n$ and $n+1$ finite (real or complex) values $y_0,y_1,\ldots,y_n$, find a rational function $F \in \mathbb{F}(\ell,m)$, i.e. a function representable in the form (1), for which

$$F(x_g) = y_g, \quad g=0,1,\ldots,n. \tag{4}$$

It should be noticed that the apparent requirement of equality of the number of conditions with the number of independent parameters is only suggested by the naive (but false) hope that an interpolation problem can always be solved providing it is fulfilled. Its actual justification lies rather in the remarkable property shared by all the functions representable in the form (1) to be uniquely determined by the set of constraints (4); indeed, since the numerator of the difference between any two elements of $F(\ell,m)$ satisfying (4) has at most degree n and vanishes at n+1 distinct points, it must vanish identically, which establishes the uniqueness of the solution of the Cauchy problem whenever there is one.

The distinction, within $\mathbb{F}(\ell,m)$, between a rational function F and its representations P/Q strongly suggests to replace (4) by

$$P(x_g) = y_g Q(x_g), \quad g=0,1,\dots,n \tag{5}$$

in the formulation above. However, owing to the possibility for Q(x) to vanish at one of the points x_g, the "modified" interpolation problem which arises from this substitution cannot be regarded a priori as equivalent to the Cauchy interpolation problem. Since it turns out that most of the known approaches to the solution of the Cauchy problem yield only the always existing solution of the modified problem, the detailed investigation of the essential relations between these two problems clearly deserves close attention. An excellent analysis of this preliminary question was given by Maehly and Witzgall in [21] (see also Stoer [33], in particular Sec. 1.2, for an alternative presentation). For the reader's convenience we shall give hereafter a resume of the main results of that important discussion, which was planned, unlike most others in the field (see e.g. [14,19,22,24,40] and [33], Sec. 1.3), independently of any particular algorithm for solving either of the interpolation problems, gaining thereby in simplicity and significance.

The set of constraints (5) can take various explicit forms, depending on the formal definitions of P and Q. Of the polynomial forms considered for various purposes in the literature (see in particular Hart [13], Sec. 4.5, and Rutishauser [32], Sec. 2), the so-called product forms and streamlined forms are in all probability not suited to a fruitful discussion of (5), contrary to the power form, the orthogonal polynomial form, the Newton form and the Lagrange form (unduly omitted in [13], Sec. 4.5). For the latter forms, as well as for the other polynomial forms which are associated with more general problems of finite interpolation (see e.g. Davis [9], Chap. 2), (5) reduces indeed to a linear algebraic system of the partitioned form

$$[X_\ell \;\; YX_m] \begin{bmatrix} p \\ -q \end{bmatrix} = 0, \tag{6a}$$

where Y is the diagonal matrix diag $\{y_0, y_1, \ldots, y_n\}$, X_ℓ (resp. X_m) is an (n+1)-rowed matrix which has $\ell+1$ (resp. m+1) columns and whose elements are known specific functions of the given points x_g, p (resp. q) is the parameter column-vector which serves for the formal definition of the polynomial P (resp. Q) and whose $\ell+1$ (resp. m+1) elements are accordingly the unknowns of the modified interpolation problem. In particular, for the conventional power form in which P and Q are given in (1), the system (6a) takes the well known explicit form

$$\left[\begin{array}{cccc|cccc} 1 & x_0 & \cdots & x_0^\ell & y_0 & y_0x_0 & \cdots & y_0x_0^m \\ 1 & x_1 & \cdots & x_1^\ell & y_1 & y_1x_1 & \cdots & y_1x_1^m \\ \cdot & \cdot & \cdot & \cdot & \cdot & \cdot & \cdot & \cdot \\ \cdot & \cdot & \cdot & \cdot & \cdot & \cdot & \cdot & \cdot \\ 1 & x_n & \cdots & x_n^\ell & y_n & y_nx_n & \cdots & y_nx_n^m \end{array}\right] \left[\begin{array}{c} p_0 \\ p_1 \\ \cdot \\ \cdot \\ \cdot \\ p_\ell \\ \hline -q_0 \\ -q_1 \\ \cdot \\ \cdot \\ \cdot \\ -q_m \end{array}\right] = 0. \qquad (6b)$$

As readily verified, the general submatrices X_ℓ and YX_m in (6a) are simply right-equivalent to those exhibited in (6b). This does not imply, however, that their explicit forms, possibly after premultiplication of $[X_\ell \; YX_m]$ by a nonsingular matrix (left-equivalence transformation), are all devoid of theoretical or practical interest, far from it; of those explicit forms whose importance must be taken for granted, only some will be really exploited later (in Secs. 4 and 5), the reader being simply referred to Opitz [29] and to [3,20,30] for the others.

The modified interpolation problem is known to have always a unique solution in the following precise sense: to any nontrivial solution of the homogeneous linear system (6) there corresponds by (1) a rational expression which actually represents one and the same rational function (called "Interpolierende" in [21] and systematically denoted by F_y in the sequel to emphasize its dependence on the vector y of the given values y_g). The proof of this remarkable theorem is straightforward (see [21], p. 295) and can be outlined as follows: nontrivial solutions of (6) always exist (since the number of unknowns, viz. n+2, exceeds the number of equations), are necessarily all such that $q \neq 0$ (since (5) forces P to vanish identically whenever Q does) and define accordingly rational expressions of the form (1); any two of these expressions must be equivalent since (5) forces the formal numerator of their difference (which polynomial has at most degree n) to vanish at the n+1 points x_g.

Whenever the Cauchy interpolation problem is soluble, its solution coincides necessarily with F_y; moreover, there is then a one-to-one correspondence between the nontrivial solutions of the homogeneous linear system (6) and those representations of F_y which belong to $\mathbb{F}(\ell,m)$. This is proved simply by combining the foregoing theorem with the trivial remark that (4) always implies (5), which means in other words that each of the representations in the form (1) of the solution of the Cauchy problem necessarily satisfies the system (5).

In the opposite case, at least one of the given points, say (x_g,y_g), must be <u>"unattainable"</u> in the sense that

$$F_y(x_g) \neq y_g, \tag{7}$$

it being understood that an irreducible representation of F_y should be used for purposes of evaluation (here as well as in (4)) whenever necessary to avoid any indeterminate form at $x = x_g$. The only possible explanation of the apparent discrepancy between each inequality (7) and its counterpart as equality constraint in (5) is that the polynomial Q(x) (and therefore also P(x)) must vanish at $x = x_g$, whichever nontrivial solution of (6) is considered (the last requirement is essential; for having overlooked this, the discussion in [33], p. 287, cannot be regarded as perfectly correct). Hence the <u>fundamental theorem</u> (which summarizes most of the analysis above): <u>there is always a one-to-one correspondence between the nontrivial solutions of the homogeneous linear system (6) and those representations of F_y in the form (1) which are undefined at each of the unattainable points</u>. It follows in particular that the Cauchy interpolation problem is soluble if, and only if, there is a nontrivial solution of (6) to which there corresponds by (1) an irreducible representation of F_y.

A simple example will help the reader to appreciate the significance of that result. Suppose we attempt to solve the Cauchy interpolation problem within $\mathbb{F}(2,1)$ for the data

x :	0	1	2	3
y :	2	3/2	μ	1/2

where the ordinate μ is a parameter. The general solution of the system (6b) is readily found to be

$$p_0 = -4p_1 - 16p_2,$$
$$q_0 = -2p_1 - 8p_2,$$
$$q_1 = -2p_2 ,$$

with the additional constraint

$$(\mu-1)(p_1+6p_2) = 0.$$

The general solution of the modified interpolation problem is accordingly

$$F_y = \frac{(4-x)(-p_1-4p_2-p_2x)}{2(-p_1-4p_2-p_2x)} \quad \text{if } \mu = 1,$$

$$F_y = \frac{(4-x)p_2(2-x)}{2\ p_2(2-x)} \quad \text{if } \mu \neq 1.$$

The fundamental theorem then leads to the conclusion that, for $\mu \neq 1$, $x = 2$ is the only unattainable point whereas, for $\mu = 1$, the Cauchy problem is solved by the irreducible fraction $F(x) = (4-x)/2$.

It should be realized that the foregoing analysis need not remain complete if rational functions are represented otherwise than as ratios of two polynomials, for example, in a continued-fraction form. Quite popular rational forms are here the associated continued fractions and the J-fractions (see [13], p. 73), fractions of the Thiele type (see e.g. [12, 13,14,19,22,24,25,28,31,33,36,38,41]) and continued fractions associated with the Euclidean algorithm (see e.g. [6], p. 151). Certain of these forms can be evaluated with appreciably less "long" arithmetic operations than the classical form (1), which may be a significant advantage (see e.g. Cheney [6], p. 151) in spite of the empirical fact that the most efficient forms generally tend to be the most ill-conditioned or unstable. Several specific algorithms making use of continued-fraction forms have been described in the literature (see the references listed above in connection with the Thiele form); however, they may fail, even though the Cauchy interpolation problem is soluble, for the continued-fraction expansion may fail to exist in the form assumed (see e.g. Hildebrand [14], p. 401).

3. The Cauchy interpolation formula

To obtain explicitly the solution $F_y(x)$ of the modified interpolation problem one has essentially to eliminate the n+2 unknown coefficients between the n+1 homogeneous linear equations (6b) and the underlying identity

$$(p_0+p_1+\dots+p_\ell x^\ell)\, Q - (q_0+q_1x+\dots+q_m x^m)\, P \equiv 0. \tag{8}$$

The natural (but cumbersome) process which consists of solving (6b) for the coefficients of P and Q explicitly and substituting them into (8) can fortunately be avoided whenever the matrix in (6b) has the rank n+1, which is quite often the case in practice (if not in theory). Under this <u>assumption of maximum rank</u> (6b) has indeed a unique solution (within a nonzero constant factor), the elimination of which is readily achieved by expressing that the resulting determinant (of order n+2) is zero; the ensuing equation

$$\delta\begin{bmatrix} Q & Qx\dots Qx^\ell & P & Px\ \dots\ Px^m \\ 1 & x_0\dots x_0^\ell & y_0 & y_0x_0\dots y_0x_0^m \\ \cdot & \cdot\ \ \cdot\ \ \cdot & \cdot & \cdot\ \ \cdot\ \ \cdot\ \ \cdot \\ \cdot & \cdot\ \ \cdot\ \ \cdot & \cdot & \cdot\ \ \cdot\ \ \cdot\ \ \cdot \\ 1 & x_n\dots x_n^\ell & y_n & y_nx_n\dots y_nx_n^m \end{bmatrix} = 0, \tag{9}$$

where δ signifies determinant, is fundamental to the study of rational interpolation and contains potentially the various possible representations of $F_y(x) = P(x)/Q(x)$; these are indeed nothing but restatements of (9) in different forms, more suitable for practical use.

Of the many possible expansions of the determinant in (9), the <u>Laplacian expansion</u> according to minors from the first ℓ+1 columns and their cofactors from the remaining m+1 columns is clearly one of the most convenient to exploit here. By this classical method (explained in detail, for example, in Aitken [1], Secs. 32,33), equation (9) readily takes the following semi-explicit form:

$$Q\sum_{(h)}(-1)^{h_1+\dots+h_\ell-\ell(\ell-1)/2}\, y_{i_1}\cdots y_{i_{m+1}}\, V(x_{h_1},\dots,x_{h_\ell},x)\,V(x_{i_1},\dots,x_{i_{m+1}})$$

$$= (-1)^{(\ell+1)m}\, P\sum_{(j)}(-1)^{j_1+\dots+j_m-m(m-1)/2}\, y_{j_1}\cdots y_{j_m}\, V(x,x_{j_1},\dots,x_{j_m})\,V(x_{k_1},\dots,x_{k_{\ell+1}})$$

Here the sum on the left extends over all ℓ-tuples $0 \leq h_1 < h_2 < \dots < h_\ell \leq n$ and the sum on the right over all m-tuples $0 \leq j_1 < j_2 < \dots < j_m \leq n$, the complementary sets of row indices (arranged in natural order) being denoted $i_1,i_2,\dots,i_{m+1}$ and $k_1,k_2,\dots,k_{\ell+1}$, respectively; as to the notation V(.), it stands for the Vandermonde determinant (or simple alternant) formed from the ordered set of arguments within brackets. As illustrated by t classical identity

$$V(x_0,x_1,\dots,x_n) = \delta \begin{bmatrix} 1 & x_0 & x_0^2 & \dots & x_0^n \\ 1 & x_1 & x_1^2 & \dots & x_1^n \\ \cdot & \cdot & \cdot & \cdot & \cdot \\ \cdot & \cdot & \cdot & \cdot & \cdot \\ 1 & x_n & x_n^2 & \dots & x_n^n \end{bmatrix} = \prod_{\substack{0 \\ i>j}}^{n} (x_i - x_j), \tag{10}$$

any Vandermonde determinant is expressible as a difference-product of its arguments (so that it does not vanish when the points x_g are all distinct). By exploiting this representation formula,the preceding restatement of (9), preliminarily divided throughout by the determinant (10), can be rewritten in a much more attractive form; after going through the requisite algebra we find indeed that the outcome P/Q can be expressed as

$$F_y(x) = \frac{P(x)}{Q(x)} \equiv \frac{\sum\limits_{(h)} y_{i_1} \cdots y_{i_{m+1}} \dfrac{P_h(x)}{P_h(x_{i_1})\cdots P_h(x_{i_{m+1}})}}{\sum\limits_{(j)} y_{j_1} \cdots y_{j_m} \dfrac{Q_j(x)}{Q_j(x_{k_1})\cdots Q_j(x_{k_{\ell+1}})}} \tag{11a}$$

where we have abbreviated

$$P_h(x) = (x-x_{h_1}) \dots (x-x_{h_\ell}), \tag{11b}$$

$$Q_j(x) = (x_{j_1}-x) \dots (x_{j_m}-x); \tag{11c}$$

the comments above on the definition of the summation symbols remain essentially unchanged, except that the subsets of row indices (denoted here concisely by h and j) need no longer be arranged in natural order.

This explicit representation (11) of the candidate $F_y(x)$ for the solution of the problem of rational interpolation dates back to Cauchy (see [5], Note V, p. 528) who gave it already in 1821, without any proof or discussion, however. The foregoing approach of the Cauchy interpolation formula was briefly described in 1846, concurrently with others but only in a purely formal way, by Jacobi (see [17], p. 501), to whom we are specially indebted for various interesting representations of P and Q (some of these formal results, obtained by equivalence transformations of the matrix in (6b), will be considered later, especially in Sec. 5). As far as the efficient numerical evaluation of $F_y(x)$ is concerned, (11) cannot compete, in general, with most other forms; that is probably the reason why it has remained practically unknown, even to specialists in interpolation problems; in fact, of the many text-books on related questions that are in general use, Noerlund [28] (see p. 423) is the only one, as far as we know, to recall that explicit result, though quite incidentally and only for $\ell=m$. The real interest of the Cauchy interpolation formula is mainly of theoretical nature: it lies indeed in the natural interpretation of (11) as the formal extension, to the class $\mathbb{F}(\ell,m)$ of rational functions, of the Lagrange interpolation formula, to which it reduces trivially for $m=0$; it should be realized that the determinant approaches of both formulas are essentially the same, being based indeed on appropriate Laplacian expansions of an alternant.

The solubility of the Cauchy interpolation problem was apparently regarded as an unquestionable fact for some sixty years. It is indeed only in 1881 that for the first time the subject was thoroughly discussed and that criteria of solubility were given; this was done by Kronecker in a most remarkable paper [18] (the leading ideas of which have inspired the next two sections), yet essentially without reference to the Cauchy interpolation formula which is only mentioned (see p. 546). In fact, the exploitation of (11) in the discussion of that solubility question was only considered in 1893, by Netto (see [27] who showed that it can lead to interesting results more readily than, for example, the elaborate Kronecker approach which is based on the continued-fraction representation of the solution; in particular, as is explained briefly hereafter, the unattainable points (x_g,y_g) can be explicitly characterized in terms of the data. As easily verified from (11), the evaluation at $x=x_g$ (where x_g is any of the given abscissas) of the numerator and denominator of the candidate $F_y(x)$ for the solution of the Cauchy problem yields the following expressions:

$$P(x_g) = y_g \sum_{(h)} \frac{y_{i_1}\cdots y_{i_m}}{P_h(x_{i_1})\cdots P_h(x_{i_m})}, \tag{12a}$$

$$Q(x_g) = \sum_{(j)} \frac{y_{j_1}\cdots y_{j_m}}{Q_j(x_{k_1})\cdots Q_j(x_{k_\ell})} = \sum_{(h)} \frac{y_{i_1}\cdots y_{i_m}}{P_h(x_{i_1})\cdots P_h(x_{i_m})}, \tag{12b}$$

where the summation symbols are to be interpreted essentially as above, the sets $\{i_1,\dots,i_m\}$ and $\{k_1,\dots,k_\ell\}$ being here, however, the respective complements of the sets $h = \{h_1,\dots,h_\ell\}$ and $j = \{j_1,\dots,j_m\}$ relative to the difference $\{0,1,\ldots,n\} - \{g\}$. It follows that the expression (11a) of $F_y(x)$ necessarily takes on the prescribed value y_g at the tabular point $x=x_g$, unless

$$Q(x_g) = \sum_{(h)} \frac{y_{i_1}\ldots y_{i_m}}{P_h(x_{i_1})\ldots P_h(x_{i_m})} = 0, \tag{13}$$

in which case it is undefined. Under the assumption of maximum rank formulated above, it turns out that condition (13) is actually necessary and sufficient for the given point (x_g,y_g) to be unattainable in the sense that $F_y(x_g) \neq y_g$; as far as we know, this convenient <u>a priori characterization of the unattainable points</u> is a novel result, though it can be regarded as a simple corollary of the fundamental theorem stated by Maehly and Witzgall and recalled at the end of Sec. 2. On the other hand, whenever the assumption of maximum rank is not verified, the expression (11a) of $F_y(x)$ is completely uninteresting, the coefficient of P and the coefficient of Q in the Laplacian expansion of the determinant in (9) vanishing then identically. Each of these two opposite cases can be recognized easily in concrete situations; useful criteria are indeed: for the former case, the existence of at least one nonzero element in the set of values calculated by (12b) and, for the latter case, the existence of at least m+1 zero elements in that same set.

By way of illustration of the foregoing we consider again the concrete interpolation problem already discussed at the end of Sec. 2. The exploitation of (12b) gives finally the set of values

$$Q(0) = 1 - \mu,$$
$$Q(1) = (1-\mu)/2,$$
$$Q(2) = 0,$$
$$Q(3) = (\mu-1)/2,$$

the examination of which leads to the conclusion that, for $\mu \neq 1$, $x=2$ is the only unattainable point, whereas, for $\mu=1$, the assumption of maximum rank is not verified. This is confirmed, of course, by the examination of the expression

$$F_y = P/Q \equiv \frac{\frac{4-x}{2}\left[\frac{2-x}{2}(1-\mu)\right]}{\left[\frac{2-x}{2}(1-\mu)\right]}$$

defined by (11), the comparison of which with its analogue in Sec. 2 is interesting as well.

4. The continued-fraction approach

Unlike Kronecker in [18] (see Sec. 1), we shall not make use of continued fractions from the outset (which indeed was an artificial starting-point) but we shall rather proceed constructively to their exploitation from an obvious polynomial identity rewritten in matrix form (it is interesting to observe that a similar idea has been exploited successfully by Talbot in different contexts; see [34,35]). It will be shown that the special determinants called bigradients (or subresultants) must play a prominent role in view of their natural association with the successive remainders in the Euclidean algorithm. Certain (possibly unknown) aspects of continued fractions will be emphasized incidentally; in particular, the classical Euler-Minding expansions are interpreted as Schweinsian expansions, the terms being generated in succession by the exchange-steps in the triangular decomposition of a certain matrix.

Let $B(x)$ designate the unique polynomial of degree not greater than n for which

$$B(x_g) = y_g, \quad g=0,1,\ldots,n. \tag{14}$$

By Lagrange's interpolation formula we have

$$B(x) = \sum_{g=0}^{n} y_g \frac{A(x)}{(x-x_g)A'(x_g)}, \tag{15a}$$

where

$$A(x) = \prod_{g=0}^{n} (x-x_g) = a_0x^{n+1}+\ldots+a_{n+1}, \quad a_0 = 1. \tag{16}$$

In the following the polynomial B (which is clearly distinct from zero, except in the uninteresting case: $y_g=0$ for every g) will be exploited mainly in its conventional power form, say

$$B(x) = b_0x^{n+1-d}+\ldots+b_{n+1-d}, \quad b_0 \neq 0, \tag{15b}$$

so that

$$\partial B = n+1-d \text{ with } 1 \leqslant d \leqslant n+1, \tag{15c}$$

the symbol ∂ standing for "actual degree". The elimination of the given values y_g between (5) and (14) yields the polynomial equation (in three "unknowns" P,Q,R)

$$P = B.Q. - A.R \tag{17}$$

which we shall now investigate in detail.

As is readily verified by comparing the formal (i.e. nominal) degrees of the three terms in (17), the polynomial R is not distinct from zero for $m < d$, in which cases the Cauchy problem is solved trivially by the unique interpolation polynomial $B(x)$ itself. We are therefore justified in assuming henceforth that $m \geqslant d$ or, equivalently, that $\ell \leqslant n-d$; R is then seen to be of formal degree $m-d$ and so can be written in the form

$$R(x) = r_{m-d}x^{m-d}+\ldots+r_0, \tag{18a}$$

its actual degree being in fact

$$\partial R = \partial Q - d \geqslant 0, \tag{18b}$$

which ensures $Q \not\equiv 0$. By equating coefficients on the two sides of (17) we obtain the set

$$\left[\begin{array}{ccccc|ccccc} b_0 & & & & & & & & \cdot & a_0 \\ b_1 & b_0 & & & & & & \cdot & & a_1 \\ b_2 & b_1 & \cdot & & & a_0 & & & & a_2 \\ \cdot & \cdot & & \cdot & b_0 & \cdot & & \cdot & \cdot & \cdot \\ \cdot & \cdot & \cdot & \cdot & \cdot & \cdot & & \cdot & \cdot & \cdot \\ b_{2m-d} & b_{2m-d-1} & \cdot & \cdot & b_{m-d} & a_m & & \cdot & \cdot & a_{2m-d} \end{array}\right] \left[\begin{array}{c} q_m \\ q_{m-1} \\ \cdot \\ \cdot \\ \cdot \\ q_0 \\ \hline -r_0 \\ \cdot \\ \cdot \\ -r_{m-d} \end{array}\right] = 0 \tag{19}$$

of $2m+1-d$ homogeneous linear equations in $2m+2-d$ unknowns (viz., the $m+1$ coefficients of Q and the $m+1-d$ coefficients of $-R$), followed by the set

$$p_{\ell-j} = \sum_{i=0}^{m} b_{2m+1-d+j-i}q_{m-i} - \sum_{i=0}^{m-d} a_{m+1+j+i}r_i \quad \text{for } j=0,1,\ldots,\ell, \tag{20}$$

of the explicit expressions of the $\ell+1$ coefficients of P in terms of those unknowns, it being understood once for all that $a_h=0$ $(h > n+1)$ and $b_k=0$ $(k > n+1-d)$.

The linear system (19) can certainly be solved for the ratios of the variables so that the polynomial equation (17) has always a nontrivial solution P,Q,R. In actual fact, to every meaningful decomposition (3) of n *corresponds a solution of (17) which is unique apart from a (possibly non-constant) common factor in P,Q,R.* For if P^*, Q^*, R^* are another such polynomial triple, then

$$P.Q^* - P^*.Q = A(Q.R^* - Q^*.R);$$

now the nominal degree of the left-hand side is n while $\partial A = n+1$, whence $Q.R^* - Q^*.R \equiv 0$ and therefore also $P.Q^* - P^*.Q \equiv 0$, and the stated result follows. It is natural to assume henceforth that, except where otherwise stated, the elements P,Q,R of each polynomial triple taken to represent a solution of (17) are relatively prime.

Whenever $m \in [d,n]$ is such that the matrix in (19) has the maximum rank (viz. $2m+1-d$), the elimination of the q's and r's between (19) and (17) rewritten as

$$P = (q_m x^m + q_{m-1} x^{m-1} + \ldots + q_0)B - (r_0 + r_1 x + \ldots + r_{m-d} x^{m-d})A$$

yields the explicit determinantal representation

$$P(x) = \delta \left[\begin{array}{cccccccccc|c} b_0 & b_1 & b_2 & \cdot & b_m & \cdot & \cdot & b_{2m-d} & & & x^m B \\ & b_0 & b_1 & \cdot & b_{m-1} & & & b_{2m-d-1} & & & x^{m-1} B \\ & & \cdot & \cdot & \cdot & \cdot & \cdot & \cdot & \cdot & \cdot & \cdot \;\; \cdot \\ & & & \cdot & & & & & & & \\ & & & & b_0 & \cdot & \cdot & b_{m-d} & & & B \\ \hline & & & a_0 & \cdot & \cdot & a_m & & & & A \\ & & \cdot & \cdot & \cdot & \cdot & \cdot & \cdot & \cdot & \cdot & \cdot \;\; \cdot \\ & a_0 & a_1 & \cdot & a_{m-d-1} & \cdot & & a_{2m-d-1} & & & x^{m-d-1} A \\ a_0 & a_1 & a_2 & \cdot & a_{m-d} & \cdot & \cdot & a_{2m-d} & & & x^{m-d} A \end{array}\right], \tag{21a}$$

from which it readily follows that

$$Q(x) = \delta \left[\begin{array}{cccccccc|c} b_0 & b_1 & b_2 & \cdot & \cdot & \cdot & b_{2m-d} & & x^m \\ 0 & b_0 & b_1 & \cdot & \cdot & \cdot & b_{2m-d-1} & & x^{m-1} \\ \cdot & \cdot & \cdot & \cdot & \cdot & \cdot & \cdot & \cdot & \cdot \\ 0 & a_0 & a_1 & \cdot & \cdot & \cdot & a_{2m-d-1} & & 0 \\ a_0 & a_1 & a_2 & \cdot & \cdot & \cdot & a_{2m-d} & & 0 \end{array}\right], \tag{22}$$

$$-R(x) = \delta \left[\begin{array}{cccccc|c} b_0 & b_1 & b_2 & \cdots & & b_{2m-d} & 0 \\ 0 & b_0 & b_1 & \cdots & & b_{2m-d-1} & 0 \\ \cdot & \cdot & \cdot & \cdots & & \cdot & \cdot \\ 0 & a_0 & a_1 & \cdots & & a_{2m-d-1} & x^{m-d-1} \\ a_0 & a_1 & a_2 & \cdots & & a_{2m-d} & x^{m-d} \end{array}\right]. \tag{23}$$

It should be noticed that for any other m the expressions (21,22,23) all vanish identically (owing to the vanishing of the cofactors of all the elements of the last column in the determinants).

By construction the polynomial P(x) must have the formal degree ℓ. This is readily verified by subtracting from the last column of the determinant in (21a) each of the others multiplied by a suitable power of x (viz., $x^{n+1-d+m-i}$ for the (i+1)-th column, i ranging from 0 to 2m-d); this sequence of elementary column operations leads eventually to the important result

$$P(x) = x^{\ell}\delta \begin{bmatrix} b_0 & b_1 & b_2 & \cdots & & b_{2m-d+1} \\ 0 & b_0 & b_1 & \cdots & & b_{2m-d} \\ \cdot & \cdot & \cdot & \cdots & & \cdot \\ 0 & a_0 & a_1 & \cdots & & a_{2m-d} \\ a_0 & a_1 & a_2 & \cdots & & a_{2m-d+1} \end{bmatrix} + \ldots, \tag{21b}$$

where the omitted terms are of degree less than ℓ. The determinants displayed in (21a) and (21b) are identical, the last column excepted; they are of order 2m+2-d, with m+1 (i.e. $\partial A-1$) rows made up of the b's and sloping down persymmetrically, followed by m+1-d (i.e. $\partial B-1$) rows made up of the a's and sloping up, it being understood that $b_0, b_1, \ldots$ and $a_0, a_1, \ldots$ are the elements of the respective sequences of coefficients of B and A possibly extended by zeros. These remarks suggest to rewrite (21a,b) in a compact form of the following type

$$P(x) = \delta \begin{bmatrix} (B)_{m+1} \\ (A)_{m+1-d} \end{bmatrix} = x^{\ell}\delta \begin{bmatrix} (b)_{m+1} \\ (a)_{m+1-d} \end{bmatrix} + \ldots, \tag{24}$$

where suitable symbols are proposed to designate unambiguously the special determinants to which the formal leading coefficient of P and P itself separately reduce, which determinants are called respectively <u>bigradients</u> and <u>polynomial bigradients</u> (apparently to emphasize their characteristic property of being persymmetric in two sequences).

Bigradients were first brought to light by Sylvester (1840) in connection with his so-called "dialytic" method of elimination. Their systematic investigation goes back more than a century to Trudi [37], whose work (first communicated in 1857 to the Naples Academy of Sciences) has suffered undeserved neglect, however. The main results obtained by Trudi were excellently summarized by Muir (see [26], Vol. 3, pp. 329-349); some of them, especially those which are directly concerned with the determinantal characterization of the greatest common divisor of two polynomials, have been recalled and exploited recently by Householder in two related papers [15,16]. It should be noted that bigradients are called <u>subresultants</u> by certain authors; thus, for example, the formal leading coefficient of P as it appears in (24) is the ℓ-th subresultant of the polynomials B and A for Bôcher (see [4], p. 197), the determinantal expression of P itself being (except for the sign) the ℓ-th (polynomial) subresultant of B and A for Collins (see [8], p. 128).

Let m be chosen so that the matrix in (19) is of maximum rank. The solution of the system (19) being then unique (within an arbitrary constant factor), it clearly follows that at least one of the actual degrees $\partial P, \partial Q$ (or ∂R) must attain its upper bound (i.e. the corresponding formal degree). By examining the expressions (22,23,24) it is easily seen that

$$\partial P = n-m = \ell \tag{25a}$$

if, and only if,

$$\delta \begin{bmatrix} (b)_{m+1} \\ (a)_{m+1-d} \end{bmatrix} \neq 0, \tag{25b}$$

and that

$$\partial Q = m, \; \partial R = m-d \tag{26a}$$

if, and only if,

$$\delta \begin{bmatrix} (b)_{m} \\ (a)_{m-d} \end{bmatrix} \neq 0. \tag{26b}$$

In other words, if we denote by $d_1 < d_2 < \dots < d_s$ (with $d_1=d \geq 1$, $d_s \leq n+1$) all the integers for which

$$\delta \begin{bmatrix} (b)_{d_i} \\ (a)_{d_i-d} \end{bmatrix} \neq 0, \tag{27a}$$

then P, defined as

$$P(x) = \delta \begin{bmatrix} (B)_{d_i} \\ (A)_{d_i - d} \end{bmatrix}, \tag{27b}$$

is of actual degree $n+1-d_i$ while Q (resp. -R), defined as the coefficient of B (resp. A) in the polynomial bigradient

$$P(x) = \delta \begin{bmatrix} (B)_{d_i+1} \\ (A)_{d_i+1-d} \end{bmatrix}, \tag{27c}$$

is of actual degree d_i (resp. d_i-d); there is no other polynomial bigradient of the form (24) which can lead by (21,22,23) to a nontrivial triple P,Q,R of relatively prime polynomials satisfying (17).

It turns out that the characterization by (27) of the nontrivial solutions of the polynomial equation (17) can be reformulated more elegantly, owing to a remarkable theorem which states that <u>the set of the nontrivial polynomial bigradients P(x) is simply the set of multiples of the remainders that occur in the Euclidean algorithm applied to A and B</u>. Already conjectured by Cayley in 1848 (see [26], Vol. 2, p. 362), this fundamental result was first established by Trudi [37]; in the summary mentioned above (see [26], Vol. 3, p. 335), Muir substituted for the original argument a simpler one of his own. For the reader's convenience, a direct proof, well adapted to the foregoing, will be outlined here; like Muir's proof it is based essentially on the simple remark that all the computations required to obtain the remainder in the division of polynomials can be translated into successive elementary row operations performed on a certain polynomial bigradient matrix.

The stated result is trivial for m=d since then, as follows from (23), the polynomial -R(x) reduces to the constant

$$-r_0 = \delta \left[\begin{array}{cccccc|c} b_0 & b_1 & \cdot & \cdot & \cdot & b_d & 0 \\ & b_0 & \cdot & \cdot & \cdot & b_{d-1} & 0 \\ & & \cdot & \cdot & \cdot & \cdot & \cdot \\ & & & & & b_0 & 0 \\ \hline a_0 & a_1 & \cdot & \cdot & \cdot & a_d & 1 \end{array}\right] = b_0^{d+1} \neq 0, \tag{28}$$

so that (17) expresses simply the fact that the polynomial

$$P(x) = \delta \begin{bmatrix} (B)_{d+1} \\ (A)_1 \end{bmatrix} = x^{n-d}\delta \begin{bmatrix} (b)_{d+1} \\ (a)_1 \end{bmatrix} + \ldots, \tag{29a}$$

of actual degree

$$\partial P = n+1-d' \text{ with } d' > d, \tag{29b}$$

is the remainder of the division of $-r_0 A$ by $-B$, the polynomial Q (of actual degree d) being itself the quotient. A similar conclusion holds evidently too for the next division in the Euclidean algorithm; the divisor B having been made the dividend and the remainder P the divisor, the actual degree of the new quotient is then $d'-d$ and accordingly the new remainder must be expressible as a polynomial bigradient in P and B, with $d'+1-d$ rows made up of the p's, followed by one row made up of the b's. This leads us to consider the following matrix identity

$$\left[\begin{array}{ccc|ccc} 1 & & & & & \\ & \cdot & & & & \\ & & 1 & & & \\ \hline & q_d \cdot & q_0 & -r_0 & & \\ & & & & \cdot & \\ q_d & \cdot & q_0 & & & -r_0 \end{array}\right] \left[\begin{array}{cccccc|c} b_0 & b_1 & \cdot & b_{d'} & \cdot & b_{2d'-d} & x^{d'}B \\ & b_0 & \cdot & \cdot & \cdot & \cdot & x^{d'-1}B \\ & & \cdot & \cdot & \cdot & \cdot & \cdot \\ & & & b_0 & & b_{d'-d} & B \\ \hline & & a_0 & \cdot & \cdot & \cdot a_{d'} & A \\ & \cdot & \cdot & & & \cdot & \cdot \\ a_0 & a_1 \cdot\cdot a_{d'-d} & & & \cdot & \cdot a_{2d'-d} & x^{d'-d}A \end{array}\right]$$

$$= \left[\begin{array}{ccccc|c} b_0 & b_1 & \cdot\ b_{d'} & \cdot & b_{2d'-d} & x^{d'}B \\ & b_0 & \cdot & \cdot & & x^{d'-1}B \\ & & \cdot & \cdot & & \cdot \\ & & b_0 & \cdot & b_{d'-d} & B \\ \hline & & & & p_0' & P \\ & & & \cdot & \cdot & \cdot \\ & & p_0' & \cdot & p_{d'-d}' & x^{d'-d}P \end{array}\right], \tag{30}$$

where the first matrix on the left accomplishes those elementary operations on the rows of the first bigradient matrix that are required for the transformation of the pair B,A into the pair B,P in accordance with (17); it will be noted that here $P(x)$ is supposed to be rewritten as $p_0'x^{n+1-d'}+\ldots+p_{n+1-d'}'$ (with $p_0' \neq 0$). By equating the determinants on the two sides of (30) we obtain

$$\delta\begin{bmatrix}(B)_{d'+1}\\(A)_{d'+1-d}\end{bmatrix} = \delta\begin{bmatrix}(P)_{d'+1-d}\\(B)_1\end{bmatrix}.(-1)^{(d'-d)(d'+1-d)/2}b_0^{d'}/r_0^{d'+1-d}; \quad (31a)$$

similarly, for d' replaced by d'-1 in (30), we find

$$\delta\begin{bmatrix}(B)_{d'}\\(A)_{d'-d}\end{bmatrix} = P.(-1)^{(d'-d)(d'+1-d)/2}b_0^{d'}(p_0')^{d'-d-1}/r_0^{d'-d}. \quad (31b)$$

From the discussion which led us to formulas (27), it follows that d' must coincide with d_2 in the two elementary examples (31a,b) of "condensation of bigradient matrices"; moreover, it must be emphasized that (31b) gives, for $d'=d_2$, that alternative definition of the polynomial (29a) whose formal degree coincides with $\partial P=n+1-d_2$. Clearly the argument can be continued, which completes the proof. For additional details the reader is referred to the recent papers [7,8] by Collins.

Let the Euclidean algorithm be applied to the polynomial pair

$$A_0 = A, A_1 = B \quad (32a)$$

and carried to completion in the form

$$\begin{aligned} A_0 &= A_1.D_1-A_2,\\ A_1 &= A_2.D_2-A_3,\\ &\cdot\quad\cdot\quad\cdot\\ A_{s-1} &= A_s.D_s, \end{aligned} \quad (32b)$$

where

$$\begin{aligned}\partial A_0 &= n+1,\\ \partial A_i &= n+1-d_i \quad \text{for } i=1,2,\ldots,s,\end{aligned} \quad (32c)$$

and

$$\partial D_i = \partial A_{i-1}-\partial A_i = d_i-d_{i-1} \geq 1, \quad (32d)$$

in accordance with the characterization (27) of the integers $d_0 = 0 < d_1 = d < d_2 < \ldots < d_s \leq n+1$. Consider now the associated sequence of continued fractions

$$\frac{R_i}{Q_i} = \frac{1}{D_1} - \frac{1}{D_2} - \cdots - \frac{1}{D_i}, \quad i=1,2,\ldots,s, \quad (33)$$

the first s-1 of these being the so-called convergents (or approximants) to the final one, which is clearly equivalent to the rational function B/A in view of (32); the successive numerators R_i and denominators Q_i are known to satisfy the fundamental recurrence formulas

$$R_0 = 0,\ R_1 = 1, \dots,\ R_i = R_{i-1}D_i - R_{i-2} \quad \text{for } 1 < i \leqslant s, \tag{34a}$$

$$Q_0 = 1,\ Q_1 = D_1, \dots,\ Q_i = Q_{i-1}D_i - Q_{i-2} \quad \text{for } 1 < i \leqslant s, \tag{34b}$$

from which follow the determinant formulas

$$R_iQ_{i-1} - R_{i-1}Q_i = 1 \quad \text{for } 1 \leqslant i \leqslant s, \tag{35}$$

and accordingly the Euler-Minding expansions

$$\frac{R_i}{Q_i} = \frac{1}{Q_1Q_0} + \frac{1}{Q_2Q_1} + \dots + \frac{1}{Q_iQ_{i-1}} \quad \text{for } 1 \leqslant i \leqslant s. \tag{36}$$

It should be observed that the discrete analogue (35) of the Liouville-Ostrogradskii formula (which is classical in the theory of linear differential equations) is only a particular case of what is called Heymann's theorem in the calculus of finite differences (see e.g. Milne-Thomson [25], p. 357); as a matter of fact, the Casorati determinant relative to any two independent solutions (and not only to the polynomial pair R,Q) of the tri-term recurrence relation (34) does not depend on i; so we have, for example,

$$A_0 = \delta \begin{bmatrix} Q_i & A_{i+1} \\ Q_{i-1} & A_i \end{bmatrix} \quad \text{for } 1 \leqslant i < s, \tag{37a}$$

$$A_1 = \delta \begin{bmatrix} R_i & A_{i+1} \\ R_{i-1} & A_i \end{bmatrix} \quad \text{for } 1 \leqslant i < s, \tag{37b}$$

since A_{i+1} is seen to satisfy the same tri-term recurrence relation as R_i and Q_i. Interpreted as a linear system in the unknowns A_i and A_{i+1}, (37) yields by exploiting (35) the important Cayley-Muir identities

$$A_i = A_1 \cdot Q_{i-1} - A_0 \cdot R_{i-1}, \quad i=1,2,\dots,s, \tag{38}$$

which express the successive remainders in the Euclidean algorithm (32) as linear combinations of the dividend A_0 and the divisor A_1, displaying thereby particular solution triples (viz. A_i, Q_{i-1}, R_{i-1}) of the polynomial equation (17); it should be noted that Q_i and R_i, as defined by (34), are relatively prime for any i because of (35).

The theory of continued fractions is connected with the theory of <u>continuant matrices</u> (or Jacobi matrices) by a fundamental result which takes here the following form

$$R_i/Q_i \equiv K(2,i)/K(1,i) \quad \text{for } 1 < i \leqslant s, \tag{39}$$

the symbol $K(h,i)$ being used to denote the symmetric continuant of the standard form (see e.g. [1], p. 127)

$$K(h,i) = \delta \begin{bmatrix} D_h & -1 & & & \\ -1 & D_{h+1} & -1 & & \\ & -1 & \cdot & \cdot & \\ & & \cdot & \cdot & -1 \\ & & & -1 & D_i \end{bmatrix} \quad \text{for } 1 \leqslant h \leqslant i \leqslant s. \tag{40}$$

To prove (39) it suffices to notice that $K(1,i)$ and $K(2,i)$, regarded as functions of i, satisfy the same recurrence relations and initial conditions as Q_i and R_i, respectively; this owing to the Cauchy expansion of continuants in terms of elements of the last row and of the last column and the joint cofactors. As leading element of the reciprocal of the continuant matrix of diagonal elements $D_1, D_2, \ldots, D_i$, the convergent R_i/Q_i must clearly satisfy the equation

$$\delta \left[\begin{array}{ccccc|c} D_1 & -1 & & & & -1 \\ -1 & D_2 & -1 & & & \\ & -1 & \cdot & \cdot & & \\ & & \cdot & \cdot & -1 & \\ & & & -1 & D_i & \\ \hline -1 & & & & & R_i/Q_i \end{array}\right] = 0, \tag{41}$$

which strongly suggests to rewrite the numerator in (39) as the negative of the determinant formed by bordering symmetrically the continuant $K(1,i)$ with the suffixed row $(-1,0,\ldots,0)$ and its transpose. This last expression of $-R_i/Q_i$ as a determinant quotient has a most interesting interpretation we will mention in passing; it coincides indeed with the explicit expression, classically obtained by exploiting the Binet-Cauchy theorem of corresponding minors, of the last pivot in the so-called <u>LDU (or triangular) decomposition</u> of the bordered matrix we have just described; moreover, the expansion in (36) can be interpreted as the <u>Schweinsian expansion</u> (see [1], p. 109) of the negative of that pivot, its successive terms giving separately the contributions to $-R_i/Q_i$ of the successive exchange-steps (supposed to be performed without any pivoting for size).

After this digression concerning certain hardly known aspects of continued fractions, we return to the Cauchy interpolation problem and come to the final conclusion already formulated by Kronecker (see [18], pp. 544-546). From the foregoing it should be perfectly clear that the only triples of relatively prime polynomials satisfying (17) are those displayed in (38). Consequently the only candidates for the "economical" solution of the Cauchy problem are the rational functions

$$F_y \equiv A_i/Q_{i-1}, \quad i=1,2,\dots,s, \tag{42}$$

it being understood that here the index i is uniquely determined, for any prescribed decomposition (3) of n, by either of the two equivalent conditions

$$n+1-d_i \leq l < n+1-d_{i-1}, \tag{43a}$$

$$d_{i-1} \leq m < d_i, \tag{43b}$$

which result from (32c) and from (32d) combined with (34b), i.e. from the known identities $\partial A_i = n+1-d_i$ and $\partial Q_i = d_i$ for all i. The rational expression (42) clearly solves the Cauchy problem whenever it is irreducible. In the opposite case (42) solves only the modified interpolation problem and the Cauchy problem is not soluble; this owing to the identities (35, 38) which force the greatest common divisor of A_i and Q_{i-1} to divide A_0 itself and accordingly to have only simple roots which must coincide with some of the given abscissas x_g.

5. The Jacobi-Kronecker approach

The interesting fact that the polynomial P can readily be eliminated from the system (6) was exploited for the first time by Jacobi (see [17], p. 482). The homogeneous linear system he obtained for determining the coefficients of Q, namely

$$\begin{bmatrix} v_0 & v_1 & \cdot & v_m \\ v_1 & v_2 & \cdot & v_{m+1} \\ \cdot & \cdot & \cdot & \cdot \\ \cdot & \cdot & \cdot & \cdot \\ v_{m-1} & v_m & \cdot & v_{2m-1} \end{bmatrix} \begin{bmatrix} q_0 \\ q_1 \\ \cdot \\ \cdot \\ \cdot \\ q_m \end{bmatrix} = [0] \tag{44}$$

with the following general definition

$$v_k = \sum_{g=0}^{n} y_g x_g^k / A'(x_g), \quad k=0,1,\ldots, \tag{45}$$

was only discussed much later, by Kronecker; it was in effect the main object of [18] to show that the complete solution of the polynomial equation (17) can always be derived from the system (44), without resorting in any way to the foregoing method based on continued fractions. Apparently rediscovered by Werner a few years ago, the system (44) proved very interesting to investigate and has been exploited repeatedly since, especially in connection with the extension to the case of rational functions of Remes' second algorithm for Chebyshev polynomial approximation (see e.g. [39]). A useful variant of (44) has been proposed by Opitz [29], P and Q being then supposed to be written in Newton form rather than in power form.

A remarkably simple method for eliminating P and for deriving (44,45) from (6b) is based on the well known fact that the divided difference of order n of a polynomial of degree smaller than n is identically zero. So we have, for example, the m identities

$$[x_0, x_1, \ldots, x_n](x^k P) \equiv 0 \text{ for } k=0,1,\ldots,m-1; \tag{46}$$

rewriting them in the Lagrangian form and eliminating P by (5), we readily get the expected result (44,45) in the compact form

$$\sum_{g=0}^{n} y_g x_g^k Q(x_g)/A'(x_g) = 0, \quad k=0,1,\ldots,m-1. \tag{47}$$

The vectors $(x_0^k/A'(x_0),\ldots,x_n^k/A'(x_n))$, for $k=0,1,\ldots,m-1$, can be interpreted as forming a basis for the m-dimensional orthogonal complement of the $(\ell+1)$-dimensional subspace of C_{n+1} (i.e. the space of (n+1)-tuples of complex numbers) that is spanned by the columns of the first matrix block in (6b). An alternative method for obtaining (44,45) is based on the natural interpretation of the rational expression V=B/A as the generating function of the infinite sequence of the v_k (k=0,1,...); as a matter of fact, (15a) yields immediately the partial fraction decomposition

$$V(x) = B(x)/A(x) = \sum_{g=0}^{n} \frac{y_g}{(x-x_g)A'(x_g)} \tag{48a}$$

and consequently the formal power expansion

$$V(x) = \sum_{k=0}^{\infty} v_k/x^{k+1}. \tag{48b}$$

The original discussion of the linear system (44) is rather lengthy (it takes some fifty pages in [18]) and hard to follow. Although it can be greatly simplified by exploiting the richness of the Frobenius theory of Hankel matrices (see e.g. Gantmacher [11], vol. 1, pp. 310-319, and vol. 2, pp. 180-183), we shall rather proceed to reduce the discussion to that of the foregoing section. This is readily achieved by the typical identity (holding for $m \geqslant d$)

$$\delta \begin{bmatrix} v_0 & v_1 & \cdot & v_{m-1} \\ v_1 & v_2 & \cdot & v_m \\ \cdot & \cdot & \cdot & \cdot \\ \cdot & \cdot & \cdot & \cdot \\ v_{m-1} & v_m & \cdot & v_{2m-2} \end{bmatrix} = \delta \begin{bmatrix} (a)_{m-d} \\ (b)_m \end{bmatrix}, \tag{49}$$

which shows that the sequence of integers $d=d_1 < d_2 < \ldots < d_s$ defined by the condition (27a) can be characterized as well by the non-vanishing of certain Hankel determinants. In actual fact, (49) is not essentially easier to establish than the more general identity

$$\delta \begin{bmatrix} v_p & v_{p+1} & \cdot & v_{p+k-1} \\ v_{p+1} & v_{p+2} & \cdot & v_{p+k} \\ \cdot & \cdot & \cdot & \cdot \\ \cdot & \cdot & \cdot & \cdot \\ v_{p+k-1} & v_{p+k} & \cdot & v_{p+2k-2} \end{bmatrix} = \delta \begin{bmatrix} (a)_{p+k-1} \\ (b')_k \end{bmatrix} \tag{50a}$$

where b' denotes the sequence of formal coefficients of $B(x)$ rewritten as

$$B(x) = b'_0 x^n + b'_1 x^{n-1} + \ldots + b'_n; \tag{51}$$

of course, in view of the actual definition (15b) of $B(x)$, the following correspondence must hold

$$\begin{aligned} & b'_0 = \ldots = b'_{d-2} = 0, \\ & b'_i = b_{i+1-d} \quad \text{for } i=d-1,d,\ldots,n, \end{aligned} \tag{52}$$

so that the bigradient on the right in (50a) can be condensed as follows

$$\delta \begin{bmatrix} (a)_{p+k-1} \\ (b')_k \end{bmatrix} = \delta \begin{bmatrix} (a)_{p+k-d} \\ (b)_k \end{bmatrix} \quad \text{for } p+k \geq d. \tag{50b}$$

The key to (50a) lies in the extension, stated recently by Householder (see [15], p. 61, and [16], p. 136), of a nearly forgotten theorem by Netto (1896), which itself is an extension of one by Wronski (1811). The proof is surprisingly simple: it consists in equating determinants on the two sides of a suitably chosen matrix identity expressing (with some redundance) the polynomial identity B=AV.

For m equal to any of the d_i, the homogeneous linear system (44) yields for the polynomial Q of the determinantal expression

$$Q(x) = \delta \begin{bmatrix} 1 & x & . & x^m \\ v_0 & v_1 & . & v_m \\ . & . & . & . \\ . & . & . & . \\ v_{m-1} & v_m & . & v_{2m-1} \end{bmatrix} \quad \text{with } \partial Q = m, \tag{53}$$

which defines it uniquely up to a scalar factor. Now (17), rewritten as

$$V(x) = R(x)/Q(x) + O(x^{-2m-1}), \tag{54}$$

expresses that the formal expansion of R+Q in a series of decreasing powers must agree with (48b) to as many terms as possible (viz. 2m) and is therefore an entry in its Padé table. An obvious determinantal reduction then shows that

$$R(x) = \delta \begin{bmatrix} 0 & xV_1 & . & x^m V_m \\ v_0 & v_1 & . & v_m \\ . & . & . & . \\ . & . & . & . \\ v_{m-1} & v_m & . & v_{2m-1} \end{bmatrix} \tag{55}$$

where V_i, the i-th section of V, is defined as

$$V_i(x) = \sum_{k=0}^{i-1} v_k/x^{k+1}. \tag{56}$$

The explicit representations (53,55) were already given by Frobenius in [10]; interesting applications can be found in [16].

References

1. AITKEN, A. C. Determinants and matrices. Oliver and Boyd, 1956.
2. AKHIEZER, N. I. The classical moment problem and some related questions in analysis. Oliver and Boyd, 1965.
3. BELEVITCH, V. 'Interpolation with rational functions and applications to passive network synthesis'. Proceedings of the Prague Symposium on Circuit Theory, 1968.
4. BOCHER, M. Introduction to higher algebra. Macmillan, 1907.
5. CAUCHY, A. L. 'Sur la formule de Lagrange relative à l'interpolation'. Analyse algébrique. Paris, 1821.
6. CHENEY, E. W. Introduction to approximation theory. McGraw-Hill, 1966.
7. COLLINS, G. E. 'Polynomial remainder sequences and determinants'. Amer. Math. Monthly, 73 (1966), pp. 708-712.
8. COLLINS, G. E. 'Subresultants and reduced polynomial remainder sequences'. J. Assoc. Comp. Mach., 14 (1967), pp. 128-142.
9. DAVIS, P. J. Interpolation and approximation. Blaisdell, 1963.
10. FROBENIUS, G. 'Ueber Relationen zwischen den Näherungsbruchen von Potenzreihen'. J. Reine Angew. Math. 90 (1881), pp. 1-17.
11. GANTMACHER, F. R. The theory of matrices. Chelsea, 1959.
12. HAMMING, R. W. Numerical methods for scientists and engineers, Chap. 20. McGraw-Hill, 1962.
13. HART, J. F. et al. Computer approximations. Wiley, 1968.
14. HILDEBRAND, F. B. Introduction to numerical analysis, Chap 9, pp. 395-412. McGraw-Hill, 1956.
15. HOUSEHOLDER, A. S. 'Bigradients and the problem of Routh and Hurwitz'. SIAM Rev., 10 (1968), pp. 56-66.
16. HOUSEHOLDER, A. S. and STEWART, G. W. 'Bigradients, Hankel determinants and the Padé table'. In Dejon, B. and Henrici, P. (Eds.), Constructive aspects of the fundamental theorem of algebra, pp. 131-150. Wiley-Interscience, 1969.
17. JACOBI, C. G. I. 'Ueber die Darstellung einer Reihe gegebener Werte durch eine gebrochene rationale Funktion'. Crelle J. reine u. angew. Math. 30 (1846), pp. 127-156, or Gesammelte Werke 3 (1884), pp. 481-511.
18. KRONECKER, L. 'Zur Theorie der Elimination einer Variabeln aus zwei algebraischen Gleichungen'. Monatsber. königl. Preuss. Akad. Wiss. Berlin (1881), pp. 535-600.
19. KUNTZMANN, J. Méthodes numériques, interpolation, dérivées, Chap. 8, pp. 232-244. Dunod, 1959.
20. LOEWNER, K. 'Ueber monotone Matrixfunktionen'. Math. Z., 38 (1934), pp. 177-216.
21. MAEHLY, H. and WITZGALL, Ch. 'Tschebyscheff-Approximationen in kleinen Intervallen II, Stetigkeitssätze für gebrochen rationale Approximationen' Num. Math., 2 (1960), pp. 293-307.
22. MAYERS, D. F. 'Interpolation by rational functions', in Handscomb, D. C. (ed.), Methods of numerical approximation, pp. 105-116. Pergamon Press, 1966.

23. MEINGUET, J. 'A "gutartig" algorithm for computing the element values in reactance ladders' (in preparation).

24. MILNE, W. E. Numerical calculus, Chap. 8. Princeton Univ. Press, 1949.

25. MILNE-THOMSON, L. M. The calculus of finite differences. Macmillan, 1933.

26. MUIR, Th. The theory of determinants in the historical order of development. Dover, 1960.

27. NETTO, E. 'Zur Cauchy'schen Interpolationsaufgabe'. Math. Ann., 42 (1893), pp. 453-456.

28. NOERLUND, N. E. Vorlesungen über Differenzenrechnung. Springer, 1924.

29. OPITZ, G. 'Steingungsmatrizen'. Z. Angew. Math. Mech., 44 (1964), pp. T52-54.

30. PREDONZAN, A. 'Su una formula d'interpolazione per le funzioni razionali'. Rend. Sem. Mat. Univ. Padova, 22 (1953), pp. 417-425.

31. RALSTON, A. A first course in numerical analysis, pp. 311-313. McGraw-Hill, 1965.

32. RUTISHAUSER, H. 'Zur Problematik der Nullstellenbestimmung bei Polynomen', in Dejon, B. and Henrici, P. (Eds.), Constructive aspects of the fundamental theorem of algebra, pp. 281-294. Wiley-Interscience, 1969.

33. STOER, J. 'Ueber zwei Algorithmen zur Interpolation mit rationalen Funktionen'. Num. Math., 3 (1961), pp. 285-304.

34. TALBOT, A. 'The evaluation of integrals of products of linear system responses'. Quart. J. Mech. Appl. Math., 12 (1959), pp. 488-503 and 504-520.

35. TALBOT, A. 'The number of zeros of a polynomial in a half-plane'. Proc. Camb. Phil. Soc., 56 (1960), pp. 132-147.

36. THIELE, T. N. Interpolationsrechnung. Teubner, 1909.

37. TRUDI, N. Theoria dei determinanti e loro applicazion. Napoli, 1862.

38. TUKEY, J. and THACHER, H. C. 'Recursive algorithm for interpolation by rational functions' (unpublished manuscript, 1960).

39. WERNER, H. 'Rationale Tshcebyscheff-Approximation, Eigenwerttheorie und Differenzenrechnung'. Arch. Rat. Mech. Anal., 13 (1963), pp. 330-347.

40. WETTERLING, W. 'Ein Interpolationsverfahren zur Lösung der linearen Gleichungssysteme, die bei der rationalen Tshcebyscheff-Approximation auftreten'. Arch. Rat. Mech. Anal., 12 (1963), pp. 403-408.

41. WYNN, P. 'Ueber einen Interpolations-Algorithmus und gewisse andere Formeln, die in der Theorie der Interpolation durch rationale Funktionen bestehen'. Num. Math., 2 (1960), pp. 151-182.

RATIONAL APPROXIMATION TO ANALYTIC FUNCTIONS ON AN INNER PART OF THE DOMAIN OF ANALYTICITY

J. Szabados

(Hungarian Academy of Sciences, Budapest)

1. Introduction

We consider the following two types of function:

(A) $f(z)$ analytic in the circle $C_r = \{z : |z| < r\}$ $(r > 1)$,

(B) $f(z)$ analytic in the ellipse

$$\Gamma_r = \left\{ z; \left(\frac{\mathrm{Re}z}{\frac{1}{2}(r + \frac{1}{r})} \right)^2 + \left(\frac{\mathrm{Im}z}{\frac{1}{2}(r - \frac{1}{r})} \right)^2 < 1 \right\} \quad (r > 1) \tag{1}$$

whose foci are -1 and +1. Denote by $A(C_r)$ and $A(\Gamma_r)$ the sets of these functions, respectively.

Let $\mathbb{P}_n$ and $\mathbb{R}_n$ be the sets of all polynomials and rational functions of degree at most n, respectively. Further let

$$E_n(f,D) = \inf_{p_n(z) \in \mathbb{P}_n} \max_{z \in D} |f(z) - p_n(z)|$$

$$R_n(f,D) = \inf_{r_n(z) \in \mathbb{R}_n} \max_{z \in D} |f(z) - r_n(z)|$$

be, respectively, the best polynomial and rational approximation of $f(z)$ on the closed domain D of the complex plane. Corresponding to (A) and (B), we shall consider two special cases:

$$D = C = \{z : |z| \leq 1\}$$

and

$$D = I = [-1,+1]$$

2. Negative results

It is known (see Erohin [4]) that

$$\sup_{f\in A(C_r)} \limsup_{n\to\infty} [R_n(f,C)]^{1/n} = \sup_{f\in A(C_r)} \limsup_{n\to\infty} [E_n(f,C)]^{1/n} = \frac{1}{r} \quad (r > 1). \quad (2)$$

This means that in this case turning from polynomials to rational functions, the order of approximation does not increase

First of all, we prove that the same holds in the second case.

Theorem 1

$$\sup_{f\in A(\Gamma_r)} \limsup_{n\to\infty} [R_n(f,I)]^{1/n} = \sup_{f\in A(\Gamma_r)} \limsup_{n\to\infty} [E_n(f,I)]^{1/n} = \frac{1}{r} \quad (r > 1). \quad (3)$$

Proof. The right hand side equality in (3) is a well-known theorem of S. N. Bernstein. The first relation in (3) evidently holds with $\leq$ instead of =. To prove the equality, it is sufficient to construct a special function $\overline{f}(z) \in A(\Gamma_r)$ for which

$$\limsup_{n\to\infty} [R_n(\overline{f},I)]^{1/n} = \frac{1}{r}$$

holds. The method used here is similar to that of Szabados [6]. Let

$$\overline{f}(z) = \sum_{i=1}^{\infty} r^{-n_i} T_{n_i}(z) \quad (n_i = (2i+1)!!,\ i = 1,2,\ldots) \quad (4)$$

where $T_n(z)$ is the Chebyshev polynomial degree n. Since $|T_n(x)| \leq 1$ for $|x| \leq 1$ *, we have

$$|T_n(z)| \leq r_1^n \text{ for } z \in \Gamma_{r_1} \quad (r_1 > 1,\ n = 0,1,\ldots)$$

(see e.g. Bernstein [3]). Thus the series in (4) converges uniformly in every $\overline{\Gamma}_{r_1}$ $(1 < r_1 < r)^{\dagger}$. Consequently, by Weierstrass's theorem, $\overline{f}(z)$ is analytic in Γ_r.

Consider the polynomial

$$p_{n_{k-1}}(x) = \sum_{i=1}^{k-1} r^{-n_i} T_{n_i}(x) \quad (5)$$

of degree n_{k-1}, and let

$$x_{j,k} = \cos\frac{j\pi}{n_k} \quad (j = 0,1,\ldots,n_k;\ k = 1,2,\ldots).$$

Then $|x_{j,k}| \leq 1$ and

* In what follows x or z always denote real or complex variable, respectively.

† $\overline{\Gamma}_r$ denotes the closed ellipse-domain corresponding to (1).

$$T_{n_i}(x_{j,k}) = \cos\frac{n_i j\pi}{n_k} = \cos\frac{(2i+1)!!}{(2k+1)!!}j\pi = (-1)^j \quad (i\geq k;\ j=0,1,\ldots,n_k).$$

Hence by (4) and (5) we have

$$\overline{f}(x_{j,k}) - p_{n_{k-1}}(x) = \sum_{i=k}^{\infty} r^{-n_i}\, T_{n_i}(x_{j,k}) = (-1)^j \sum_{i=k}^{\infty} r^{-n_i} \quad (j=0,1,\ldots,n_k),$$

i.e. $\overline{f}(x) - p_{n_{k-1}}(x)$ assumes the maximum of its absolute value in $[-1,+1]$ with alternating signs at the points $x_{j,k}$ $(j=0,1,\ldots,n_k)$. Therefore by a theorem of Chebyshev (see e.g. Achieser [1]) the polynomial $p_{n_{k-1}}(x) \in \mathbb{P}_{n_{k-1}}$ is the best approximating polynomial of degree n_{k-1}, $n_{k-1}+1, \ldots, n_k - 1$ at the same time. Since

$$n_k + 1 \geq 2n_{k-1} + 2$$

the polynomial $p_{n_{k-1}}(x)$ is also the best approximating <u>rational function</u> of degree n_{k-1} to $\overline{f}(x)$, and

$$R_{n_{k-1}}(\overline{f},I) = \sum_{i=k}^{\infty} r^{-n_i} \quad (k=1,2,\ldots).$$

Moreover, we have

$$R_{n_{k-1}}(\overline{f},I) = R_{n_{k-1}+1}(\overline{f},I) = \ldots = R_{n_k-n_{k-1}-1}(\overline{f},I) = \sum_{i=k}^{\infty} r^{-n_i}. \qquad (6)$$

For if

$$R_{n_k-n_{k-1}-1}(\overline{f},I) < R_{n_{k-1}}(\overline{f},I),$$

i.e. (denoting by $r_{n_k-n_{k-1}-1}(x)$ the corresponding best approximating rational function)

$$\max_{x\in I} |\overline{f}(x) - r_{n_k-n_{k-1}-1}(x)| < \max_{x\in I} |\overline{f}(x) - p_{n_{k-1}}(x)|$$

then the rational function

$$p_{n_{k-1}}(x) - r_{n_k-n_{k-1}-1}(x) = [p_{n_{k-1}}(x) - \overline{f}(x)] + [\overline{f}(x) - r_{n_k-n_{k-1}-1}(x)]$$

would have as numerator a polynomial $\in \mathbb{P}_{n_k-1}$. On the other hand, by the above mentioned Chebyshev theorem this numerator would have $n_k - 1 + 2 = n_k + 1$ alternations of signs, i.e. n_k roots, which is impossible.

By (6) and the definition of n_k we have

$$\liminf_{k\to\infty}[R_{n_k-n_{k-1}-1}(\bar{f},I)]^{1/(n_k-n_{k-1}-1)} \geq \lim_{k\to\infty} r^{-n_k/(n_k-n_{k-1}-1)}$$

$$= \lim_{k\to\infty} r^{-1/(1-\frac{1}{2k+1}-\frac{1}{n_k})} = \frac{1}{r}. \quad //$$

Remark. If $f^{(p)}(z)$ exists on the periphery of Γ_r (in the one-dimensional sense) and satisfies there a Lipschitz condition of order $\alpha (0 < \alpha \leq 1)$, then

$$E_n(f,I) \leq \frac{c(f)}{n^{p+\alpha} r^n}$$

where $c(f) > 0$ depends only on f (see Sewell [5], p. 208). By a slight modification of the above method it would be easy to construct a function which shows the above-mentioned structural property and

$$\limsup_{n\to\infty}[R_n(f,I)]^{1/n} = \frac{1}{r}.$$

By refinement of the method one may hope to get a function with the property

$$\limsup_{n\to\infty}[r^n n^{p+\alpha} R_n(f,I)] > 0.$$

3. Approximation on the unit circle

We have seen that the rational approximation in $A(C_r)$ and $A(\Gamma_r)$ is *generally* not better than the polynomial one. To obtain different orders of magnitude of the polynomial and rational approximation, we have to make some restrictions on the behaviour of the function on the periphery of the domain of analyticity.

Definition 1. Denote by $A(C_r,\phi,s)$ the following subset of $A(C_r)$. We shall say that $f(z) \in A(C_r,\phi,s)$ if $f(z) \in A(C_r)$, and the singularities of $f(z)$ on $|z| = r$ can be covered by s distinct open arcs each of them having angle at centre $\leq \phi$ (of course, $s\phi \leq 2\pi$).

By definition, to every $f(z) \in A(C_r,\phi,s)$ there corresponds an $R = R(f) > r$ such that $f(z)$ is analytic in $C(r,R)$ where $C(r,R)$ is the following star-like domain: $z \in C(r,R)$ if (i) $|z| < r$, or (ii) $r \leq |z| \leq R$ but $f(z)$ is analytic at the point $\frac{r}{|z|} z$ (see Fig. 1).

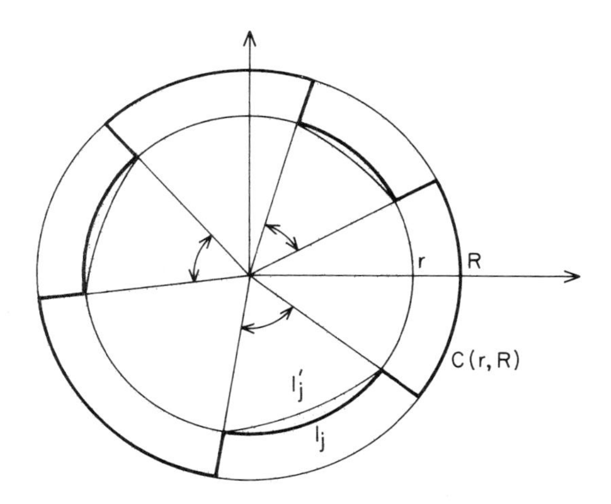

Fig. 1

Theorem 2

If $f(z) \in A(C_r,\phi,s)$ and

$$\cos \frac{\phi}{2} > \frac{R-r}{Rr-1} \frac{r^2+1}{2r} \tag{7}$$

then for sufficiently large n we have

$$R_n(f,C) \leqslant K\, q^{n/s} \tag{8}$$

where

$$q = \frac{1-\sqrt{a}}{1+\sqrt{a}},\quad a = \frac{R-1}{R+1} \cdot \frac{r(R-1)\cos\phi/2 + r^2 - R}{r(R+1)\cos\phi/2 + r^2 + R} \tag{9}$$

and K is independent of n.

<u>Remarks</u>. One has to choose ϕ and s so that the right hand side of (8) should be the smallest possible value. By (2), Theorem 2 gives a better order of approximation if

$$s < \frac{|\log q|}{\log r}.$$

Here the right hand side tends to infinity when $r \to 1+0$ (with fixed $R(\, > r)$).

It is worthwhile to mention the special case when f(z) has s <u>isolated</u> singularities on $|z| = r$. Then ϕ can be chosen arbitrarily small and by (9) a approaches the value

$$\frac{R-1}{R+1} \cdot \frac{r-1}{r+1}$$

from below. Thus we have from (8)

$$\limsup_{n\to\infty}[R_n(f,C)]^{1/n} \leq \left\{\frac{R + r}{Rr + 1 + \sqrt{[(R^2-1)(r^2-1)]}}\right\}^{1/s} \tag{10}$$

Theorem 2 of Szabados [7] is a weaker form of (10). Namely, the estimate (10) is better than that in [7]; the singularities of $f(z)$ can be poles (in [7] the continuity of $f(z)$ on $|z| \leq r$ is assumed), and these poles are not necessarily isolated. Moreover, we do not assume anything about $f(z)$ outside of $|z| \leq r$.

Another interesting special case is when $s=1$, i.e. when the singularities of $f(z)$ on $|z| = r$ can be covered by <u>one arc</u>. Then - as is easily checked -

$$\limsup_{n\to\infty}[R_n(f,C)]^{1/n} \leq q$$

which, when the restriction (7) holds, is less than $1/r$, i.e. is better than the order of polynomial approximation (see (2)). In particular, if there is only <u>one singularity</u> on $|z| = r$, then ϕ can be arbitrarily small, and

$$\limsup_{n\to\infty}[R_n(f,C)]^{1/n} \leq \frac{R + r}{Rr + 1 + \sqrt{[(R^2-1)(r^2-1)]}} .$$

If $f(z)$ has no other (finite) singularity on the z-plane, then R can be chosen arbitrarily large, and

$$\limsup_{n\to\infty}[R_n(f,C)]^{1/n} \leq \frac{1}{r + \sqrt{(r^2-1)}} . \tag{11}$$

<u>Proof of Theorem 2</u>. Let $F(z) = f(rz)$. Then $F(z) \in A(C_1,\phi,s)$, and $F(z)$ is analytic in $C(1,R/r)$ (see Definition 1). Let the singularities of $F(z)$ on $|z| = 1$ be covered by distinct open arcs of lengths $\ell_j (\ell_j \leq \phi;\ j=1,2,\dots,s)$ with centres $z_j (|z_j| = 1;\ j=1,2,\dots,s)$, respectively, and put (see (9))

$$g_j(z) = \left(\frac{z - z_j(1-2\sqrt{a})}{z - z_j(1+2\sqrt{a})}\right)^n \qquad (j=1,2,\dots,s). \tag{12}$$

Denote by L_j the tangent of $|z| = 1$ at the point z_j, and P_j the closed half-plane bordered by L_j which does not contain $|z| = 1$ (see Fig. 2). Then by an easy calculation we obtain

$$|g_j(z)| \geq 1 \text{ for } z \in P_j \quad (j=1,\dots,s) \tag{13}$$

and

$$|g_j(z)| = q^n \text{ for } |z + az_j| = 1 - a \quad (j=1,\dots,s). \tag{14}$$

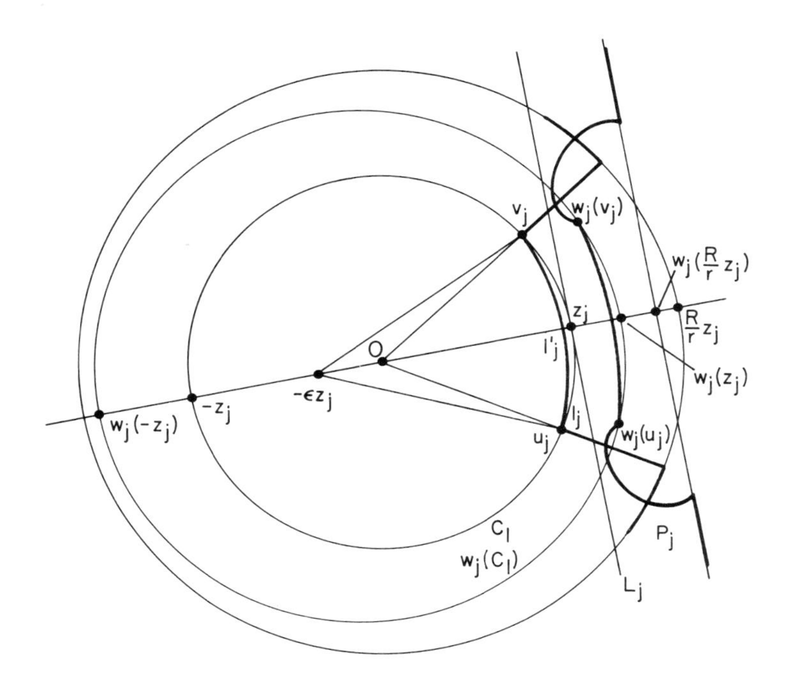

Fig. 2

On the other hand,

$$|g_j(z)| \geqslant q^n \text{ for } |z| \geqslant 1 \quad (j=1,\ldots,s). \tag{15}$$

Further let

$$w_j(z) = \frac{r[R - a(R+1)]z + [1 - a(R+1)]z_j}{rz + Rz_j} z_j \quad (j=1,\ldots,s), \tag{16}$$

then

$$w_j(-\frac{1}{r}z_j) = -z_j, \; w_j(\frac{1}{r}z_j) = (1-2a)z_j, \; w_j(-\frac{R}{r}z_j) = \infty \; (j=1,\ldots,s). \tag{17}$$

Therefore $w_j(z)$ maps the circle $|z| \leqslant \frac{1}{r}$ into the circle $|z + az_j| \leqslant 1 - a \quad (j=1,\ldots,s)$, and by (14)

$$g_j(w_j(z)) \leqslant q^n \text{ for } |z| \leqslant \frac{1}{r} \quad (j=1,\ldots,s). \tag{18}$$

Now let

$$z_j = e^{it_j}, \; z = e^{it}, \; |t - t_j| \leqslant \frac{\ell_j}{2} \leqslant \frac{\phi}{2} \quad (1 \leqslant j \leqslant s)$$

(i.e. z is on the arc ℓ_j), then by (16)

$$\operatorname{Re}\frac{w_j(z)}{z_j} = R - a(R+1) + (R^2-1)(a-1)\operatorname{Re}\frac{1}{R+rz/z_j} \tag{19}$$

$$= R - a(R+1) - \frac{(R^2-1)(1-a)[r\cos(t-t_j)+R]}{R^2+r^2+2Rr\cos(t-t_j)}$$

$$\geqslant R - a(R+1) - (R^2-1)(1-a)\frac{r\cos\phi/2+R}{R^2+r^2+2Rr\cos\phi/2}$$

$$= 1 + (R-1)\left\{1-\frac{(R+1)(R+r\cos\phi/2)}{R^2+r^2+2Rr\cos\phi/2}\right\} - a(R+1)\left\{1-\frac{(R-1)(R+r\cos\phi/2)}{R^2+r^2+2Rr\cos\phi/2}\right\}$$

$$= 1 + \frac{(R-1)(r^2-R+(R-1)r\cos\phi/2) - a(R+1)(r^2+R+(R+1)r\cos\phi/2}{R^2+r^2+2Rr\cos\phi/2}$$

$$= 1 \quad (z \in \ell_j).$$

This means that the w_j-image of the arc $\ell_j = \widehat{u_j v_j}$ is in P_j (see Fig. 2). Moreover

$$w_j(-z_j) = \frac{-r[R-a(R+1)]+1-a(R+1)}{R-r}z_j = \frac{a(R+1)(r-1)-rR+1}{R-r}z_j,$$

$$|w_j(-z_j)| > 1.$$

This together with $|w_j(z_j)| > 1$ (see (19)) means that the w_j-image of $|z| \leqslant 1$ $(j=1,\dots,s)$ is a circle containing $|z| \leqslant 1$:

$$w_j(C_1) \supset C_1. \tag{20}$$

Thus taking $\varepsilon > 0$ small enough,

(i) the w_j-images $(j=1,\dots,s)$ of the arcs ℓ_k' with centre $-\varepsilon z_k$ and with endpoints u_k and v_k $(k=1,\dots,s)$, are external to C_1,

(ii) the w_j-image of ℓ_j' is in P_j $(j=1,\dots,s)$, and

(iii) ℓ_j' does not intersect $|z| = \frac{1}{r}$ $(j=1,\dots,s)$.

Now let $K(r,R)$ be the curve obtained from the boundary of $C(1,\frac{R}{r})$ by replacing ℓ_j by ℓ_j' (see Fig. 1). Then $F(z)$ is analytic in the closed region bounded by $K(r,R)$.

Let $R_{ns}(z) \in \mathbb{R}_{ns}$ be the rational function which interpolates to $F(z)$ at the roots of $g_j(w_j(z))$, $j=1,\dots,s$ (with multiplicity n) and at $z=0$, and which has the same poles as $g_j(w_j(z))$, $j=1,\dots,s$ (with multiplicity n). Then (see Walsh [8], Ch. 8, Theorem 2)

$$F(z) - R_{ns}(z) = \frac{z \prod_{j=1}^{s} g_j(w_j(z))}{2\pi i} \int_{K(r,R)} \frac{F(\xi)d\xi}{\xi(\xi-z) \prod_{j=1}^{s} g_j(w_j(\xi))} \quad (|z| \leqslant \frac{1}{r}).$$

Thus, by (18) we have, if $M = \max_{z \in K(r,R)} |F(z)|$,

$$|F(z) - R_{ns}(z)| \leqslant \frac{q^{ns}M}{2\pi r(1-\varepsilon)(1-\varepsilon-\frac{1}{r})} \int_{K(r,R)} \frac{|d\xi|}{\prod_{j=1}^{s} |g_j(w_j(\xi))|} \quad (|z| = \frac{1}{r}).$$

First of all, let $|\xi| = \frac{R}{r}$, $\xi \in K(r,R)$. Now by (16)

$$\mathrm{Re}\, \frac{w_j(\frac{R}{r} z_j)}{z_j} = \frac{R[R-a(R+1)]+1-a(R+1)}{2R} = \frac{R^2+1-a(R+1)^2}{2R} > 1,$$

therefore the w_j-image of $|z| = \frac{R}{r}$ is a line in P_j (see (17)). Hence, by (13),

$$|g_j(w_j(\xi))| \geqslant 1 \quad (j=1,\ldots,s).$$

On the other hand, if $\xi \in K(r,R)$ but $|\xi| < \frac{R}{r}$, i.e. $\xi \in \ell'_k (1 \leqslant k \leqslant s)$ or ξ is on one of the line-segments connecting u_k or v_k with $|z| = \frac{R}{r}$, then by the above considerations $w_k(\xi) \in P_k$ and so (13) gives

$$|g_k(w_k(\xi))| \geqslant 1.$$

As regards $g_j(w_j(\xi))$ $(j \neq k)$ in this case, we get by (20) and (15)

$$|g_j(w_j(\xi))| \geqslant q^n \quad (j \neq k).$$

Thus we can write

$$|F(z) - R_{ns}(z)| \leqslant K_1 \frac{q^{ns}}{q^{n(s-1)}} \quad (|z| = \frac{1}{r}),$$

i.e.

$$|f(z) - R_{ns}(\frac{1}{r} z)| \leqslant K_1 q^n \quad (|z| = 1).$$

This completes the proof of Theorem 2.

4. Approximation on an interval of the real axis

Consider now the class of functions $A(\Gamma_r)$, i.e. which are analytic in (1). Let

$$z_j = \tfrac{1}{2}(r + \tfrac{1}{r})\cos t_j + i\, \tfrac{1}{2}(r - \tfrac{1}{r})\sin t_j, \quad 0 \leqslant t_j < 2\pi \quad (j=1,2)$$

be two points on the boundary of Γ_r. We shall call $|t_1 - t_2|$ the <u>angle</u> of the ellipse-arc $\widehat{z_1 z_2}$.

<u>Definition 2</u>. Denote by $A(\Gamma_r,\phi,s)$ the following subset of $A(\Gamma_r)$: $f(z) \in A(\Gamma_r,\phi,s)$ if $f(z) \in A(\Gamma_r)$ and the singularities of $f(z)$ on the boundary of Γ_r can be covered by s distinct open ellipse-arcs each of them having angle $\leq \phi(\leq \pi)$ (in the above sense).

Map the z-plane onto the w-plane by

$$z = \tfrac{1}{2}(w + \frac{1}{w}).$$

Then the map of $I = [-1,+1]$ in the w-plane is the unit circle $|w| = 1$ counted twice, and the image in the z-plane of Γ_r in the w-plane counted twice is the annular region $\frac{1}{r} < |w| < r$. The map of the boundary Γ_r consists of two circles, $|w| = \frac{1}{r}$ and $|w| = r$. Put

$$F(w) = f[\tfrac{1}{2}(w + \frac{1}{w})] \tag{21}$$

where $f(z) \in A(\Gamma_r,\phi,s)$. This function is analytic in the annulus $\frac{1}{r} < |w| < r$, and its singularities on $|w| = \frac{1}{r}$ and $|w| = r$ can be covered by s+s arcs having angle at centre $\leq \phi$. This is easily seen by (21).

By (21), $F(w) = F(\frac{1}{w})$, which implies

$$F(w) = G(w) + G(\frac{1}{w}) \tag{22}$$

where $G(w)$ is analytic in $|w| < r$, and $G(w) \in A(C_r,\phi,s)$. Applying Theorem 2, we obtain a rational function $R_{2n}(w) \in \mathbb{R}_{2n}$ such that

$$|G(w) - R_{2n}(w)| \leq K\, q^{2n/s} \quad \text{for } |w| = 1.$$

Hence

$$|F(w) - [R_{2n}(w) + R_{2n}(\frac{1}{w})]| \leq 2K\, q^{2n/s} \quad \text{for } |w| = 1. \tag{23}$$

Consider the rational function

$$r_{2n}(w) = R_{2n}(w) + R_{2n}(\frac{1}{w}) = \frac{\sum_{k=0}^{2n} a_k w^k}{\sum_{k=0}^{2n} b_k w^k}. \tag{24}$$

We prove that this is a rational function of the variable $w + \frac{1}{w}$ of degree at most n. Namely, by (24) $r_{2n}(w) = r_{2n}(\frac{1}{w})$, i.e.

$$\frac{\sum_{k=0}^{2n} a_k w^k}{\sum_{k=0}^{2n} b_k w^k} = \frac{\sum_{k=0}^{2n} a_{2n-k} w^k}{\sum_{k=0}^{2n} b_{2n-k} w^k} .$$

nce

$$a_k = \lambda a_{2n-k},\ b_k = \lambda b_{2n-k} \quad (k=0,1,\ldots,2n) \tag{25}$$

ich implies $\lambda = \pm 1$. Thus

$$r_{2n}(w) = \frac{\sum_{k=0}^{n-1} a_k(w^{n-k} + \lambda\, w^{k-n}) + \alpha}{\sum_{k=0}^{n-1} b_k(w^{n-k} + \lambda\, w^{k-n}) + \beta},$$

here

$$\alpha = a_n,\ \beta = b_n \text{ for } \lambda = +1; \quad \alpha = \beta = 0 \text{ for } \lambda = -1.$$

ow for $s = 1,2,\ldots,\ w^s + w^{-s} = 2T_s(z),\ w^s - w^{-s} = (w - w^{-1})U_{s-1}(z)$, here U_{s-1} is a Chebyshev polynomial of the 2nd kind. It follows at once hat $r_{2n}(w)$ is rational in z of degree at most n, say $\overline{R}_n(z)$. Then by (23) nd (21),

$$|f(x) - \overline{R}_n(x)| \leqslant 2K\, q^{2n/s} \text{ for } -1 \leqslant x \leqslant 1.$$

So we are led to the following

Theorem 3

If $f(z) \in A(\Gamma_r,\phi,s)$ and (7) holds, then for sufficiently large n we have

$$R_n(f,I) \leqslant K\, q^{2n/s} \tag{26}$$

where K depends only on f, and q is defined by (19). Here R is the value corresponding to the function $G(w)$ (see (21) and (22)) in the sense of Definition 1.

Remarks

1. The same remarks as made after Theorem 2 can be applied to Theorem 3, but with 2n instead of n (i.e. with better estimates).

2. It must be noted that if $f(z)$ is real on $I = [-1,+1]$ then we can construct a rational function with real coefficients realizing (26), but in this case we have to rewrite n instead of 2n in (26). Namely, if an

approximating rational function realizing (26) is of the form

$$r_n(x) = \frac{p_{n,1}(x) + ip_{n,2}(x)}{p_{n,3}(x) + ip_{n,4}(x)} = \frac{p_{n,1}(x)p_{n,3}(x) + p_{n,2}(x)p_{n,4}(x)}{p_{n,3}^2(x) + p_{n,4}^2(x)}$$

$$+ i\,\frac{p_{n,2}(x)p_{n,3}(x) - p_{n,1}(x)p_{n,4}(x)}{p_{n,3}^2(x) + p_{n,4}^2(x)} = r_{2n,1}(x) + i\, r_{2n,2}(x)$$

where $p_{n,k}(x)$ $(k=1,\dots,4)$ are polynomials with real coefficients of degree at most n, then $r_{2n,1}(x)$ is a rational function with real coefficients of degree at most $2n$; and

$$|f(x) - r_{2n,1}(x)| \leqslant |f(x) - r_n(x)| \qquad (-1 \leqslant x \leqslant +1).$$

3. However, if $f(z)$ is real-valued for real z and has singularities <u>only</u> on the real axis, then the best approximating rational function has real coefficients and (26) holds. This can be easily seen from the proofs of Theorems 2 and 3.

5. Examples

For

$$f_1(z) = (r - z)^\alpha \qquad (r > 1,\ \alpha \text{ real})$$

the order of polynomial approximation in C is

$$E_n(f_1, C) \leqslant \frac{K_2}{n^{\alpha+1} r^n}$$

(cf. Sewell [5], pp. 171-172). Theorem 2 gives (by (11))

$$\limsup_{n\to\infty} [R_n(f_1, C)]^{1/n} \leqslant \frac{1}{r + \sqrt{(r^2-1)}} \tag{27}$$

which is much better. Similarly, for

$$f_2(z) = \log(r - z)$$

we have (cf. [5], p. 174)

$$E_n(f_2, C) \leqslant \frac{K_3}{nr^n}$$

and for $R_n(f_2, C)$ the same holds as in (27).

The functions f_1 and f_2 on $I = [-1,+1]$ were investigated by S. N. Bernstein [2] who showed that

$$E_n(f_1, I) \sim \frac{K_4}{n^{\alpha+1}(r + \sqrt{r^2-1})^n}, \quad E_n(f_2, I) \sim \frac{K_5}{n(r + \sqrt{r^2-1})^n}.$$

n the other hand, f_1 and f_2 being analytic in $\Gamma_{r+\sqrt{r^2-1}}$ we have (by emark 3 of Theorem 3)

$$\lim_{n\to\infty} \sup[R_n(f_i,I)]^{1/n} \leq \left(\frac{1}{r + \sqrt{(r^2-1)} + \sqrt{([r + \sqrt{(r^2-1)}]^2-1)}}\right) (i=1,2).$$

These examples always refer to the case when r is <u>real</u>. But our heorems 2 and 3 give reasonable estimates for complex r as well. Let

$$f_1(z) = (u-z)^\alpha,\ f_2(z) = \log(u-z) \quad (u \text{ complex}).$$

hen

$$\lim_{n\to\infty} \sup[R_n(f_i,C)]^{1/n} \leq \frac{1}{|u| + \sqrt{(|u|^2-1)}} \quad (i=1,2;\ |u| > 1)$$

nd

$$\lim_{n\to\infty} \sup[R_n(f_i,I)]^{1/n} \leq \frac{1}{b + \sqrt{(b^2-1)}} \quad (i=1,2)$$

here

$$b = \left(\frac{|u|^2 + 1 + |u^2-1|}{2}\right)^{1/2} + \left(\frac{|u|^2 - 1 + |u^2-1|}{2}\right)^{1/2} \quad (u \notin I).$$

References

1. ACHIESER, N. I. <u>Theory of approximation</u>. Ungar, 1956.
2. BERNSTEIN, S. N. 'Sur la valeur asymptotique de la meilleure approximation des fonctions analytiques admettant des singularités données'. Bull. de l'Acad. Roy. de Belgique, Classe des Sciences, (1913), pp. 76-90.
3. BERNSTEIN, S. N. <u>Extremal properties of polynomials and best approximation of continuous functions of one real variable</u>. (Russian). Moscow, 1937.
4. EROHIN, V. D. 'On the best approximation of analytic functions by rational fractions with free poles' (Russian). Dokl. Akad. Nauk SSSR, <u>128</u>(1) (1959), pp. 29-32.
5. SEWELL, W. E. <u>Degree of approximation by polynomials in the complex domain</u>. Princeton Univ. Press, 1965.
6. SZABADOS, J. 'Negative results in the theory of rational approximation'. Studia Sci. Math. Hung., <u>2</u> (1967), pp. 385-390.
7. SZABADOS, J. 'Rational approximation in complex domains'. Studia Sci. Math. Hung. <u>4</u> (1969) (to appear).
8. WALSH, J. L. <u>Interpolation and approximation by rational functions in the complex domain</u>. Amer. Math. Soc., Colloquium Publ., 1960.

THE DETERMINATION OF H-SETS FOR THE INCLUSION THEOREM IN NONLINEAR TSCHEBYSCHEFF APPROXIMATION

L. Collatz

(University of Hamburg)

1. Introduction and statement of basic concepts

The application of approximation theory to differential equations, integral equations etc. frequently leads to approximation problems which differ from the usual problems by aggravating circumstances. In the simplest case we have to approximate a given function $f(x)$ continuous in the interval $B = [a,b]$ by an element w of a set $W = \{w(x,a)\}$ of functions depending on a parameter $a = \{a_1,\dots,a_p\}$. Let $C(B)$ denote the Banach-space of functions $g(x)$ continuous in B, with norm

$$||g|| = \sup_{x \in B} p(x)\ |g(x)|. \tag{1}$$

Here, $p(x)$ is a chosen positive function of $C(B)$. To approximate in the Tschebyscheff sense means to ask for the minimal distance ρ_o:

$$\rho_o = \inf_{w \in W} ||w - f|| . \tag{2}$$

An element $\hat{w} \in W$ fulfilling

$$||\hat{w} - f|| = \rho_o \tag{3}$$

is called a minimal solution. If the parameters a_ν appear linearly in the functions of W, we speak of linear Tschebyscheff-approximation, otherwise is called non-linear. Function sets consisting of polynomials, Tschebyscheff-systems, rational functions, sums of exponentials, etc. are often considered.

In contrast to this classical case, the following complications often occur in the applications:

1. The function set W involved has been little or not at all investigated up to now.

2. Often the function f(x) depends on several independent variables $x = \{x_1,\ldots,x_n\}$, and B denotes a region in the n-dimensional space R^n. Even rational approximation with two independent variables has been far less investigated than the case of only one variable. In particular, the theory of Tschebyscheff systems does not apply.

3. Frequently the parameters a_ν appear in a much more complicated and intricate manner than in the classical case. For instance, if we try to approximate a solution y(x) of the boundary value problem

$$y'' = y^2, \; y(\pm 1) = c, \tag{4}$$

c a given constant, by the functions

$$w(x) = c + (1 - x^2)(a_1 + a_2 x^2) \tag{5}$$

which fulfil the boundary conditions, the parameters a_1 and a_2 appear linearly. But, if we insert w in the differential equation, we get a problem of polynomial approximation in which the parameters a_1 and a_2 appear several times at different places:

$$\frac{a_2}{a_1}(1-6x^2) - \frac{1}{2a_1}[c + (1-x^2)(a_1+a_2x^2)]^2 \simeq 1. \tag{6}$$

4. The type of approximation may be more complicated. "Syn-approximation" (D. G. Moursund [8]) involves approximating simultaneously several functions derived from f, for instance f, $\partial f/\partial x_1$, $\partial f/\partial x_2$. In "simultaneous approximation" (E. Bredendiek, [2]), several regions $B_1,\ldots,B_s$ may occur, and in "combi-approximation" we have different function sets $W_1,\ldots,W_s$ (L. Collatz, [7]). Sometimes the limits of the regions B_σ in simultaneous approximation are not known a priori.

In the following we describe how to get information about the minimal deviation (or, sometimes, the statement that a given approximation w is a minimal solution) in favourable and not too complicated cases, in spite of all complications mentioned above. This will be achieved by the theory of H-sets, and we shall give some methods for the determination of H-sets.

The basis for this is a theorem, which will be quoted for completeness: To approximate a given function $f(x) \in C(B)$ by the functions of a class $W = \{w(x,a)\}$ in the sense of the norm (1) we suppose M_1, M_2 to be parts of B with the property that for no pair $\tilde{w}, w \in W$ is the function $\delta = w - \tilde{w}$

positive on M_1, negative on M_2. We let $H = M_1 \cup M_2$ and call this an "H-set". Then if $g \in W$ and the error $\varepsilon = g-f$ is positive on M_1, negative on M_2, we have the inclusion

$$\mu_1 \leqslant \rho_o \leqslant \mu_2 \tag{7}$$

where we have set

$$\mu_1 = \inf_{x \in H} p(x)|\varepsilon(x)|, \quad \mu_2 = \|\varepsilon\|. \tag{8}$$

If $\mu_1 = \mu_2$, then g is a minimal solution. Therefore we may use the theorem to prove that some function is in fact a minimal solution. Frequently, μ_1 will be a little smaller than μ_2 in applications, especially if a computer is used. Then we know that we have reached almost the best possible result within the function class W. For numerical methods see for instance Wetterling [10].

2. The linear and rational cases

Now we discuss different methods A,B,C,D,E to prove that some set of points is an H-set.

A. Linear approximations.

For this there is an algorithm easy to realize on the computer which also applies to more general approximations including the linear case of the combi-approximations (Full details are given in Collatz [6] Sec.25.6); for linear functions see G. D. Taylor [9].
We give only one example which will be used later:
W is to contain the functions

$$w = w(x,y) = a_1x^2+a_2x+a_3y^2+a_4y+a_5 \tag{9}$$

involving 5 free parameters a_ν. No term of the form xy appears in w. Here we can give a lot of H-sets. We shall consider several types:

a) Let P_1,P_2,P_3,P_4 be the corners of a rectangle the sides of which are parallel to the coordinate axes (Fig. 1(a)). For instance, P_1 and P_3 may belong to the set M_1 (black circles), P_2 and P_4 to the set M_2 (white circles). For the proof that these four points constitute a H-set we may choose the coordinate axes in such a way that P_1 is the origin and P_3 has the coordinates $x = r$, $y = s$. The difference $\delta = w - \tilde{w}$ of two polynomials of W is again of the form (9). Now we can write down the conditions for the sign of δ at the four points $P_j (j=1,2,3,4)$, and we have to show that these conditions are not consistent. For the practical computation we use

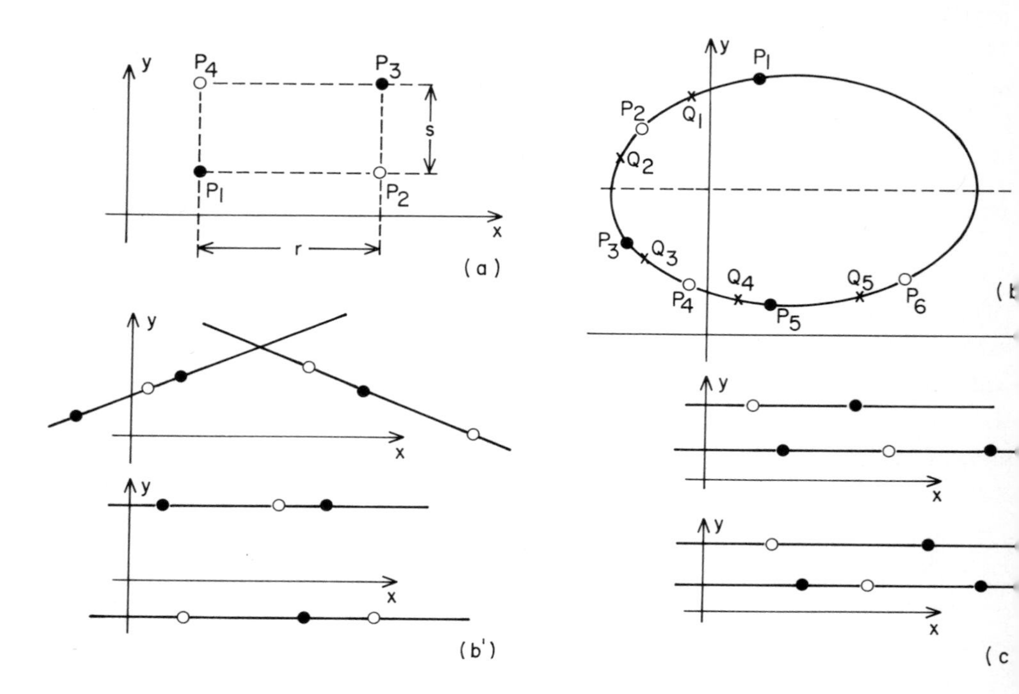

Fig. 1

a scheme which shows in an obvious manner only the coefficients of the parameters a_ν. This gives the first four rows, and the fifth row is the sum of the second, the third and the fourth row. The, the first and the fifth row already lead to the contradiction $+1.a_5 > 0$, $-1.a_5 > 0$. Hence, the points P_j constitute an H-set.

points	coordinates x	y	coefficients of a_1	a_2	a_3	a_4	a_5	
P_1	0	0	0	0	0	0	1	> 0
P_2	r	0	$-r^2$	$-r$	0	0	-1	> 0
P_3	r	s	r^2	r	s^2	s	1	> 0
P_4	0	s	0	0	$-s^2$	$-s$	-1	> 0
			0	0	0	0	-1	> 0

b) Let $P_j (j=1,2,\ldots,6)$ be on an ellipse, on a parabola or on a branch of a hyperbola the axes of which are parallel to the coordinate axes. Tracing along the curves, we add the points by turns to M_1 and M_2 respectively (Fig. 1(b)). These points constitute again an H-set. In fact, if a difference δ is positive on M_1 and negative on M_2, δ vanishes at some points $Q_j (j=1,\ldots,5)$ between adjacent points P_j by continuity. Hence, δ vanishes on the whole curve. This contradicts the fact that δ is positive at P_1. The argument also applies to the singular cases in Fig. 1(b'), a detailed discussion is superfluous.

c) Of course, there are further H-sets for our set of functions. Examples are sketched in Fig. 1(c). We omit the analytical description.

B. Rational approximation

If the elements of W are of the form $w = Z/N$ where the parameters a_ν appear linearly in Z and N and take only values for which the denominator is positive in B, then the difference of two elements of W may be written

$$\delta = w - \tilde{w} = Z/N - \tilde{Z}/\tilde{N} = \hat{Z}/\hat{N} \tag{10}$$

Here the denominator $\hat{N} = N\tilde{N}$ is positive in B. Hence we may investigate the sign of $\hat{Z} = Z\tilde{N} - \tilde{Z}N$ instead the sign of δ. This wellknown artifice has been used in the investigation of several function sets (see for instance Collatz [5]). If Z and N are polynomials in one or more independent variables, everything depends on the number

$$k = (\deg Z + \deg N). \tag{11}$$

Collatz [5] gives H-sets for k=1,2,3,4 in the case of two independent variables.

For instance, each H-set with respect to a polynomial

$$N = a_1x^2 + a_2xy + a_3y^2 + a_4x + a_5y + a_6 \tag{12}$$

is also an H-set for the rational function $w = 1/N$ if we suppose that the denominator N is positive in B. In another example, B is the quadrant $x \geq 0$, $y \geq 0$ and W denotes the function set

$$W = \{w = \frac{1}{N} = \frac{1}{a_1+a_2x+a_3y} \text{ with } N > 0 \text{ in } B\}. \tag{13}$$

It is well known that for linear functions, an arbitrary convex quadrangle is an H-set if the two pairs of opposite corners constitute the sets M_1, M_2

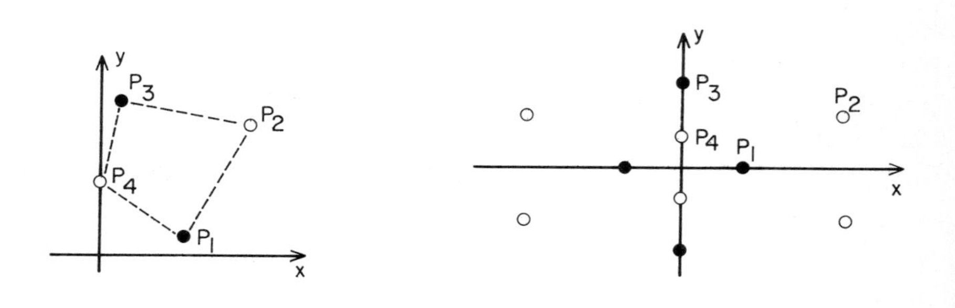

Fig. 2 Fig. 3

respectively. Hence, every convex quadrangle (as in Fig. 2) is an H-set for the class (13).

3. Further principles of reduction

C. Monotonicity

Let $W = \{w(x,a)\}$ be a set of functions. Let I denote the range of $w(x,a)$ if x varies in B and a varies in the region A of parameter vectors. Let ϕ be a real-valued strictly monotonic function on I (decreasing or increasing If H is an H-set with respect to W, then H is also an H-set for the class

$$\hat{W} = \{\phi(w(x,a))\}. \tag{14}$$

In fact, if there is no pair $w,\tilde{w} \in W$ satisfying

$$w > \tilde{w} \text{ in } M_1,\ w < \tilde{w} \text{ in } M_2, \tag{15}$$

then we certainly cannot find a pair $w,\tilde{w}$ with the property

$$\phi(w) > \phi(\tilde{w}) \text{ in } M_1,\ \phi(w) < \phi(\tilde{w}) \text{ in } M_2. \tag{16}$$

This simple remark has many applications. If, for instance, the range consists only of positive numbers, we may choose $\phi(z) = 1/z$.

If we take $\phi(z) = e^z$, we see that all H-sets for the quadratic polynomials N in (12) are at the same time H-sets for the non-linear class e^w. Corresponding results hold for more than two dimensions.

Example: Heat-conducting-equation with three independent variables.

We ask for a function $u(x,y,t)$ which satisfies the differential equation

$$Lu = k\frac{\partial u}{\partial t} - \frac{\partial^2 u}{\partial x^2} - \frac{\partial^2 u}{\partial y^2} = 0 \quad \text{in } D: -\infty < x,y < +\infty,\ t > 0 \tag{17}$$

and which satisfies the initial condition

$$u(x,y,0) = f(x,y) = 1/(1+x^2+y^4) \quad \text{on } \Gamma: -\infty < x,y < +\infty,\ t=0 \tag{18}$$

The function

$$v(x,y,t) = \frac{c_1}{t+t_o} \exp\left[-\frac{k}{4(t+t_o)}((x-x_o)^2 + (y-y_o)^2)\right] \tag{19}$$

is an exact solution of the differential equation (17) reducing to

$$v(x,y,0) = w(x,y) = a_1 e^{-a_2x^2-a_3y^2} \tag{20}$$

if $t=0$, where we have taken $x_o=y_o=0$ in account of the symmetry. Hence we are led to the problem of approximating the function f on Γ by the function w as well as possible. In fact we approximate in the Tschebyscheff sense because the relation $|\varepsilon| \leq \delta$ on Γ for the error $\varepsilon = w-f$ implies the same inequality on the whole region D.

Numerical computation gives the values

$$a_1 = 0.9749; \quad a_2 = 0.4954; \quad a_3 = 0.5905,$$

and the maximal error is

$$|\varepsilon| \leq \delta = 0.1010 \text{ on } \Gamma$$

(I thank Mr. P. Budde and Mr. H. G. Zimmermann for the calculation on the computer.)

The following table gives the coordinates of the extremals of the error function ε, where we may restrict ourselves to the quadrant $x \geq 0$, $y \geq 0$ on account of the symmetry.

point	coordinates		ε
P_1	$x = 0.8484$	$y = 0$	$+ 0.1010$
P_2	$x = 2.391$	$y = 0.772$	$- 0.1010$
P_3	$x = 0$	$y = 1.346$	$+ 0.1010$
P_4	$x = 0$	$y = 0.5332$	$- 0.1010$

If we put $x^2 = s$, $y^2 = t$ in the quadrant $x \geq 0$, $y \geq 0$ and $a_1 = e^{\alpha_1}$

(supposing $a_1 > 0$), the function w in (20) becomes

$$w = \exp [\alpha_1 - a_2 s - a_3 t] = \exp \phi, \tag{21}$$

i.e. we have a usual exponential approximation in the region B: $s \geq 0$, $t \geq 0$; the stated linear function of s and t is denoted by ϕ for abbreviation. Therefore we only have to consider the points $P_1, \ldots, P_4$ (see Fig. 3) and a comparison with Fig. 2 shows that these points constitute an H-set for the linear function ϕ and hence for w (the change of variables does not influence the convexity).

Now the inclusion theorem immediately tells us that we cannot make the minimal deviation and hence the global error bound δ smaller than 0.1010 if we use the functions v of (19). If we want to have a better approximation, we must use other sets of functions, for instance we may enlarge the number of free parameters.

D. Reduction to simpler cases

Such reductions are possible in many cases. We give a simple example concerning a segment-combi-approximation. The function $f(x) = e^{-x}$ is to be approximated in the interval $I = [0, +\infty]$ by decomposing I into two parts $I_1 = [0, a]$, $I_2 = [a, +\infty]$. In I_1 we use polynomials of degree k whereas in I_2 we take a rational function, in particular the reciprocal of a polynomial with degree m. At x = a the values of the two approximating functions may be different. Here we may prove the inclusion theorem (7), (8) in the same way as if we had used functions of only one class in the intervals I_1 and I_2, for instance rational functions in both intervals, see Collatz [5].

Numerical example k = m = 1

In I_1 we approximate by the function $a_{0(1)} + a_{1(1)}x$, in I_2 by the function $a_{0(2)}/(1 + a_{1(2)}x)$.

The calculation on the computer (for which I thank Mr. H. Krisch) yields the values

σ	a = 0.98	Extremal points	$a_{0(\sigma)}$	$a_{1(\sigma)}$
1	$I_{(1)} = [0, a]$	0; 0.44; 0.952	0.964	-0.645
2	$I_{(2)} = [a, \infty]$	0.952; 1.36; 4.37	-0.375	-1.986

The inclusion theorem gives for the total minimal deviation the bounds

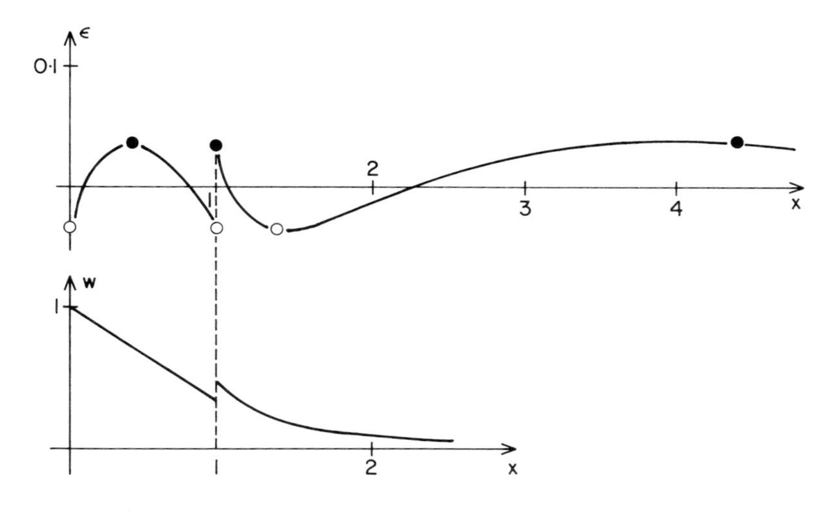

Fig. 4

$0.0355 \leqslant \rho_o \leqslant 0.0365$. Graphs of w and ε are shown in Fig. 4.

E. Special investigation of the systems of nonlinear inequalities

If the foregoing methods do not yield a result, we sometimes may succeed in showing that the system of nonlinear inequalities is not consistent and hence has no solution.

A simple example will illustrate this. Suppose we are given the integral equation:

$$y(s) + \int_{-\infty}^{+\infty} K(s,t)y(t)dt = 1 \tag{22}$$

If we approximate the kernel K by a degenerate Kernel $K^*(s,t)$ the resulting integral equation can be solved explicitly. In another paper (of Collatz, see Abadie [1]) the example was considered, of approximating the kernel

$$K = \frac{1}{1+s^2+t^2} \quad \text{by } K^* = \frac{a_1}{(a_2+s^2)(a_2+t^2)}$$

in the domain $-\infty < s,t < +\infty$. With the values

$$a_1 = 1.748\ 37, \quad a_2 = 1.357\ 30$$

the error $\varepsilon = K^* - K$ takes the extrema of its modulus at the points of Fig. 5:

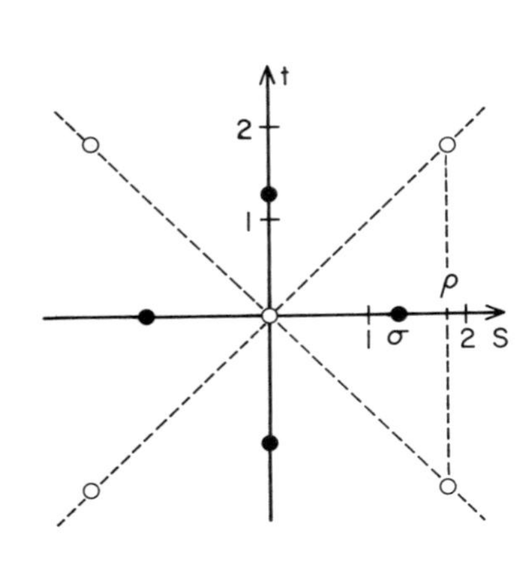

Fig. 5

P_1	$s_1 = t_1 = 0$	$\varepsilon = -0.05097$
P_2	$s_2 = \sigma,\ t_2 = 0$ $\sigma = 1.28357..$	$\varepsilon = 0.05097$
P_3	$s_3 = t_3 = \rho$ $\rho = 1.81583$	$\varepsilon = -0.05097$

The inclusion theorem (7), (8) gives then $\rho_o = 0.050\,97$. For this we prove that the above mentioned points are an H-set with $P_2 \in M_1$ and $P_1, P_3 \in M_2$. In fact, we prove that the inequalities

$$\Phi(P_1) < 0,\ \Phi(P_2) > 0,\ \Phi(P_3) < 0\ ,$$

where

$$\Phi = \frac{a}{(b+s^2)(b+t^2)} - \frac{c}{(d+s^2)(d+t^2)},\quad b > 0,\ d > 0$$

have no real solution a,b,c,d in the case $2\rho^2 \geq \sigma^2$. For they imply:

$$\text{for } P_1 :\quad -\frac{a}{b^2} + \frac{c}{d^2} > 0 \tag{23}$$

$$\text{for } P_2 :\quad \frac{a}{b(b+\sigma^2)} - \frac{c}{d(d+\sigma^2)} > 0 \tag{24}$$

$$\text{for } P_3 :\quad -\frac{a}{(b+\rho^2)^2} + \frac{c}{(d+\rho^2)^2} > 0. \tag{25}$$

This gives, using an obvious notation

$$[b(23) + (b+\sigma^2)(24)] :\ \frac{c\sigma^2(b-d)}{d^2(d+\sigma^2)} > 0 \quad\text{or}\quad c(b-d) > 0 \tag{26}$$

and

$$[b(b+\sigma^2)(24) + (b+\rho^2)^2(25)] :\ \frac{c(d-b)\psi}{d(d+\sigma^2)(d+\rho^2)^2} > 0 \quad\text{or}\quad c(d-b)\psi > 0 \tag{27}$$

with $\psi = (b+d)\rho^4 + 2bd\rho^2 - bd\sigma^2 + \sigma^2\rho^4$. For $2\rho^2 \geq \sigma^2$ we have $\psi > 0$ and a contradiction in (26), (27).

References

1. ABADIE, J. (Ed.). Integer and Nonlinear Programming, Proceedings of a

Symposium, June 1969, at Ile de Bendor, France.

2. BREDENDIEK, E. 'Simultan-Approximation'. Arch. Rat. Mech. Anal. 33 (1969), pp. 307-330.

3. BROSOWSKI, E. 'Ueber Extremalsignaturen linearer Polynome in n Veränderlichen'. Num. Math., 7 (1965), pp. 396-405.

4. COLLATZ, L. 'Approximation von Funktionen bei einer und mehrer unabhängigen Veränderlichen'. Z. Angew. Math. Mech., 36 (1956), pp. 198-211.

5. COLLATZ, L. 'Inclusion theorems for the minimal distance in rational Tschebyscheff approximation with several variables', in H. L. Garabedian (Ed.), Approximation of Functions, pp. 43-56. Elsevier, 1965.

6. COLLATZ, L. Functional Analysis and Numerical Mathematics. Academic Press, 1966.

7. COLLATZ, L. 'Nichtlineare Approximation bei Randwertaufgaben', to appear in der Wissenschaftlichen Zeitschrift der Hochschule fur Architektur und Bauwesen, Weimar, 1969.

8. MOURSUND, D. G. 'Some computational aspects of the uniform approximation of a function and its derivative', SIAM J. Numer. Anal., 2 (1965), pp. 464-472.

9. TAYLOR, G. D. 'On minimal H-sets', to appear in Proc. Symposium on Numerical Problems of Approximation Theory, June 1969, Oberwolfach. Birkhäuser Verlag.

10. WETTERLING, W. 'Anwendung des Newtonschen Iterationsverfahrens bei der Tschebyscheff-Approximation, insbesondere mit nicht-linear auftretenden Parametern'. Mathematik-Technik-Wirtschaft, 10 (1963), Part I, pp. 61-63, Part II, pp. 112-115.

GENERAL PURPOSE CURVE FITTING

J. R. Rice*

(Purdue University, W. Lafayette, Indiana)

1. Introduction

The purpose of this paper is to discuss some approaches to the approximation of functions and curves which have no special mathematical structure. The distinction between functions and curves is discussed in some detail in Section 3 and meanwhile the terms are used interchangeably. Such curves arise, in general, from the physical world rather than the mathematical world. The theory of approximation of mathematically defined functions is highly developed and fairly well understood (Hart et al. [3]). This is not so for the functions considered here. These functions have three main attributes which distinguish them from mathematically defined functions:

(a) low accuracy
(b) frequent uncertainty in values
(c) frequent occurrence of "disjointed" behavior.

There are a number of different objectives in general purpose curve fitting. These include

(a) <u>mathematical representation</u> (usually with certain properties)
(b) <u>data analysis</u> (smoothing, information extraction)
(c) <u>compactification</u> (elimination of redundant information)
(d) <u>easy manipulation and evaluation</u>.

Only the fourth of these objectives is normally relevant for mathematically defined functions. It is,of course, irrational to expect that one approach or algorithm will excel in all of the objectives of general purpose curve

* This work was supported in part by a grant from the National Science Foundation, GP-07163.

fitting. The most delicate of these objectives is that of data analysis. A more detailed discussion of this question is given in Rice [6]. Note that these objectives do not, in general, impose any direct requirement on the nature of the approximating functions to be used and this opens the door for considering many approaches not usually met in approximation.

The organization of this paper is as follows. The next section presents several points concerning algorithms, both general and specific to this context. The third section gives a discussion of the relationship between the approximation of functions and of curves. Some possible ad hoc approaches are presented along with remarks on the need for more analysis. The fourth section contains some remarks on the imposition of constraints an a new approach is presented.

The final two sections concern two algorithms for curve fitting. One (de Boor and Rice [1], [2]) is oriented toward data analysis and not analyzed in detail. The second is oriented toward mathematical representation and is presented in some detail.

2. Algorithm properties and constituents

The ultimate objective in curve fitting is to construct an algorithm for obtaining approximations. Such algorithms and approximations produced would ideally have the following properties:

Algorithm	Approximation
A. High Speed	A. Efficient, Rapid Evaluation
B. High Flexibility and Reliability	B. Compactness
C. Smoothing Power	C. Smoothness
D. Easy Constraint Imposition	

It is clear that one is not able to attain all of these objectives simultaneously. Thus there is a need for a variety of algorithms, each of which excels in several of these areas and which is tailored for some area of application.

There is considerable lack of precision in our normal use of the word algorithm and the usual "algorithms" discussed in the literature are not algorithms at all. Rather than dwell on this here, the interested reader is referred to Rogers [8]. The closest approximation to an algorithm in normal circumstances is a computer program written in some "standard" language like Algol or Fortran. Even though it is not practical to discuss algorithms specifically, we can consider the major constituents of such algorithms. These constituents are subdivided into three basic groups:

A. Approximation Form: polynomials, rational functions, exponential sums, piecewise polynomials (includes splines and tables with interpolation), constrained subsets of these, etc.

B. Norm - Error Measure: least squares, Tchebycheff, one-sided, L_1, interpolation, etc.

C. General "Method": orthogonalization, steepest descent, Remes algorithm, simplex algorithm, etc.

These are the constituents upon which algorithm construction is based, but one must keep in mind that extremely different algorithms can be constructed from the same constituents. One is tempted to make a comparison with cooking in this respect.

It is perhaps constructive to examine two algorithms (loosely speaking) in the present context. First consider least squares polynomial approximation using an orthogonalization scheme. A good algorithm with these constituents would have the following properties:

Speed: fast
Flexibility: poor
Smoothing power: fair - good
Constraint imposition: relatively easy
Evaluation: moderately fast
Compactness: fair - excellent
Smoothness: fair- excellent

The poor flexibility of polynomials induces the wide range in the properties of the approximation obtained. Thus when low degree polynomials are adequate, then one has a very smooth, compact (and easy to evaluate) approximation. However, in many cases a very high degree polynomial is required and the quality of the approximation deteriorates drastically. Indeed, the value of the algorithm deteriorates in all respects in this situation.

The second set of constituents we consider is piecewise polynomials using interpolation in tables. A good algorithm with these constituents would have the following properties:

Speed: excellent (no time at all required)
Flexibility: great (can be used for any set of data)
Smoothing Power: terrible
Constraint Imposition: impractical (?)
Evaluation: moderately fast
Compactness: poor
Smoothness: poor

The main attraction of this algorithm is that it is very simple and has great flexibility. Certain variants of this approach also lead to extremely fast evaluation. Of course, the price for this is paid in the areas of compactness, smoothing power and smoothness.

3. On curves and functions

There are a number of applications where one needs to have approximations which are good in the geometric sense rather than as functions. This is, of course, most apparent in the case of closed curves as shown in Figure 1, but it also occurs when the curve is the graph of an ordinary function. The most obvious approach in the case of closed curves is to parameterize the curve with two functions and then approximate each of them independently. This is often very effective but experience shows that there is a significant number of curves where this gives an unsatisfactory result. This is because the geometric distance is not closely enough related to the parameterization distance.

The definition, use and evaluation of the distance between two curves leads to a large number of difficulties both on the theoretical level and in practical applications. Consider the curves Γ_1 and Γ_2 in Figure 1A. One might measure the distance between them by

$$d = \max_{y\in\Gamma_1} \left(\min_{x\in\Gamma_2} \|x - y\|\right)$$

where $\|.\|$ is the particular norm used in the plane. If one parameterizes Γ_1 by arc length, one can alternatively use

$$\int_{\Gamma_1} \min_{x\in\Gamma_2} \|x - y\|^2$$

as a kind of least squares distance. These distances are not symmetric as one can see in Figure 1B. The Fréchet distance between Γ_1 and Γ_2 is the maximum of the distance from Γ_2 to Γ_1 and from Γ_1 to Γ_2 and is symmetric (but not a norm - the curves do not form a Banach space). Recent

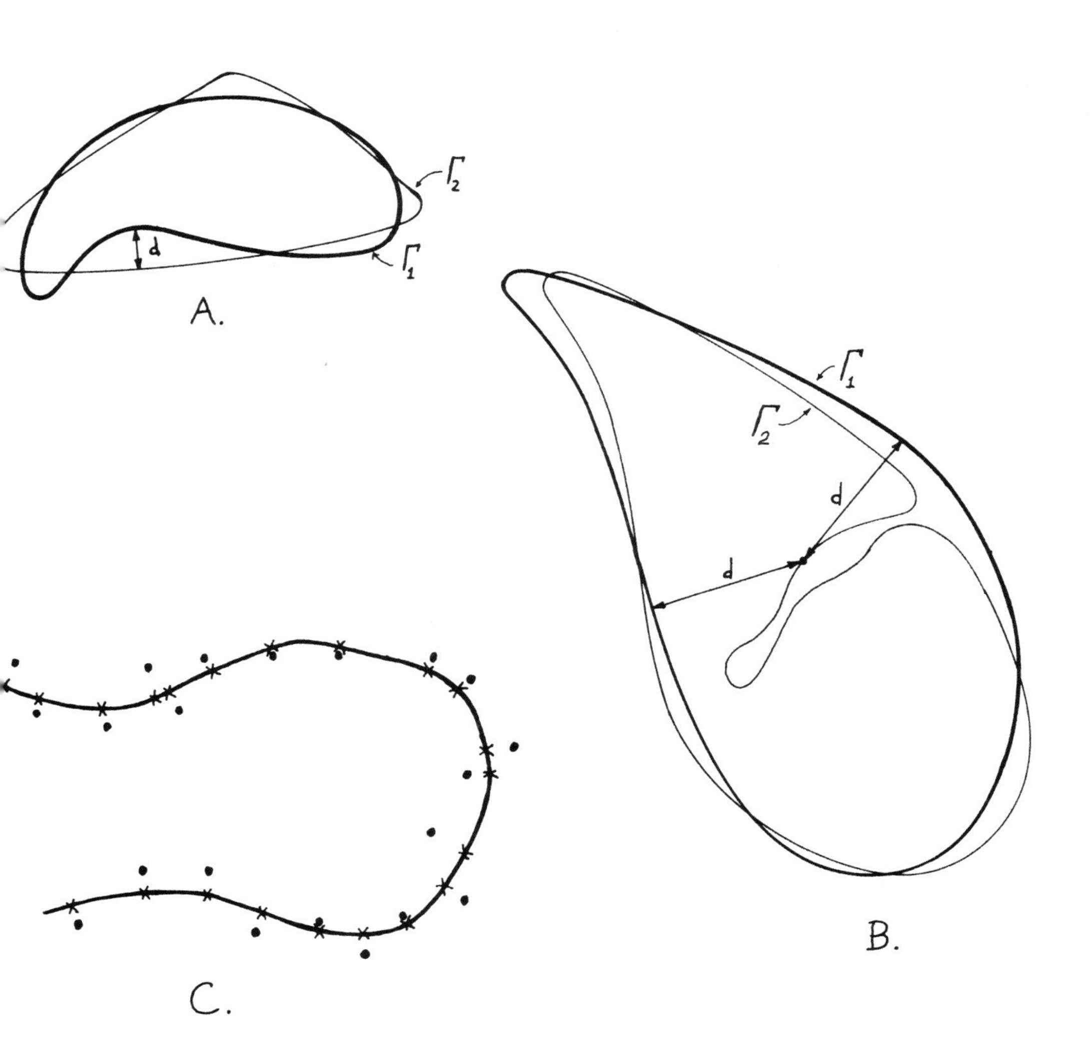

Fig. 1

theoretical results involving this distance are presented in the interesting paper, Sendov [9], in these Proceedings. The further development of this and related questions is an important area for research. Note that there is an alternation theorem involving approximation by conic sections in Motzkin [4].

The practical difficulties are perhaps even more severe than the theoretical ones. Note that the computational effort required to evaluate

$$\max_{x \in \Gamma_2} ||x - y||$$

is already much more than that required to evaluate the norm of the error in ordinary function approximation. One must evaluate this for every y in Γ_1 and this is a very substantial increase in a basic computation of an algorithm. Several strategies come to mind to make these computations more efficient, but the example in Figure 1B shows that they are not always correct. Unfortunately, the closest point projection can be discontinuous in much simpler situations than shown in Figure 1B.

Further difficulties occur in the approximation of a finite set of data as shown in Figure 1C. The approximation to be computed is normally a curve and thus one has to associate points on this curve with data points. Alternatively, one can make the data set into a curve by something like linear interpolation. This is very satisfactory if the data are on a nice smooth curve. If they are not, then this approach is not so helpful.

There are three ad hoc schemes which have been used with some success in computation. The first of these is to use parameterizations and approximate them independently. As noted above, this sometimes gives unsatisfactory results. Furthermore, most curves do not have natural parameterizations and thus the choice of parameterization is nebulous and a source of ambiguity in an algorithm. One can remove this problem by using arc length, but this means that one has to make a non-trivial computation to obtain the parameterization.

The second scheme is a refinement of the first. One takes the approximations of the parameterizations and estimates the normal derivatives of the approximate curve. These normal derivatives are then used in weight functions for a second approximation. This somewhat more than doubles the computational effort, but users of this scheme report very satisfactory results. This is clearly the first step of an iterative process and perhaps one could establish its convergence under

Thus one has to backtrack along the curve to find a suitable point which is to be the (k+1)-th knot. The 1-pass algorithm includes a sub-algorithm (the joining algorithm) to determine this point. Experiments indicate that (with the low values of n and Q likely to be used in practice) the best place is at the first local extremum of the error curve preceeding the right end point. Unfortunately, there are many non-standard situations possible, especially for discrete functions, and a useful joining algorithm is fairly complex. Once the joining algorithm determines ξ_k, the situation is set to compute $P_{k+1}(x)$ and ξ_{k+1} in a similar manner and thus construct the desired approximation A(x).

The complete algorithm contains a number of special procedures to be used in "failure" situations. These can occur because of unreasonable requests (one sets ε smaller than the random noise level in f(x))or because of inadequacies in the algorithm. Experiments indicate that the algorithm is noticeably less successful when n - Q = 1 than for $n - Q \geq 2$. One would, of course, expect perhaps twice as many knots for n - Q = 1 as for n - Q = 2 and this expectation is about what happens. The difficulty for n - Q = 1 manifests itself in the joining algorithm where there is rarely a local extremum in the error curve except at the end points.

As an example of the possible gain in speed, this algorithm was compared with that of the preceding section for a particularly complex curve [5, page 164]. The nonlinear least squares cubic spline algorithm requires about 16-18 minutes on an IBM 7094 to obtain an approximation (with 16 knots) which cannot be distinguished from the original by the eye. A preliminary version of the 1-pass algorithm with n=3 and Q=1 obtained an equally accurate approximation (with 35 knots) in 4-6 seconds. Note that the first approximation has only 36 independent parameters while the second has 109. However, the more efficient forms for the evaluation of splines involve a redundant parameterization and thus some of the advantages in compactness are lost for splines when efficiency in evaluation is important. If the value and slope at the knots are used as the representation of these approximations, the first requires 52 numbers while the second requires 109.

Running orthogonalization is described in more generality and detail in Rice [7] than necessary here. We present a brief resume of the pertinent points in the specific case of polynomial approximation on a discrete set. In the 1-pass algorithm the situation is as follows: We have data (f_i, x_i), i=1,2,...,k and polynomials

```
C     ****THE HEART OF THE ONE-PASS ALGORITHM****
C     THE FUNCTION DOT(I,J,NOW,NEXT) RETURNS THE DOT PRODUCT OF
C     THE I-TH AND J-TH BASIS FUNCTIONS OVER THE INTERVAL NOW
C     TO NEXT. I,J = 20 CORRESPOND TO THE DATA FUNCTION.
C     IF NEXT .LT. NOW THIS CODE IS CORRECT IF DOT CHANGES SIGN
C     NBASIS = NUMBER OF BASIS FUNCTIONS
C     ORTHO RELATES THE ORTHOGONAL POLYNOMIALS TO ORIGINAL BASIS
C     AOLD, ANEW ARE COEFFICIENTS OF THE APPROXIMATION
C     ERX IS THE SQUARE OF THE LEAST SQUARES ERROR
      PROD(1,1) = DOT(1,1,NOW,NEXT)
      SIZE = SQRT(1.+PROD(1,1))
      ANEW(1) = (AOLD(1) + DOT(1,20,NOW,NEXT))/SIZE
      ORTHO(1,1) = ORTHO(1,1)/SIZE
      IF( NBASIS .EQ.1 )                 GO TO 40
C                               MAIN LOOP
      DO 30 K = 2,NBASIS
      K1 = K - 1
      ANEW(K) = AOLD(K) + DOT(K,20,NOW,NEXT)
C         COMPUTE INNER PRODUCTS AND FIND NEW BASIS
      DO 5 J = 1,K
    5 PROD(J,K) =  DOT(J,K,NOW,NEXT)
      DO 8 J=1,K1
      DO 8 L = 1,J
    8 ORTHO(K,L) = ORTHO(K,L) - PROD(J,K)*ORTHO(J,L)
      SIZE = 1. +PROD(K,K)
C                    FIND NEW COEFFICIENTS AND NORMALIZE
      DO 10 L = 1,K1
      ANEW(K) = ANEW(K) - PROD(L,K)*ANEW(L)
   10 SIZE = SIZE - PROD(L,K)**2
      SIZE = SQRT(SIZE)
      DO 20 L=1,K
   20 ORTHO(K,L) = ORTHO(K,L)/SIZE
      ANEW(K) = ANEW(K)/SIZE
   30 CONTINUE
C                    FIND ERROR, RESTORE COEFFICIENTS
   40 SUMSQR = 0.
      DO 45 K = 1,NBASIS
      SUMSQR = SUMSQR + ANEW(K)**2
   45 AOLD(K) = ANEW(K)
      SIZEF = SIZEF + DOT(20,20,NOW,NEXT)
      ERX = ABS(SIZEF - SUMSQR)
```

The heart of the 1-pass algorithm

$$\phi_j(x) = \sum_{m=0}^{j} \sigma_{jm} x^m \quad j=0,1,\ldots,n$$

orthogonal on $\{x_i\}$ with the dot product defined by the trapezoidal rule. Furthermore, we have the coefficients a_j of the least squares approximation to the data and the L_2-error d. The problem is to obtain efficiently the corresponding quantities for the data (f_i,x_i), i=1,2,...,k+1. These quantities are found by the algorithm below in Fortran labeled "the heart of the one-pass algorithm".

The data does not appear explicitly in this code as it is used in the subroutine DOT. The main ingredient of this code is the array

$$\text{PROD(I,J)} = \int_{x_k}^{x_{k+1}} \phi_I(x)\phi_J(x)dx = \text{DOT(I,J,K,K+1)}$$

and note that $\phi_{20}(x) = f(x)$ by convention. The arrays ORTHO(I,J) and AOLD(I) contain the coefficients of the orthogonal polynomials $\phi_i(x)$ and of the best approximation in terms of the $\phi_i(x)$, respectively.

Note that the algorithm only computes dot products on the interval $[x_k,x_{k+1}]$. This is the key to the efficiency of this algorithm and implies that the computation effort of the 1-pass algorithm is proportional to the number of data points (all other effects being constant). In [7] a more detailed analysis of the computational effort is made for three possible cases:

<u>Case 1</u>: Ordinary orthogonalization used for each interval $[X_1,X_k]$, K=n+1,...,M

<u>Case 2</u>: Running orthogonalization used for the same intervals

<u>Case 3</u>: Ordinary orthogonalization used for $[X_1,X_M]$ only.

These three cases have been compared on the basis of the number of "units" of arithmetic required for various values of n and M. While this gives only a rough indication of the actual computation time required, it is indicative of the general situation. The hypothetical unit used is one addition and other arithmetic operations have been expressed somewhat arbitrarily in these units.

	n=2			n=4		
	M=5	M=15	M=25	M=5	M=15	M=25
Case 1	328	2168	5608	2408	12968	31528
Case 2	134	334	534	806	1736	2666
Case 3	98	258	418	613	1413	2213

Table of the number of units of arithmetic required for orthogonalization using the three cases.

This comparison indicates that the effort needed to compute all the intermediate approximations is moderate compared to the effort to compute the final one. Of course, in the 1-pass algorithm one does not know beforehand which value of M is to be used.

References

1. de BOOR, C. W. and RICE, J. R. 'Least squares cubic spline approximation, I: Fixed knots'. Num. Math.

2. de BOOR, C. W. and RICE, J. R. 'Least squares cubic spline approximation, II: Variable knots'. Num. Math.

3. HART, J. F. et al. Computer Approximations. John Wiley, 1968.

4. MOTZKIN, T. S. 'Approximation by curves of a unisolvent family'. Bull. Amer. Math. Soc., 55 (1949), pp. 789-793.

5. RICE, J. R. The Approximation of Functions, Vol. II: Nonlinear and Multivariate Theory. Addison Wesley, 1969.

6. RICE, J. R. 'Approximation formulas for physical data', Pyrodynamics, 6 (1968), pp. 231-256.

7. RICE, J. R. 'Running orthogonalization'. To appear.

8. ROGERS, H. Theory of Recursive Functions and Effective Computability. McGraw Hill, 1967.

9. SENDOV, B. 'Approximation relative to Hausdorff distance'. These Proceedings, pp. 101-108.

ON COMPUTING BEST L_1 APPROXIMATIONS

I. Barrodale

(University of Victoria, Canada)

"Least-first-power" approximation has not received as much attention in the literature as approximation in the sense of least-squares or Chebyshev. Here we present a brief summary of linear and nonlinear L_1 approximation on both intervals and discrete point sets, with emphasis on the actual computation of best approximations. The notation used is that adopted by Rice [8], in which book much of the linear theory can be found.

PART I

Approximation of a continuous function defined on an interval

For a given finite real interval $X = [a,b]$ and a given function $f(x) \in C[a,b]$, we choose an approximating function $F(A,x) \in C[a,b]$, where $A = \{a_1, a_2, \ldots, a_n\}$ is a set of real parameters, and try to determine $F(A^*,x)$ such that for all $A \in E_n$,

$$\int_a^b |f(x) - F(A^*,x)|dx \leq \int_a^b |f(x) - F(A,x)|dx.$$

A. Linear approximation

Now $F(A,x) = L(A,x) = \sum_{j=1}^{n} a_j\phi_j(x)$ where the n given $\phi_j(x)$'s are linearly independent. It is convenient both here and in what follows to summarize the known results by answering four questions. Specifically, these are the questions of existence, uniqueness, characterization and determination of best approximations.

(i) Existence of best approximations. This is guaranteed by a standard compactness argument (see Rice [8, p. 27]).

(ii) Uniqueness. The L_1 norm is not strict so uniqueness cannot be guaranteed in general.

Example: $X = [-1,1]$; $f(x) = 1$; $L(A,x) = a_1 x$.

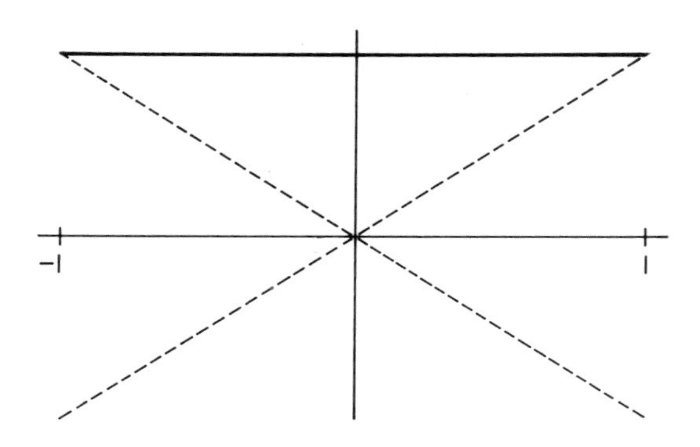

Here, any $L(A^*,x) = a_1^* x$ for which $|a_1^*| \leq 1$ is a best approximation.

However if $\{\phi_1,\phi_2,\ldots,\phi_n\}$ forms a Chebyshev set on X then best approximations are unique. (This result is due to Jackson and is proved in Achieser [1, p. 67]. Recall that $\{\phi_1,\phi_2,\ldots,\phi_n\}$ is a Chebyshev set on X iff the n-th order determinant $|\phi_j(x_i)| \neq 0$ for any choice of n distinct points x_i from X.)

(iii) Characterization. The following result, which is actually a corollary of the general characterization theorem, appears in various forms in Achieser [1, p. 84], Cheney [4, p. 220], Kripke and Rivlin [5, p. 104], Lorentz [6, p. 112], Rice [8, p. 105] and Timan [14, p. 58].

Theorem 1A

If $\int_a^b \phi_j(x)\,\mathrm{sgn}\,[f(x) - L(A^*,x)]dx = 0$ for $j = 1,2,\ldots,n$ then

$L(A^*,x) = \sum_{j=1}^{n} a^*_j \phi_j(x)$ is a best approximation to $f(x)$ on X.

(iv) Determination. In (a,b) suppose that n points $x_1,\ldots,x_n$, $a = x_0 < x_1 < x_2 < \ldots < x_n < x_{n+1} = b$, can be found for which the sign function

$$s(x) = \begin{cases} +1 & x_i < x < x_{i+1} \quad i \text{ even} \\ -1 & x_i < x < x_{i+1} \quad i \text{ odd} \end{cases}$$

satisfies $\int_a^b \phi_j(x)\, s(x)dx = 0$ for $j = 1,2,\ldots,n$. Then any $L(A^*,x)$ defined by putting $s(x) = \mathrm{sgn}[f(x) - L(A^*,x)]$ is a best approximation. Now $L(A^*,x)$ can be obtained by solving the interpolation problem $f(x_i) = L(A,x_i)$ for $i = 1,2,\ldots,n$, provided that the resulting curve $f(x) - L(A^*,x)$

changes sign on (a,b) only at these n points x_i.

This interpolation problem has been investigated by Rice and Hobby [11] who prove that for any choice of $\{\phi_1, \phi_2, \ldots, \phi_n\}$ there exists a sign function $s(x)$ with at most n sign changes that satisfies $\int_a^b \phi_j(x)s(x)dx = 0$ for $j = 1,2,\ldots,n$. (This result also has application to nonlinear L_1 approximation). It follows almost from the definition that if $\{\phi_j\}$ is a Chebyshev set and $\int_a^b \phi_j(x)s(x)dx = 0$ for $j = 1,2,\ldots,n$, then $s(x)$ must have at least n sign changes in (a,b). Kripke and Rivlin [5, p. 120] show that if both $\{\phi_1, \phi_2, \ldots, \phi_n\}$ and $\{\phi_1, \phi_2, \ldots, \phi_n, f\}$ form a Chebyshev set and if $L(A^*,x)$ is the (unique) best approximation to $f(x)$, then $f(x) - L(A^*,x)$ changes sign in (a,b) at exactly n distinct points x_i which are independent of $f(x)$.

In the case of polynomial approximation these n nodes can be determined by computing the best approximation to x^n. The monic polynomial of degree n which best approximates the zero function on $[-1,1]$ is $2^{-n}U_n(x)$, where $U_n(x)$ is the Chebyshev polynomial of degree n of the second kind, and therefore $x_i = \cos[i\pi/(n+1)]$ for $i = 1,2,\ldots,n$. Thus for any function $f(x)$ where $\{1,x,\ldots,x^{n-1},f(x)\}$ is a Chebyshev set, the best L_1 polynomial approximation to $f(x)$ of degree less than n is the polynomial of interpolation for these n nodes x_i. The remarkable situation occurs where a best approximation to a function $f(x)$ may be computed by interpolation at points x_i which are independent of $f(x)$ itself.

Example:

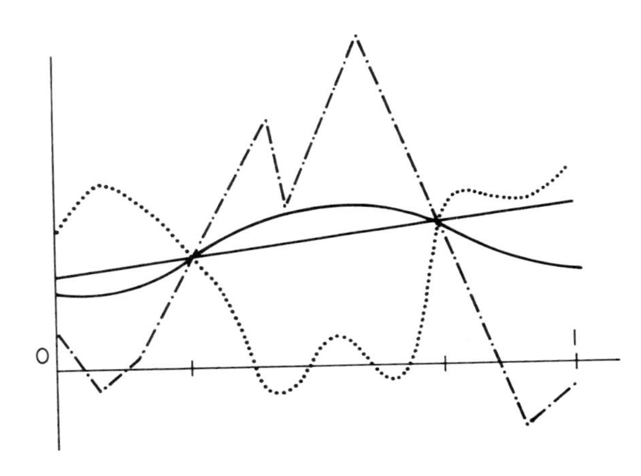

The diagram illustrates three continuous functions on [0,1] which have the same best straight line approximation; the error curves change sign only at the zeros of $U_2^*(x)$.

Generally however we are more interested in polynomial approximation to an arbitrary continuous function $g(x)$ where $\{1,x,\dots,x^{n-1},g(x)\}$ is not a Chebyshev set. We revert to the technique outlined above and determine $L(A_0,x)$ by interpolation to $g(x)$ at the zeros of the suitably translated $U_n(x)$. Provided that $g(x) - L(A_0,x)$ changes sign on X at just these n nodes then $L(A_0,x)$ is a best approximation. If this error curve does not have this desired property, then $L(A_0,x)$ can be used as a starting value in an iterative scheme due to Usow [15] which converges to a best approximation.

Geometrically this scheme is the following. Consider the set $K = \{(A,d): \int_a^b |f(x) - L(A,x)|dx < d\}$. K is a convex set in E_{n+1} and the best approximation $L(A^*,x)$ corresponds to a point (A^*,d^*) which is in fact the lowest point on K. If $L(A_0,x)$ is not the best approximation Usow shows how to make a systematic descent on K to find $L(A^*,x)$, provided that $L(A,x)$ is derived from a Chebyshev set.

Finally we note that the nodes x_i are also known for some other approximating functions besides polynomials.

B. Nonlinear approximation

(i) Existence of best approximations. For particular cases this question can sometimes be decided by imposing restrictions on $F(A,x)$. See Rice [9, p. 66].

(ii) Uniqueness. The question of uniqueness is completely open.

(iii) Characterization. Provided that the set of points of interpolation of $F(A^*,x)$ to $f(x)$ has measure zero then in most cases (i.e. when the mild assumptions regarding $f(x)$ and $F(A,x)$ specified in Rice [9] are valid) the following result is available:

Theorem 1B

$F(A^*,x)$ is a best approximation to $f(x)$ iff

$$\int_a^b \frac{\partial F(A^*,x)}{\partial a_j} \operatorname{sgn}[f(x) - F(A^*,x)]dx = 0, \quad j = 1,2,\dots,n$$

(iv) Determination. For each set $\{\partial F(A,x)/\partial a_j\}$ there exists a sign function $s(x)$ with n or less sign changes and its nodes x_i can usually be determined numerically by solving a set of simultaneous nonlinear equations.

In practice the best approximation can sometimes be determined iteratively whereby the k-th approximation $F(A_k,x)$ is obtained by interpolating $f(x)$ at the nodes $\{x_i\}_{k-1}$ that correspond to $F(A_{k-1}, x)$. The procedure is started by guessing $F(A_1,x)$ and terminates when $\{x_i\}_{k-1} = \{x_i\}_k$, for then $F(A_k,x)$ interpolates $f(x)$ at the nodes associated with A_k. Finally if $f(x) - F(A_k,x)$ has no other sign changes and is not zero on a set of positive measure, we have a best approximation. (For numerical evidence of this algorithm see Rice [10]).

In an analogous fashion to the linear case, Usow [15] shows how to use an unsuccessful $F(A_k,x)$ as a starting approximation for a descent on K. However no proof of convergence is supplied for this nonlinear case.

PART II

Approximation of a function defined on a discrete point set

For a given point set $X = \{x_1,x_2,\ldots,x_N\}$ and a given function $f(x) = \{(x_i, f(x_i)): i = 1,2,\ldots,N\}$, we choose an approximating function $F(A,x)$ which is usually defined continuously on some interval $I \supset X$, and try to determine $F(A^*,x)$ such that for all $A \in E_n$,

$$\sum_{i=1}^{N} |f(x_i) - F(A^*,x_i)| \leq \sum_{i=1}^{N} |f(x_i) - F(A,x_i)|$$

A. Linear approximation

Now $F(A,x) = L(A,x) = \sum_{j=1}^{n} a_j\phi_j(x)$ and we write $f(x_i) = f_i$ and $\phi_j(x_i) = \phi_{j,i}$.

(i) Existence of best approximations. Existence is again a consequence of the fundamental theorem for normed linear spaces. It can also be established in this finite dimensional case by the existence theorem of linear programming.

(ii) Uniqueness. Uniqueness cannot be guaranteed even for best polynomial approximations.

Example: $f(x) = \{(0,1),(1,-1),(2,-1),(3,1)\}$; $L(A,x) = a_1 + a_2x$

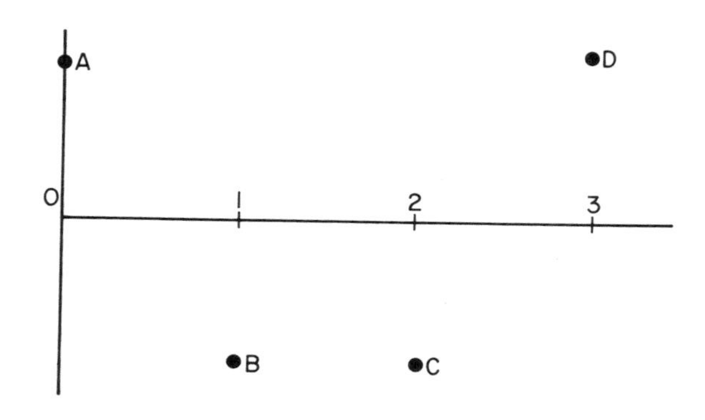

Here, any straight line that passes through both of the sloping sides AB and CD is a best approximation.

(iii) Characterization. The following theorem appears in Rice [8, p. 114].

Theorem 2A

$L(A^*,x) = \sum_{j=1}^{n} a_j^* \phi_j(x)$ is a best approximation to $f(x)$ iff

$$\left|\sum_{x\in X} L(A,x)\,\mathrm{sgn}[f(x) - L(A^*,x)]\right| \leq \sum_{x\in Z} |L(A,x)|, \quad \forall A \in E_n,$$

where $Z = \{x \in X:\ f(x) = L(A^*,x)\}$.

However best approximations are computed without reference to this theorem.

(iv) Determination. Best approximations can be obtained by linear programming as follows (see Barrodale and Young [2]).

Put $\sum_{j=1}^{n} a_j\phi_{j,i} - f_i = u_i - v_i$ where $u_i \geq 0$, $v_i \geq 0$ for $i = 1,2,\ldots,N$, and define $\phi_{n+1}(x) = -\sum_{j=1}^{n} \phi_j(x)$, $\alpha_{n+1} = \max(0, -\min a_j)$, and $\alpha_j = a_j + \alpha_{n+1}$ for $j = 1,2,\ldots,n$. Then

$$f_i = \alpha_1\phi_{1,i} + \ldots + \alpha_n\phi_{n,i} + \alpha_{n+1}\phi_{n+1,i} - u_i + v_i \quad \ldots \text{(A)}.$$

Now the problem is to minimize $\sum_{i=1}^{N} |u_i - v_i|$ and this can be accomplished by solving the linear program:

$$\text{minimize } \sum_{i=1}^{N} (u_i + v_i) \text{ subject to the N constraints (A).}$$

This l.p. can be represented in a simplex tableau with N equality constraints and effectively n+1 variables. Fortran and Algol programs are available for this algorithm; its efficiency decreases as N increases.

For large values of N the dual problem should be solved instead. The dual is a bounded variable l.p. (see Rabinowitz [7, p. 127]) and this problem in turn may be expressed as an interval l.p. (see Robers [12] and Robers and Ben Israel [13]). An empirical comparison between these three algorithms is presently being undertaken by the author.

Usow [16] describes an alternative approach to this linear discrete problem. Defining $K = \{(A,d): \sum_{x\in X} |f(x) - L(A,x)| \leq d\}$, then K is a convex polytope and (A^*,d^*) is at a lowest vertex of K. To find this lowest vertex a descent path is defined on K from vertex to vertex. However, convergence to a best approximation does not always occur with this method.

B. Nonlinear approximation

The literature contains virtually no references to the problems of existence, uniqueness, characterization, or determination of nonlinear discrete best approximations in this norm. In practice we can, for example, examine existence for functions F(A,x) which have just one parameter appearing nonlinearly: since nonuniqueness is possible for polynomial approximation it must clearly be allowed for with any nonlinear approximating function. Experience with the following algorithms suggests that even though no characterization theorems are available it is not difficult to obtain good approximations, and even best approximations when they exist, with several nonlinear functions F(A,x).

Algorithm 1. This is an adaptation of an iterative minimax algorithm due to Loeb for generalized rational approximation.

Suppose $F(A,x) = R(x) = \dfrac{P(x)}{Q(x)} = \dfrac{a_1\phi_1(x) + \ldots + a_n\phi_n(x)}{\psi_1(x) + b_2\psi_2(x) + \ldots + b_m\psi_m(x)}$.

Now $\sum_{i=1}^{N} |f(x_i) - R(x_i)| = \sum_{i=1}^{N} \dfrac{1}{|Q_i|} |f_iQ_i - P_i|$ and an approximation $F(A_t,x)$ is computed by determining $\min_{a_j^{(t)},b_k^{(t)}} \sum_{i=1}^{N} \dfrac{1}{|Q_i^{(t-1)}|} |f_iQ_i^{(t)} - P_i^{(t)}|$ where $1/|Q_i^{(t-1)}|$ is regarded as a known weight function and (say) $Q_i^{(0)} = \psi_1(x_i)$. This method can be extended to cover approximation by

$[R(x)]^p$ for any fixed p.

In many cases the method works well in practice; usually convergence takes place in just a few iterations to what appears to be a best approximation. Sometimes the scheme does not begin to converge within twenty or thirty iterations, and this behavior is independent of the starting value $Q^{(0)}(x)$. Furthermore, the following example demonstrates that even when convergence does occur it may not be to a best approximation.

Example:

$$f(x) = \{(0,1), (0.2,1), (0.4,1), (0.5,0), (0.6,-1), (0.8,-1), (1,-1)\}$$

$$F(A,x) = (a_0 + a_1x + a_2x^2)/(1 + b_1x + b_2x^2)$$

1

0

-1

Now both of the functions $\dfrac{1 - 2x}{1 - 10x/3 + 10x^2/3}$ and $\dfrac{5/7 - 10x/7}{1 - 25x/7 + 25x^2/7}$ are symmetric and interpolate five of the seven data points with an error of approximation of 4/7; these are both best approximations and there are no others. However, the above algorithm converges to the function $\dfrac{1 - 29x/12 + 10x^2/12}{1 - 41x/12 + 40x^2/12}$ from several different initial choices for $Q^{(0)}(x)$, including the denominators of both best approximations. This function still interpolates five of the data points but it is unsymmetric and has a larger error of approximation equal to 58/99. (Private communication with Loeb has established that the above phenomenon is not restricted to this norm; an example of convergence to a good approximation which is not best has also been provided for the minimax case.)

Algorithm 2. The idea here is to recast the approximation problem as a separable programming problem of the type:

$$\min \sum_{j=1}^{n} f_j(x_j)$$

subject to

$$x_j \geq 0$$

and

$$\sum_{j=1}^{n} g_{ij}(x_j) = b_i \qquad i = 1,2,\ldots,m.$$

The basic technique used is to replace the functions $g_{ij}(x_j)$ and $f_j(x_j)$ by polygonal approximations and solve the resulting approximation to the problem by the simplex method.

Every linear and some nonlinear L_p approximation problem, including $0 < p < 1$, can be restated in separable form, but here we are only concerned with the nonlinear case for $p=1$. A simple illustrative example is the following.

Suppose $F(A,x) = a + e^{cx}$, and assume $a \geq 0$ and $c \geq 0$. Put $f(x_i) - (a + e^{cx_i}) = u_i - v_i$ where $u_i \geq 0$ and $v_i \geq 0$. Then the task is to minimize $\sum_{i=1}^{N} (u_i + v_i)$ subject to $f(x_i) = a + e^{cx_i} + u_i - v_i$ for $i = 1,2,\ldots,N$.

This technique is capable of yielding almost best approximations for a variety of functions $F(A,x)$.

Algorithm 3. This algorithm has been used successfully with functions $F(A,x)$ which are nonlinear in just one variable, e.g. $a_1 + a_2e^{cx}$, $P_n(x)/(1 + cx)$, $e^{cx}(P_n(x))$, $a_1 + a_2 \sin cx$, $a_1 + a_2x^c$, $P_n(x) + b(x - c)_+^n$. In general suppose that $F(A,x)$ depends linearly upon parameters $a_1,a_2,\ldots,a_{n-1}$ and nonlinearly upon c, where $A = \{a_1,\ldots,a_{n-1},c\}$. Let $A^* = \{a_1^*,\ldots,a_{n-1}^*,c^*\}$ be a set of best parameters. The success of the algorithm depends upon the validity of the following assumption.

Assumption: $G(c) = \min\limits_{a_j(c)} \sum_{i=1}^{N} |f(x_i) - F(A,x_i)|$ is unimodal in c, at least for some sizable interval containing c^*. (Recall that a function is unimodal in a region if it has just one local minimum which is also a global minimum for the region.)

Two comments are in order here. Firstly, by a "sizable interval" we mean one that contains the upper and lower bounds on c^* that we supply to the algorithm initially. Secondly, if the assumption is valid for some given interval one can locate c* to within prescribed accuracy (and hence a best approximation) in a minimal number of calls of the linear algorithm, by using a Fibonacci search technique. See Wilde [17].

By tabulating G(c) for a fine mesh of c values over quite large intervals, this assumption has been tested empirically for several functions f(x) and F(A,x). It has been found to be valid in most cases for intervals of reasonably large width.

Applications

Least-first-power approximation seems to be most useful in approximating empirical data where the observations contain wild points. See Barrodale [3].

Acknowledgements

The author has collaborated with Dr. J. C. Mason of Toronto and Dr. F. D. K. Roberts of Victoria in studying algorithms for nonlinear discrete approximations. Documented evidence of the behavior of these and other algorithms will be available shortly. The financial assistance provided by NRC grant No. A5251 is gratefully acknowledged.

References

1. ACHIESER, N. I. Theory of Approximation. Ungar, 1956.

2. BARRODALE, I. and YOUNG, A. 'Algorithms for best L_1 and L_∞ linear approximations on a discrete set'. Numer. Math., 8 (1966), pp. 295-306.

3. BARRODALE, I. 'L_1 approximation and the analysis of data'. Applied Stat., 17 (1968), pp. 51-57.

4. CHENEY, E. W. Introduction to Approximation Theory. McGraw-Hill, 1966.

5. KRIPKE, B. R. and RIVLIN, T. J. 'Approximation in the metric of $L^1(x,\mu)$'. Trans. Amer. Math. Soc., 119 (1965), pp. 101-122.

6. LORENTZ, G. G. Approximation of Functions. Holt, Rinehart and Winston, 1966.

7. RABINOWITZ, P. 'Applications of linear programming to numerical analysis'. SIAM Review 10 (1968), pp. 121-159.

8. RICE, J. R. The Approximation of Functions, Vol. 1. Addison-Wesley, 1964.

9. RICE, J. R. 'On nonlinear L_1 approximation'. Arch. Rat. Mech. Anal., 17 (1964), pp. 61-66.

10. RICE, J. R. 'On computation of L_1 approximations by exponentials, rationals, and other functions'. Math. Comp., 18 (1964), pp. 390-396.

11. RICE, J. R. and HOBBY, C. R. 'A moment problem in L_1 approximation'. Proc. Amer. Math. Soc., 16 (1965), pp. 665-670.

12. ROBERS, P. D. Interval Linear Programming. Doctoral Thesis, Northwestern University, 1968.

13. ROBERS, P. D. and BEN-ISRAEL, A. 'An interval programming algorithm for discrete linear L_1 approximation problems'. Systems Research Memorandum No. 223, Northwestern University, 1968.

14. TIMAN, A. F. Theory of Approximation of Functions of a Real Variable. Pergamon Press, 1963. (Transl. from Russian)

15. USOW, K. H. 'On L_1 approximation, I: Computation for continuous functions and continuous dependence'. SIAM J. Numer. Anal., 4 (1967), pp. 70-88.

16. USOW, K. H. 'On L_1 approximation, II: Computation for discrete functions and discretization effects'. SIAM J. Numer. Anal., 4 (1967), pp. 233-244.

17. WILDE, D. J. Optimum Seeking Methods. Prentice-Hall, 1964.

MATHEMATICAL PROGRAMMING AND APPROXIMATION

P. Rabinowitz

(Weizmann Institute of Science, Israel)

1. Introduction

In a previous paper on the applications of linear programming to numerical analysis, Rabinowitz [27], the author discussed in detail the connection between linear programming and approximation. The main applications were to discrete linear real L_1 and L_∞ approximation, unconstrained or with linear constraints and with the possibility of introducing weights. Further topics mentioned there included fitting by cubic splines and discrete L_∞ approximation by rational functions. In the present work, we shall pursue this matter further by pointing out some connections between nonlinear programming and approximation. The best results attained in this field so far are in the application of quadratic programming to discrete linear real L_2 approximation with linear constraints. Other results are in the application of convex programming to continuous linear and rational real L_∞ approximation, to discrete real L_p approximation and to discrete linear complex L_∞ approximation and in the application of geometric programming to L_p-constrained discrete linear real L_p approximation. Finally, we indicate how to formulate a general discrete real nonlinear approximation problem as a nonlinear programming problem which is not convex in general, and speculate as to the best way to solve such problems.

2. Linear Programming

There are many formulations of the linear programming problem and many algorithms to solve such problems. A vast literature has arisen around this subject and much effort has been expended in developing efficient and versatile computer packages. A brief theoretical summary together with a collection of computer routines for solving linear and quadratic programming problems is given in Künzi et al. [21]. One standard formulation of the (primal) linear programming problem is as follows:

Find values $x_1,\ldots,x_n$ which maximize the objective function

$$z = \sum_{j=1}^{n} c_j x_j$$

subject to the constraints

$$\sum_{j=1}^{n} a_{ij}x_j \leq b_i, \quad i = 1,\ldots,m_1$$

$$\sum_{j=1}^{n} a_{ij}x_j = b_i, \quad i = m_1+1,\ldots,m$$

$$x_j \geq 0, \qquad j = 1,\ldots,n_1$$

$$x_j \text{ unrestricted}, \quad j = n_1+1,\ldots,n$$

The dual to this problem is as follows: Find values $u_1,\ldots,u_m$ which minimize the objective function

$$w = \sum_{i=1}^{m} u_i b_i$$

subject to the constraints

$$\sum_{i=1}^{m} u_i a_{ij} \geq c_j, \quad j = 1,\ldots,n_1$$

$$\sum_{i=1}^{m} u_i a_{ij} = c_j, \quad j = n_1+1,\ldots,n$$

$$u_i \geq 0, \qquad i = 1,\ldots,m_1$$

$$u_i \text{ unrestricted}, \quad i = m_1+1,\ldots,m$$

For other formulations of the linear programming problem and ways to transform one formulation to another, see Rabinowitz [27].

The discrete linear real weighted L_∞ approximation problem is as follows: Given n+1 vectors $\underline{v}_0,\ldots,\underline{v}_n$ in m-dimensional real space $R^m, m > n$, and a set of positive weights $\{w_i, i=1,\ldots,m\}$, to find real coefficients $a_1,\ldots,a_n$ so that

$$\| \underline{v}_0 - \sum_{i=1}^{n} a_i \underline{v}_i \|_\infty = \text{minimum}$$

where for any vector $\underline{v}_i = \{v_{i1},\ldots,v_{im}\}$, $\|\underline{v}_i\|_\infty = \max_{1\leq j\leq m} |w_j v_{ij}|$. Thus the problem is to find $a_1,\ldots,a_n$ to minimize

$$\max_{1 \leq j \leq m} |w_j(v_{0j} - \sum_{i=1}^{n} a_i v_{ij})|.$$

To this problem may be added any combination of linear constraints of the form:

1) $a_j \geq 0$ (non-negativity of coefficient)
2) $|a_j| \leq K$ (boundedness of coefficient)
3) $\sum a_i v_{ik} \geq v_{0k}$ (one-sided approximation)
4) $\sum a_i v_{ik} = v_{0k}$ (equality constraint)

and similar and possibly other forms.

The linear programming formulation of this problem is: Find $a_0, a_1, \ldots, a_n$ which minimize the objective function $z = a_0$ subject to the constraints

$$w_j(\sum_{i=1}^{n} v_{ij} a_i) - a_0 \leq w_j v_{0j}, \qquad j = 1, \ldots, m$$

$$-w_j(\sum_{i=1}^{n} v_{ij} a_i) - a_0 \leq -w_j v_{0j}, \qquad j = 1, \ldots, m$$

$$a_0 \geq 0$$

$$a_i \text{ unrestricted}, \quad i = 1, \ldots, m$$

plus any additional constraints of the problem.

The discrete linear real weighted L_1 approximation problem is similar to the corresponding L_∞ problem except that in this case we are called upon to minimize $\| \underline{v}_0 - \sum_{i=1}^{n} a_i \underline{v}_i \|_1$ where for any vector $\underline{v}_i$

$$\| \underline{v}_i \|_1 = \sum_{j=1}^{m} w_j |v_{ij}|.$$

In this problem too, there may be any combination of linear constraints. One possible linear programming formulation of the L_1 approximation problem is as follows: Find $a_1, \ldots, a_n, e_1, \ldots, e_m$ which minimize the objective function

$$z = \sum_{j=1}^{m} w_j e_j$$

subject to the constraints

$$\sum_{i=1}^{n} v_{ij}a_i - e_j \leq v_{0j} \quad , \qquad j = 1,\ldots,m$$

$$-\sum_{i=1}^{n} v_{ij}a_i - e_j \leq -v_{0j} \quad , \qquad j = 1,\ldots,m$$

$$e_j \geq 0 \qquad j = 1,\ldots,m$$

$$a_i \text{ unrestricted}, \qquad i = 1,\ldots,n$$

plus any additional constraints of the problem. For alternative formulations of these two problems and additional details and references, see Rabinowitz [27] and for L_∞ Collatz [8].

Discrete real linear weighted linearly constrained L_1 and L_∞ approximation by cubic splines with fixed pre-assigned knots can also be handled by linear programming, Barrodale and Young [2]. In this case we are given n knots $z_1,\ldots,z_n$ and m pairs of real numbers (x_i,y_i), $i = 1,\ldots,m$ and we are required to find n+4 coefficients $b_0,\ldots,b_3,a_1,\ldots,a_n$ which minimize $\| \underline{y} - \underline{S}(x) \|$ where the norm is either the weighted L_1 or L_∞ norm and $\underline{S}(x) = \{S(x_1),\ldots,S(x_m)\}$, where

$$S(x) = \sum_{j=0}^{3} b_j x^j + \sum_{j=1}^{n} a_j (x-z_j)_+^3.$$

Here

$$(x-z_j)_+^3 = \begin{cases} (x-z_j)^3 & \text{for } x \geq z_j, \\ 0 & \text{for } x \leq z_j. \end{cases}$$

The linear program for this problem, e.g., in the (unweighted) L_∞ case is as follows: Find $a_0,\ldots,a_n$, $b_0,\ldots,b_3$ which minimize the objective function $z = a_0$ subject to the constraints

$$\sum_{j=0}^{3} b_j x_i^j + \sum_{j=1}^{n(i)} a_j (x_i - z_j)^3 - a_0 \leq y_i \quad , \qquad i = 1,\ldots,m$$

$$-\sum_{j=0}^{3} b_j x_i^j - \sum_{j=1}^{n(i)} a_j (x_i - z_j)^3 - a_0 \leq -y_i \quad , \qquad i = 1,\ldots,m$$

$$a_0 \geq 0$$

$$a_j \text{ unrestricted} \qquad j = 1,\ldots,n$$

$$b_j \text{ unrestricted} \qquad j = 0,\ldots,3$$

where n(i) is the number of knots $z_j \leq x_i$. Here also linear constraints may be added. The approximation points x_i and the set of knots z_j may be disjoint or not. Stability may be a problem in this formulation since the form of the spline given by the formula for $S(x)$ is not computationally stable. An alternative formulation of cubic splines is discussed in the next section. Fitting by splines of higher degree can be treated in a similar fashion.

The final application of linear programming to approximation is that of discrete real weighted rational L_∞ approximation. In this case, a sequence of linear programming problems is solved and the solutions to these problems converge to the solution of the rational approximation problem. In addition to the methods reported in [27], we mention here the differential correction method of Cheney and Loeb [7]. The problem is as follows: Given m pairs of real numbers (x_i,y_i), $i = 1,\ldots,m$, to find coefficients $a_0,\ldots,a_n$ and $b_0,\ldots,b_p$ which minimize $\max_{1\leqslant i\leqslant m} |y_i - R(x_i)|$ where

$$R(x) \equiv P(x)/Q(x) = \sum_{j=0}^{n} a_j x^j / \sum_{j=0}^{p} b_j x^j$$

subject to $C_1 \geqslant Q(x_i) \geqslant C_2 > 0$ for some fixed constants C_1, C_2.

The differential correction algorithm proceeds as follows: At step k we assume an approximation $R_k(x) = P_k(x)/Q_k(x)$. We compute

$$e_k = \max_{1\leqslant i\leqslant m} |y_i - R_k(x_i)|$$

and use it to define an auxiliary function

$$d_k(R) = \max_{1\leqslant i\leqslant m} \{|y_i Q(x_i) - P(x_i)| - e_k Q(x_i)\} .$$

We now solve the linear programming problem: Find $a_0,\ldots,a_n,b_0,\ldots,b_p$ which minimize $d_k(R)$ subject to the constraints $C_1 \geqslant Q(x_i) \geqslant C_2$, $i = 1,\ldots,m$ and $|b_j| \leqslant 1$, $j = 1,\ldots,p$. This gives us $R_{k+1}(x)$. When $d_k(R_{k+1}) \geqslant 0$ we stop and $\{R_k(x_i)\}$ is a best approximation to $\{y_i\}$. This algorithm is shown to be effective.

As far as discrete real rational L_1 approximation is concerned, nothing has been proposed to the best of my knowledge. However, a possible approach could be along the line of one of Loeb's algorithms mentioned in [27]. The problem is to find coefficients $a_0,\ldots,a_n$ and $b_1,\ldots,b_p$ to minimize $\sum_{i=1}^{m} |y_i - P(x_i)/Q(x_i)|$ subject to $Q(x_i) \geqslant C$, with $b_0=1$. Writing this as

$$\sum_{i=1}^{m} \left| \frac{1}{Q(x_i)} \right| \, |y_i Q(x_i) - P(x_i)|$$

we can set up the iteration, minimize

$$\sum_{i=1}^{m} \left|\frac{1}{Q_k(x_i)}\right| \left|y_i Q_{k+1}(x_i) - P_{k+1}(x_i)\right|$$

subject to $Q_{k+1}(x_i) \geq C$, $i = 1,\ldots,m$. This yields a discrete real linear weighted linearly constrained L_1 approximation problem which can be solved by linear programming. However, there is no practical experience with this algorithm, and as in the L_∞ equivalent of this algorithm, no convergence theorem.* This algorithm and possibly others used in discrete rational L_∞ approximation should be looked into as candidates for corresponding L_1 approximation.

3. Quadratic Programming

Quadratic programming is concerned with the problem of minimizing a quadratic function subject to linear constraints. Specifically, it solves the following problem: Find $\underline{x} = (x_1,\ldots,x_n)$ which minimizes the quadratic function $z = \underline{p}^t\,\underline{x} + \underline{x}^t\,B\,\underline{x}$ subject to the constraints

$$A\underline{x} \leq \underline{b}$$
$$\underline{x} \geq 0$$

where $\underline{p}$ is a vector of n elements, $\underline{b}$ one of m elements, A an $m \times n$ matrix and C an $n \times n$ symmetric positive semi-definite matrix. There are many algorithms for solving this problem, most of which are covered in Künzi et al. [20]. Several computer routines in ALGOL and FORTRAN are given in Künzi et al. [21], while comparisons among some of the methods as to efficiency are given in Dorn [10], Moore and Whinston [22], van de Panne and Whinston [31].

Quadratic programming is eminently suitable for solving real linear least squares (L_2) approximation problems with linear constraints. Both discrete and continuous problems can be solved and weights can be incorporated at will. We shall discuss the discrete unweighted case, for simplicity, but all other cases can be derived from this one by replacing sums by integrals and by introducing weights in the sums or integrals. The problem then is as follows: Given n+1 vectors $\underline{v}_0,\ldots,\underline{v}_n$ in R^m, $m > n$, to find $a_1,\ldots,a_n$ so that $\|\underline{v}_0 - \sum_{i=1}^{n} a_i\underline{v}_i\|_2$ = minimum subject to certain

* But see the paper by Barrodale in these Proceedings, pp. 205–215.

linear constraints where $\| \underline{v}_i \|_2 = (\sum_{j=1}^{m} v_{ij}^2)^{\frac{1}{2}}$. This is equivalent to minimizing

$$\sum_{j=1}^{m} (v_{0j} - \sum_{i=1}^{m} a_i v_{ij})^2$$

which in turn is equivalent to minizing

$$z = \underline{p}^t \underline{a} + \underline{a}^t B \underline{a},$$

where

$$B = (b_{rs}),\ b_{rs} = \sum_{j=1}^{m} v_{rj} v_{sj},\ r,s=1,\ldots,n$$

and

$$\underline{p} = (p_1,\ldots,p_n),\ p_r = -2 \sum_{j=1}^{m} v_{0j} v_{rj},\quad r = 1,\ldots,n.$$

The following constrained L_2 problems have been treated:

Krabs [19] assumes that we have a bound K on the L_∞ error of an approximation to a given vector $\underline{v}_0$ by a linear combination of vectors $\underline{v}_i$, i=1,...,n in R^m, m > n. He now wants to compute a least-squares approximation of $\underline{v}_0$ by $\sum_{i=1}^{n} a_i \underline{v}_i$, subject to the constraint that

$$|\underline{v}_0 - \sum_{i=1}^{n} a_i \underline{v}_i|_\infty \leqslant K.$$

The quadratic program formulation of this problem is as follows: Find $a_1,\ldots,a_n$ which minimize

$$z = \underline{a}^t B \underline{a} - 2 \underline{v}_0^t A \underline{a}$$

subject to the constraints

$$A\underline{a} \leqslant \underline{v}_0 + K\underline{e}$$

$$-A\underline{a} \leqslant -v_0 + K\underline{e}$$

where $A = (v_{ij})$, i = 1,...,n, j=1,...,m, is assumed to have rank n, $B = A^t A$, and $\underline{e} = (1,\ldots,1)$ is a vector of m elements.

Gorenflo and Kovetz [16] were concerned with the problem of finding coefficients $a_1,\ldots,a_n$ to minimize

$$\int_0^1 [f(x) - \sum_{i=1}^{n} a_i g_i(x)]^2 dx$$

subject to the constraint

$$\sum_{i=1}^{n} a_i h_i(x) \geq 0, \quad 0 \leq x \leq 1,$$

where $f(x)$, $g_i(x)$ and $h_i(x)$ are given functions. Discretizing the problem leads to the following: Minimize

$$\sum_{j=0}^{m} (f(j/m) - \sum_{i=1}^{n} a_i g_i(j/m))^2$$

subject to

$$\sum_{i=1}^{n} a_i h_i(j/p) \geq 0, \quad 1 \leq j \leq p.$$

The formulation as a quadratic program: minimize $\underline{a}^t B \underline{a} + \underline{p}^t \underline{a}$ subject to $A\underline{a} \leq 0$ is straightforward.

Strauss [30] is concerned with fitting a set of data points by a cubic spline with fixed knots subject to certain smoothness conditions. Specifically, given m pairs of real numbers (x_i, y_i), $i=1,\ldots,m$, n knots $z_1,\ldots,z_n$, and n+1 numbers $S_0,\ldots,S_n$ which can be either 1, 0, or -1, to find a cubic spline $S(x)$ which minimizes

$$\sum_{i=1}^{m} (y_i - S(x_i))^2$$

subject to the constraints $S_j S''(x) \geq 0$, $z_j \leq x \leq z_{j-1}$, $j=0,\ldots,n$ with $z_0 = a$, $z_{n+1} = b$, the endpoints of the closed interval $[a,b]$ containing all x_i and z_j. $S(x)$ can be represented by n+1 groups of numbers (a_j, b_j, c_j, d_j) $j=0,\ldots,n$ which are related by 3n equalities, leaving n+4 free parameters:

$$S(x) = a_j x^3 + b_j x^2 + c_j x + d_j, \quad z_j \leq x \leq z_{j+1}.$$

The equalities relating these numbers are as follows:

$$a_j z_j^3 + b_j z_j^2 + c_j z_j + d_j = a_{j-1} z_j^3 + b_{j-1} z_j^2 + c_{j-1} z_j + d_{j-1},$$

$$3a_j z_j^2 + 2b_j z_j + c_j = 3a_{j-1} z_j^2 + 2b_{j-1} z_j + c_{j-1},$$

$$6a_j z_j + 2b_j = 6a_{j-1} z_j + 2b_{j-1}, \quad j=1,\ldots,n.$$

The constraint $S_j S''(x) \geq 0$, $z_j \leq x \leq z_{j+1}$ is equivalent to the two constraints

$$S_j(3a_jz_j + b_j) \geq 0$$
$$S_j(3a_jz_{j+1} + b_j) \geq 0 \qquad j=0,\ldots,n$$

Thus we finally have set up our quadratic programming problem in 4n+4 variables subject to 3n equality constraints and 2n+2 inequality constraints, where the objective function is, of course, derived from $\sum_{i=1}^{m}(y_i - S(x_i))^2$. For fuller details see Strauss [30] and Amos and Slater [1].

4. Convex Programming

Most of the algorithms for nonlinear programming were developed for the case of convex programming. The reader is referred to recent articles by Zoutendijk [35], [36], Wolfe [32], and Beale [3] and to the books by Fiacco and McCormick [12], Hadley [17], Künzi et al. [20], Saaty and Bram [29], Zukhovitskiy and Avdeyeva [37]. The problem here is to find a point $\underline{x}$ in R^n which minimizes the convex function $f(\underline{x})$ subject to the constraints $g_i(\underline{x}) \leq 0$ where the $g_i(\underline{x})$ are also convex functions. Any constraints in the components x_j of $\underline{x}$ are included in the constraints of the $g_i(\underline{x})$. The reasons that convex programming is important are that a local minimum of $f(\underline{x})$ is a global minimum and that duality theorems hold.

Several approximation problems can be formulated as convex programming problems. The simplest is discrete real linear L_p approximation with weights and linear constraints. In the simplest case, it reduces to the following convex program: Find coefficients $a_1,\ldots,a_n$ and errors $e_1,\ldots,e_m$ which minimize the convex function $\sum_{j=1}^{m} e_j^p$ subject to the linear (and hence convex) constraints

$$v_{0j} - \sum_{i=1}^{n} a_i v_{ij} - e_j \leq 0$$
$$-v_{0j} + \sum_{i=1}^{n} a_i v_{ij} - e_j \leq 0 \qquad j=1,\ldots,m$$
$$-e_j \leq 0.$$

Alternatively, we can reduce the number of constraints at the cost of increasing the number of variables to get the following formulation: Find coefficients $a_1,\ldots,a_n$, positive errors $e_1,\ldots,e_m$ and negative errors

$d_1,\dots,d_m$ which minimize the convex function $\sum_{j=1}^{m}(e_j^p + d_j^p)$ subject to the linear equality constraints

$$v_{0j} - \sum_{i=1}^{n} a_i v_{ij} - e_j + d_j = 0 \qquad j=1,\dots,m$$

$$e_j \geq 0, \quad d_j \geq 0.$$

We point out that this problem is of a special form, consisting of a nonlinear objective function and linear constraints for which more special methods of solution exist, Goldfarb and Lapidus [15], Rosen [28], Zangwill [34]. An ALGOL procedure for the case of linear inequality constraints is given by Fletcher [14].

The next application of convex programming to approximation is in complex approximation. Given a set of n+1 complex vectors $\underline{w}_i$, $i=0,\dots,n$ in complex m-dimensional space C^m, $m > n$, to find a set of complex coefficients a_i, $i=1,\dots,n$ so that

$$\max_{1 \leq j \leq m} |w_{0j} - \sum_{i=1}^{n} a_i w_{ij}| = \text{minimum}.$$

It is equivalent, of course, to require $\max_{1 \leq j \leq m} |w_{0j} - \sum_{i=1}^{n} a_i w_j|^2 = \text{minimum}$, so that the problem reduces to that of minimizing e subject to the constraints

$$|w_{0j} - \sum_{i=1}^{n} a_i w_{ij}|^2 \leq e \qquad j=1,\dots,m$$

which is a convex programming problem in the 2n real variables b_i, c_i, $i=1,\dots,n$ where $a_i = b_i + i\, c_i$ [37].

An early application of convex programming to approximation is that of Cheney and Goldstein [6] to continuous real linear L_∞ approximation. The problem is to find coefficients $a_1,\dots,a_n$ so that

$\max_{a \leq x \leq b} |f(x) - \sum_{i=1}^{n} a_i g_i(x)| = \text{minimum}$ for given real-valued continuous functions $f(x)$, $g_1(x),\dots,g_n(x)$. More generally, we can have x range over any closed convex set in R^m. This problem reduces to the convex programming problem of minimizing a_0 subject to an infinite number of linear constraints of the form

$$f(x_j) - \sum_{i=1}^{n} a_i g_i(x_j) - a_0 \leqslant 0$$

$$-f(x_j) + \sum_{i=1}^{n} a_i g_i(x_j) - a_0 \leqslant 0$$

$$- a_0 \leqslant 0$$

where j ranges over a non-denumerable well-ordered indexing set for the x's in the range of interest. Algorithms for the solution to this problem are given in Cheney and Goldstein [6].

For continuous real rational L_∞ approximation, Cheney [5] gives an analogue of the differential correction algorithm discussed in Section 2, at each stage of which one solves a convex programming problem of the form:

$$\max_{a \leqslant x \leqslant b} \{|f(x)Q(x) - P(x)| - e_k Q(x)\} = \text{minimum}.$$

A final application is to the problem of fitting a quadratic regression law subject to the condition that the fitted surface be convex or concave (Hartley et al. [18]). The problem here is as follows: given n vectors in R^m, $\underline{x}_i$, i=1,...,n and n values y_i, i=1,...,n where each y is a function of m variables, to find a scalar b_0, a vector $\underline{b}$ and a positive semi-definite matrix B such that

$$\sum_{i=1}^{n} (y_i - Q(\underline{x}_i))^2 = \text{minimum}$$

where $Q(\underline{x}_i) = b_0 + \underline{b}^t\underline{x}_i + x_i^t B\underline{x}_i$. Although this is actually a quadratic programming problem, nevertheless it is more readily solved by an algorithm for convex programming. The details may be found in [18].

5. Geometric Programming

Duffin, Peterson and Zener in their book, Geometric Programming [11], discuss the application of that subject to discrete real linear L_p approximation. For $1 < p < \infty$, the theory is straightforward since the norm is differentiable. For p=1,∞ also they show how to apply geometric programming, and they also indicate how to include constraints. A further elaboration of this is given by Peterson and Ecker [24] who show that every quadratically-constrained (convex) quadratic program and every L_p-constrained (discrete linear) L_p- approximation problem are special cases of the following geometric programming problem: Find the infimum of

$G_0(\underline{x})$ subject to the constraints $G_k(\underline{x}) \leq 0$, $k=1,\ldots,r$, $\underline{x} \in P$, where

$$G_k(x) = \sum_{i=m_k}^{n_k-1} p_i^{-1}|x_i - b_i|^{p_i} + x_{n_k} - b_{n_k}, \quad k=0,\ldots,r,$$

and $m_0 = 1$, $m_j = n_{j-1} + 1$, $j=1,\ldots,r$, $n_r = n$. The vector $\underline{b} = (b_1,\ldots,b_n)$ is an arbitrary but fixed vector in R^n and the arbitrary but fixed constants p_i satisfy the condition $p_i > 1$. The set P is a fixed but arbitrary vector subspace of R^n. The full details are in [24].

6. General Nonlinear Programming

The general discrete nonlinear approximation problem in L_p, $1 \leq p \leq \infty$, leads to a nonlinear programming problem which is not convex. For the L_∞ case, this has been discussed by Collatz and Wetterling [8] and for the general case, by Bracken and McCormick [4] who also give some examples in which nonlinear approximation problems were solved by the Sequential Unconstrained Minimization Technique [12]. The general discrete real L_∞ approximation problem is to find parameters $a_1,\ldots,a_n$ such that

$$\max_{1\leq i\leq m} |y_i - f(x_i;a_1,\ldots,a_n)| = \text{minimum}.$$

Particular cases of this are, e.g., the case where f is a rational function $\sum_{i=0}^{p} a_i x^i/[1 + \sum_{i=p+1}^{n} a_i x^{i-p}]$, a sum of exponentials $\sum_{i=1}^{p} a_i e^{a_{i+p}x}$, or a trigonometric sum $\sum_{i=1}^{p} a_i \cos(a_{i+p}x + a_{i+2p})$. Of course, there is an infinite variety of forms that f may take. The formulation as a nonlinear programming problem is the (by now) obvious one: minimize e subject to

$$\begin{aligned} y_i - f(x_i;a_1,\ldots,a_n) - e &\leq 0 \\ -y_i + f(x_i;a_1,\ldots,a_n) - e &\leq 0 \qquad i = 1,\ldots,m \\ e &\geq 0 \end{aligned}$$

For nonlinear f, it is impossible for both functions in the above inequalities for the same index i to be convex so that our nonlinear programming problem is non-convex. Similarly, for L_p, $1 \leq p < \infty$ the formulation is either: minimize $\sum_{i=1}^{m} e_i^p$ subject to

$$y_i - f(x_i;a_1,\dots,a_n) - e_i \leqslant 0$$
$$-y_i + f(x_i;a_1,\dots,a_n) - e_i \leqslant 0$$
$$e_i \geqslant 0 \qquad i = 1,\dots,m$$

or: minimize $$\sum_{i=1}^{m} (e_i^p + d_i^p)$$

subject to

$$y_i - f(x_i;a_1,\dots,a_n) + e_i - d_i = 0$$
$$e_i \geqslant 0,\ d_i \geqslant 0, \qquad i = 1,\dots,m$$

It is an open question whether it is more economical to solve these problems by nonlinear programming techniques or by unconstrained minimization methods for non-differentiable functions, such as those reviewed by Fletcher [13]. For nonlinear L_∞ approximation, there is also an algorithm by Osborne and Watson [23] as well as that of Demjanov [9]. For the case p = an even integer, there are more powerful minimization algorithms available for which the reader is referred to Powell [25], [26].

7. Conclusions

It is clear from the examples cited above that there is a close connection between nonlinear programming and approximation. Almost all real finite discrete approximation problems and many continuous approximation problems can be approximated by discrete problems with suitably chosen weights. On the other hand, as Zangwill [33] points out, many nonlinear programming problems can be formulated as approximation problems so that there is a considerable amount of equivalence between the two. Both are closely related to the problem of optimization, unconstrained or constrained, but as Powell [25] has pointed out, the techniques developed in one discipline have not been carried over to another. Furthermore, there seems to be very little numerical work around on nonlinear approximation and the application of mathematical programming to it. In view of the many computational methods available, it would be interesting to undertake a study to determine which methods are best for approximation and to compare nonlinear programming techniques with optimization techniques.

References

1. AMOS, D. E. and SLATER, M. L., 'Polynomial and spline approximation by quadratic programming'. Comm. ACM, 12 (1969), pp. 379-381.

2. BARRODALE, I. and YOUNG, A. 'A note on numerical procedures for approximation by spline functions'. Comp. J., 9 (1966/67), pp. 318-320.

3. BEALE, E. M. L. 'Numerical Methods', in Abadie, J. (Ed.), Nonlinear Programming, pp. 135-205. North-Holland, 1967.

4. BRACKEN, J. and McCORMICK, G. P. Selected Applications of Nonlinear Programming. Wiley, 1968.

5. CHENEY, E. W. Introduction to Approximation Theory. McGraw-Hill, 1966.

6. CHENEY, E. W. and GOLDSTEIN, A. A. 'Newton's method for convex programming and Tchebycheff approximation'. Numer. Math., 1 (1959), pp. 253-268.

7. CHENEY, E. W. and LOEB, H. L. 'Two new algorithms for rational approximation'. Numer. Math., 3 (1961), pp. 72-75.

8. COLLATZ, L. and WETTERLING, W. Optimierungsaufgaben. Springer, 1966.

9. DEMJANOV, V. F. 'Algorithms for some minimax problems'. J. Comp. System Sci., 2 (1968), pp. 342-380.

10. DORN, W. S. 'Nonlinear programming - a survey'. Manag. Sci., 9 (1963), pp. 171-208.

11. DUFFIN, R. J., PETERSON, E. L., and ZENER, C. Geometric Programming - Theory and Application. Wiley, 1967.

12. FIACCO, A. V. and McCORMICK, G. P. Nonlinear Programming,Sequential Unconstrained Minimization Techniques. Wiley, 1968.

13. FLETCHER, R. 'Function minimization without evaluating derivatives - a review'. Comp. J., 8 (1965), pp. 33-41.

14. FLETCHER, R. 'An algorithm for optimization subject to linear inequalities'. I.C.I. Management Services Report MSDH/68/130, 1968.

15. GOLDFARB, D. and LAPIDUS, L. 'Conjugate gradient method for nonlinear programming problems with linear constraints'. I. and E.C. Fundamentals, 7 (1968), pp. 142-151.

16. GORENFLO, R. and KOVETZ, Y. 'Solution of an Abel-type integral equation in the presence of noise by quadratic programming'. Numer. Math., 8 (1966), pp. 392-406.

17. HADLEY, G. Nonlinear and Dynamic Programming. Addison-Wesley, 1964.

18. HARTLEY, H. O., HOCKING, R. R. and COOKE, W. P. 'Least squares fit of definite quadratic forms by convex programming'. Manag. Sci., 13 (1967), pp. 913-925.

19. KRABS, W. 'Fehlerquadrat-Approximation als Mittel zur Lösung des diskreten linearen Tschebyscheff-Problems'. Z. angew. Math. Mech., 44 (1964), T42-45 (1964).

20. KÜNZI, H. P., KRELLE, W. and OETTLI, W. Nonlinear Programming. Blaisdell, 1966.

21. KÜNZI, H. P., TZCHACK, H. G. and ZEHNDER, C. A. Numerical Methods of Mathematical Optimization. Academic Press, 1968.

22. MOORE, J. H. and WHINSTON, A. B. 'Experimental methods in quadratic programming'. Manag. Sci., 13 (1966), pp. 58-76.

23. OSBORNE, M. R. and WATSON, G. A. 'An algorithm for minimax approximation in the nonlinear case'. Comp. J., 12 (1969), pp. 64-69.

24. PETERSON, E. L. and ECKER, J. G. 'Geometric Programming: a unified duality theory for quadratically constrained quadratic programs and ℓ_p-constrained ℓ_p approximation problems'. Bull. Amer. Soc., 74 (1968), pp. 316-321.

25. POWELL, M. J. D. 'Minimization of functions of several variables', in Walsh, J. (Ed.), Numerical Analysis, pp. 143-157. Academic Press, 1966.

26. POWELL, M. J. D. 'A survey of numerical methods for unconstrained optimization'. A.E.R.E., T.P. 340, (1968).

27. RABINOWITZ, P. 'Applications of linear programming to numerical analysis'. SIAM Rev., 10 (1968), pp. 121-159.

28. ROSEN, J. B. 'The gradient projection method for nonlinear programming, Part I: linear constraints'. J. Soc. Indust. Appl. Math., 8 (1960), pp. 181-217.

29. SAATY, T. L. and BRAM, J. Nonlinear Mathematics. McGraw-Hill, 1964.

30. STRAUSS, C. M. 'Computerized curve fairing'. Division of Appl. Math., Brown Univ., June 1966.

31. VAN DE PANNE, C. and WHINSTON, A. 'A comparison of two methods for quadratic programming'. Operations Res., 14 (1966), pp. 422-441.

32. WOLFE, P. 'Methods of nonlinear programming', in Abadie, J. (Ed.), Nonlinear Programming, pp. 99-131. North-Holland, 1967.

33. ZANGWILL, W. I. 'An algorithm for the Chebyshev problem with an application to concave programming'. Manag. Sci., 14 (1967), pp. 58-78.

34. ZANGWILL, W. I. 'The convex simplex method'. Manag. Sci., 14 (1967), pp. 221-238.

35. ZOUTENDIJK, G. 'Nonlinear programming: a numerical survey'. SIAM J. Control, 4 (1966), pp. 194-210.

36. ZOUTENDIJK, G. 'Computational methods in nonlinear programming'. To appear in Proceedings of SIAM Conference on Optimization, Toronto, June 1968.

37. ZUKHOVITSKIY, S. I. and AVDEYEVA, L. I. Linear and Convex Programming. Saunders, 1966.

ONE-SIDED APPROXIMATIONS BY LINEAR COMBINATIONS OF FUNCTIONS

G. Marsaglia

(Boeing Scientific Research Laboratories, Seattle)

1. Introduction

This paper is concerned with approximating a function g(x) from one side (usually from below) by a linear combination of functions. Formally, this is the problem:

Maximize

$$p_1 + p_2 + \ldots + p_n$$

subject to the constraints

$$p_1 \geq 0, p_2 \geq 0, \ldots, p_n \geq 0 \tag{1}$$

and

$$p_1 f_1(x) + p_2 f_2(x) + \ldots + p_n f_n(x) \leq g(x), \quad -\infty < x < \infty. \tag{2}$$

The problem is equivalent to asking for the one-sided approximation that minimizes the area of the difference, i.e., the L_1 norm, but in applications the sum $p_1 + \ldots + p_n$ plays a more direct role than does the residual area.

We will give an algorithm for finding the optimal set of p's and discuss applications to Monte Carlo Theory: To develop a method for generating random variables with specified density g(x), one writes g as a mixture of the n convenient densities $f_1(x), \ldots, f_n(x)$ and a residual density r(x):

$$g(x) = p_1 f_1(x) + \ldots + p_n f_n(x) + p_{n+1} r(x), \quad \sum_1^{n+1} p_n = 1.$$

Because of constraints (1) and (2), the function $r(x)$ will be a density function, and p_{n+1} will be small, since $p_1 + \ldots + p_n$ is maximized. Details of this application are in Section 5. Figure 1 shows the fitting densities $f_1, \ldots, f_8$ we are particularly concerned with; they are associated with the random variables $U_1 + U_2 + U_3$, $1 + U_1 + U_2 + U_3$, $2 + U_1 + U_2 + U_3, \ldots$, where the U's are uniformly distributed over the interval $[0,1]$. Figure 4 shows how closely some of the common density functions may be fitted by $p_1 f_1 + \ldots + p_8 f_8$.

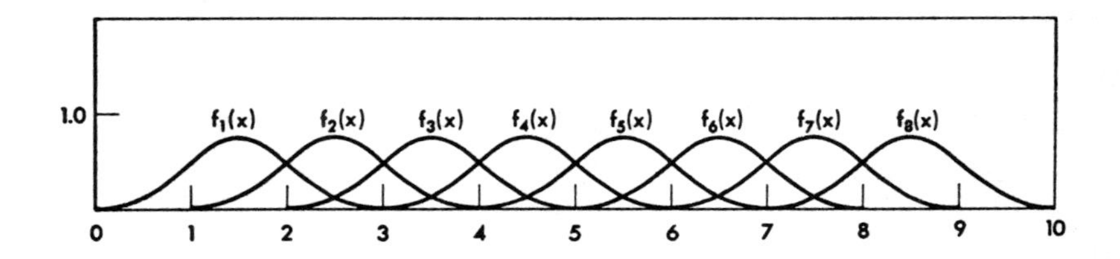

Fig. 1

2. Direct Approach

The set of points $(p_1, p_2, \ldots, p_n)$ such that

$$p_1 f_1(x) + \ldots + p_n f_n(x) \leq g(x), \quad -\infty < x < \infty$$

forms a convex set, since for each x the inequality determines a half-space and the intersection of any number of half-spaces is a convex set. The problem is to find where the hyperplane $p_1 + p_2 + \ldots + p_n = c$ last touches this convex set as c increases. The figure below illustrates the situation when n=2. One would think that direct methods using derivatives could be used to find the last point of contact of the moving hyperplane with the convex set, but unfortunately the situation gets complicated when n is 3 or more, particularly when the approximating functions are quadratic splines which do not have the non-trivial derivatives necessary for a differential geometry approach.

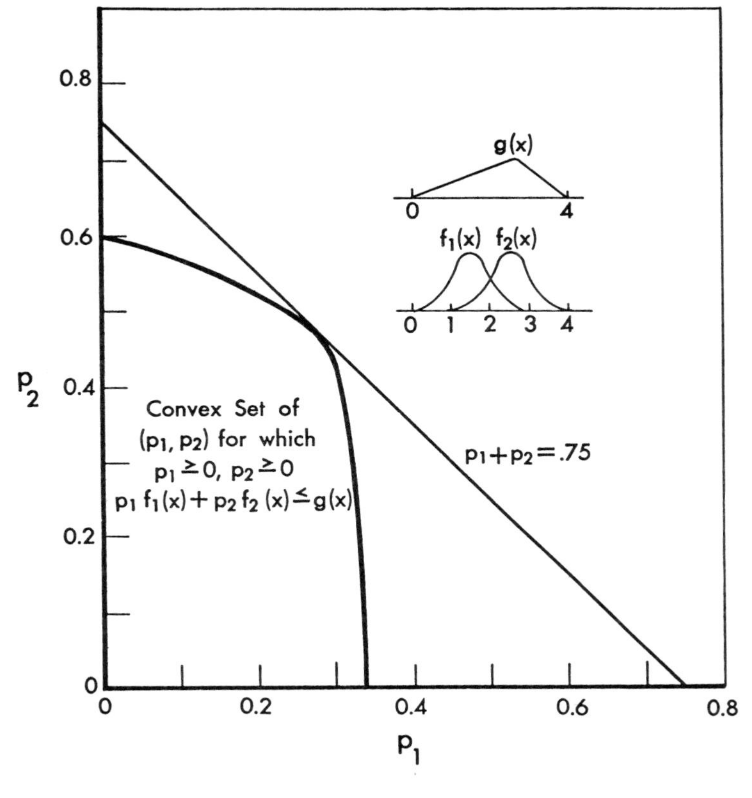

Fig. 2

3. Linear Programming Approach

If we specify that the conditions $\Sigma p_i f_i(x) \leq g(x)$ hold for a suitable fine mesh of x values, say $x_1, x_2, \ldots, x_{100}$, then we have an ordinary linear program with 100 + n constraints. Our original convex set is now slightly enlarged to a convex polytope, the intersection of 100 + n half-spaces, and we can expect that this linear program will provide a set of optimal p's which is suitably close to the optimum for the continuous case. When expressed as a linear program, this is the problem:

Maximize

$$p_1 + p_2 + \ldots + p_n$$

subject to the constraints

$$p_1 \geq 0$$
$$p_2 \geq 0$$
$$\vdots$$
$$p_n \geq 0$$

$$p_1f_1(x_1) + p_2f_2(x_1) + \ldots + p_nf_n(x_1) \leq g(x_1)$$
$$p_1f_1(x_2) + p_2f_2(x_2) + \ldots + p_nf_n(x_2) \leq g(x_2)$$
$$\vdots$$
$$p_1f_1(x_{100}) + p_2f_2(x_{100}) + \ldots + p_nf_n(x_{100}) \leq g(x_{100}).$$

An algorithm for solving this general problem will be given below. The algorithm is based on solving the dual to the above linear program, using a condensed form of the full tableau, as in the revised simplex method. See Dantzig [1], Chapter 9, for references and a discussion of the revised simplex method.

4. Algorithm for Solving the General Problem

This algorithm successively alters rows of an $n \times n$ matrix and a row $(p_1, p_2, \ldots, p_n)$ of current estimates of the optimal p's. At the beginning of each step the matrix under consideration has this form:

$$\begin{pmatrix} a_{11}a_{12} & \cdots & a_{1n} \\ a_{21}a_{22} & \cdots & a_{2n} \\ \vdots & & \vdots \\ a_{n1}a_{n2} & \cdots & a_{nn} \\ p_1p_2 & \cdots & p_n \end{pmatrix} = \begin{pmatrix} \alpha_1 \\ \alpha_2 \\ \vdots \\ \alpha_n \\ \pi \end{pmatrix} .$$

One then finds a "value" v_i for each row α_i and a "value" v for the row π. (Methods for computing "values" are in the outline below.) If α_n is the row with the best value, then replace α_m by α_m/v_m, replace π by $\pi - v\alpha_m$ and for $i \neq m$ replace row α_i by $\alpha_i - v_i\alpha_m$. Repeat the process with the new matrix: Calculate the new values $v, v_1, \ldots, v_n$, find the row with the best value, replace each row with a linear combination of itself and the row with the best value, and so on. The iteration stops when the value v of π is negligible, say $v < \varepsilon$.

To start the iteration, let $a_{ij} = \delta_{ij}$, that is, start with the identity matrix, and a set of initial guesses for $p_1, p_2, \dots, p_n$. <u>These initial guesses must be greater than the final, optimal values of the p's.</u> For example, in fitting density functions, the initial guess $p_1 = p_2 = \dots = p_n = 1$ will serve, although the number of iterations (usually about 2n) may be slightly reduced by improving the initial estimates.

In a computer program it is convenient to designate the row of p's as the (n+1)st row of the matrix A. Details of the algorithm are given in this outline:

<u>Step 1</u>. Find the highest point (x^*, v) on the error curve, that is,

$$v = \sum_{j=1}^{n} p_j f_j(x^*) - g(x^*) \geq \sum_{j=1}^{n} p_j f_j(x) - g(x), \quad -\infty < x < \infty,$$

(in the program, the value v is stored as V(N+1)).

<u>Step 2</u>. Find the row α_m with best value at x^*, where "value" is computed by using the elements of a row as weights for $f_1(x^*), \dots, f_n(x^*)$:

$$v_i = \sum_{j=1}^{n} a_{ij} f_j(x^*) .$$

m is the index for which $a_{i,n+1}/v_i$ has the least positive value.

<u>Step 3</u>. Replace α_m by α_m/v_m and then for each $i \neq m$ replace row α_i by a linear combination of rows α_i and α_m:

$$\alpha_m \to \alpha_m/v_m$$
$$\alpha_i \to \alpha_i - v_i \alpha_m, \quad i \neq m.$$

Return to Step 1 and repeat unless v (stored as V(N+1)) is small. If $v < \varepsilon$, then the iteration is complete and the current values $p_1, p_2, \dots, p_n$ give the solution (stored as A(n+1,1),...,A(n+1,n)).

The accuracy of the solution depends upon ε, of course. For most well-behaved density functions, $\varepsilon = .0001$ provides adequate precision in the optimal set $p_1, p_2, \dots, p_n$.

For the classes of fitting functions we have considered, the algorithm converges rapidly; generally after about 2n iterations. Examples will be given in the next section. A FORTRAN listing of the algorithm as a subroutine, together with comments, is given on page 240.

Figure 3 shows how successive iterations in the algorithm provide better and better approximations. A piecewise linear function g was chosen as an example; it is drawn with 6 fitting functions $f_1, \dots, f_6$ at the top left.

Below it is drawn the initial approximation with starting values $p_1 = \ldots = p_6 = 1$, $\Sigma p_i = 6$. The first iteration "brings in" a new choice of p_1 giving $\Sigma p_i = 4.42$; the second iteration provides some improvement, $\Sigma p_i = 4.0$, and so on. Suddenly after 6 iterations there is dramatic improvement, with nearly optimal values $p_1 = .069, \ldots, p_6 = .126$, $\Sigma p_i = .945$. Another set of 6 iterations produces as good a result as we require for practical purposes, and this situation is typical - the first n-1 iterations do not seem to make a lot of progress, then with the last p being "brought in", there is dramatic improvement in the n-th iteration. Another n iterations then provide a set of p's satisfactorily close to the optimal set for the original, continuous version of the problem.

5. Applications: Generating Random Variables

We are concerned with a particular set of approximating functions $f_1, f_2, \ldots, f_8$. They are translates of the density of the sum $U_1 + U_2 + U_3$, where U_1, U_2, U_3 are independent, uniformly distributed over the unit interval [0,1]. Let this density function be f(x); it is a quadratic spline function with formula

$$f(x) = \begin{cases} 0.5x^2 & 0 \leq x \leq 1 \\ 0.5x^2 - 1.5(x-1)^2 & 1 \leq x \leq 2 \\ 0.5x^2 - 1.5(x-1)^2 + 1.5(x-2)^2 & 2 \leq x \leq 3 \\ 0 & x < 0 \text{ or } x > 3. \end{cases}$$

The set of approximating functions $f_1(x), f_2(x), \ldots, f_8(x)$ takes this form:

$$f(x), f(x-1), f(x-2), \ldots, f(x-7).$$

These densities are drawn in Figure 1.

Note that if, by using the algorithm described above, we can represent a density function g(x) in the form

$$g(x) = p_1 f(x) + p_2 f(x-1) + \ldots + p_8 f(x-7) + p_9 r(x),$$

then we can generate a random variable X with density g(x) using this outline:

1. with probability p_1 put $X = U_1 + U_2 + U_3$
2. with probability p_2 put $X = U_1 + U_2 + U_3 + 1$

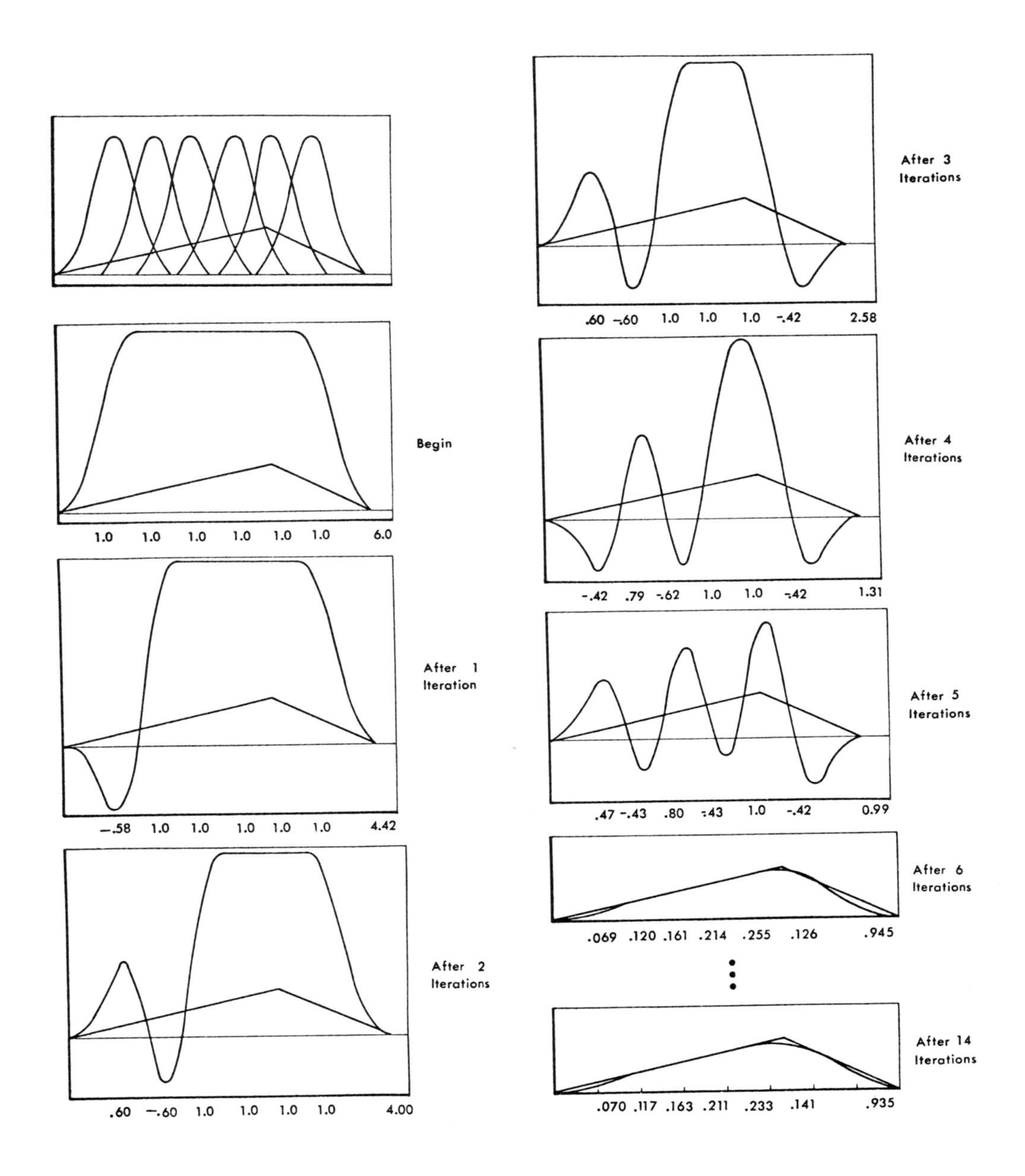
Begin
1.0 1.0 1.0 1.0 1.0 1.0 6.0
After 1 Iteration
−.58 1.0 1.0 1.0 1.0 1.0 4.42
After 2 Iterations
.60 −.60 1.0 1.0 1.0 1.0 4.00
After 3 Iterations
.60 −.60 1.0 1.0 1.0 −.42 2.58
After 4 Iterations
−.42 .79 −.62 1.0 1.0 −.42 1.31
After 5 Iterations
.47 −.43 .80 −.43 1.0 −.42 0.99
After 6 Iterations
.069 .120 .161 .214 .255 .126 .945
After 14 Iterations
.070 .117 .163 .211 .233 .141 .935

Figure 3

```
0001          SUBROUTINE P1P2PN(XL,XR,N,P)
0002          DIMENSION A(21,21),V(21),P(21),X(101),W(101)
0003          NP=N+1
0004          D=(XR-XL)/(N+2)                      ]  converts to standard
0005          DO 1 I=1,101                         ]  interval and gets
0006          X(I)=.01*(I-1)*(N+2)                 ]  functional values
0007        1 W(I)=D*H(XL+.01*(I-1)*(XR-XL))       ]
0008          DO 2 I=1,N              ]
0009          IM=I-1                  ]
0010          DO 3 J=1,IM             ]
0011          A(J,I)=0.               ]
0012        3 A(I,J)=0.               ]        assigns initial matrix values
0013          A(I,I)=1.               ]
0014          A(N+1,I)=1.             ]
0015        2 A(I,N+1)=1.             ]
0016          A(N+1,N+1)=N            ]
0017        4 S=-1000000.
0018          DO 5 I=1,101                      ]
0019          T=X(I)                            ]
0020          Y=-W(I)                           ]
0021          DO 8 J=1,N                        ]
0022        8 Y=Y+A(N+1,J)*BASIS(J,T)           ]   finds maximum of
0023          IF(Y.LE.S) GO TO 5                ]   approximation-function
0024          TS=T                              ]
0025          S=Y                               ]
0026        5 CONTINUE                          ]
0027          T=TS                              ]
0028          V(N+1)=S                          ]
0029          S=1000000.                         computes value v_i          ]
0030          DO 6 I=1,N                         of row alpha_i, finds       ]
0031          V(I)=0.                            row alpha_m with best value ]
0032          DO 7 J=1,N                                                     ]
0033        7 V(I)=V(I)+A(I,J)*BASIS(J,T)                                    ]
0034          IF(V(I).LE.0..OR.A(I,N+1).GE.S*V(I)) GO TO 6                   ]
0035          M=I                                                            ]
0036          S=A(I,N+1)/V(I)                                                ]
0037        6 CONTINUE                                                       ]
0038          DO 9 J=1,NP             ]
0039        9 A(M,J)=A(M,J)/V(M)      ]    replaces row alpha_m by alpha_m/v_m
0040          DO 10 I=1,NP                      ]
0041          IF(I.EQ.M) GO TO 10               ]    replaces row alpha_i
0042          DO 11 J=1,NP                      ]
0043       11 A(I,J)=A(I,J)-A(M,J)*V(I)         ]    by alpha_i-v_i alpha_m
0044       10 CONTINUE                          ]
0045          IF(V(N+1).GE..0001) GO TO 4 <-------- repeats iteration
0046          DO 12 I=1,NP                          if  v > epsilon
0047       12 P(I)=A(N+1,I)
0048          RETURN
0049          END
```

The given density function H(X) on the interval XL $\leq$ X $\leq$ XR is called as a FORTRAN function. The fitting functions $f_1,\ldots,f_n$ are called via function BASIS(N,T), that is, $f_1(t)$ is called as BASIS(1,T), $f_2(t)$ as BASIS(2,T), etc.

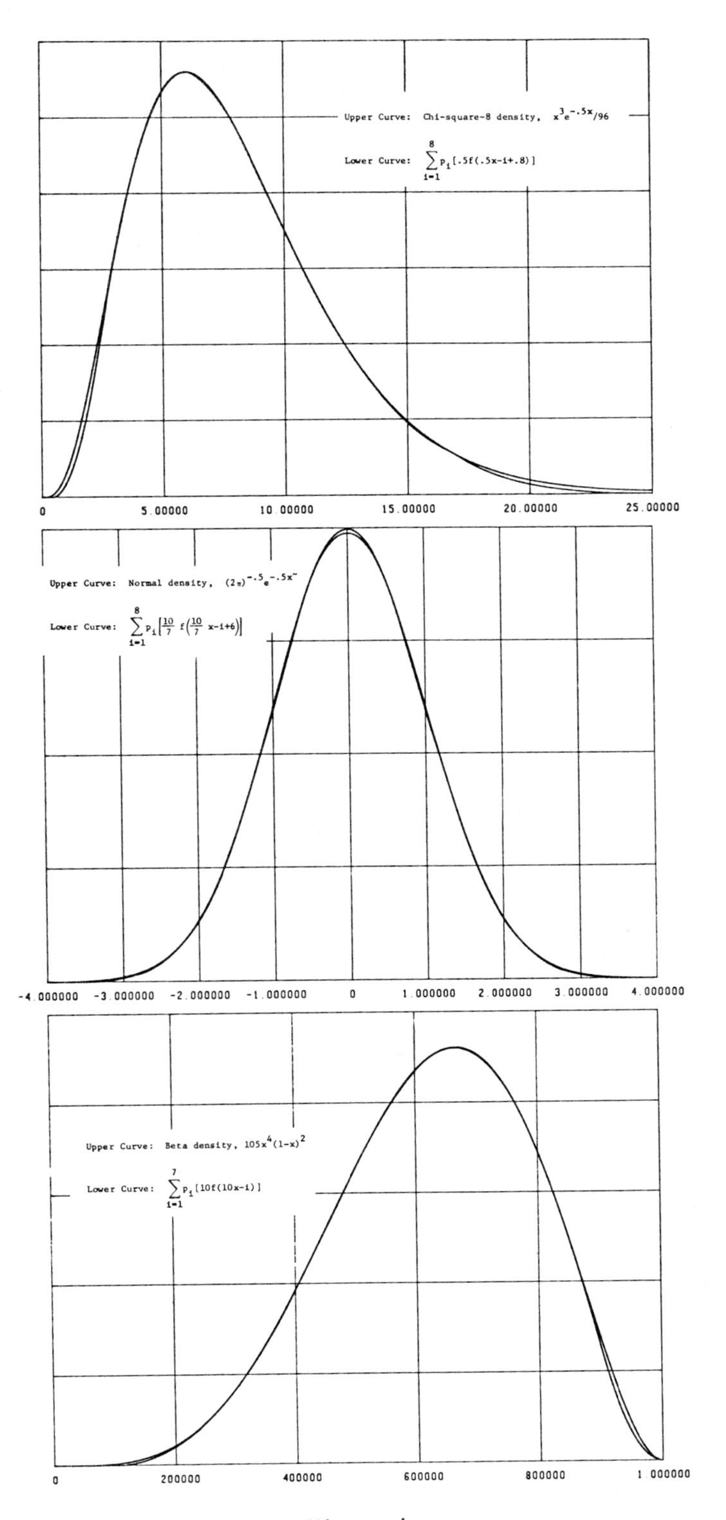
Upper Curve: Chi-square-8 density, $x^3 e^{-.5x}/96$
Lower Curve: $\sum_{i=1}^{8} p_i[.5f(.5x-i+.8)]$
0
5.00000
10.00000
15.00000
20.00000
25.00000
Upper Curve: Normal density, $(2\pi)^{-.5} e^{-.5x^2}$
Lower Curve: $\sum_{i=1}^{8} p_i\left[\frac{10}{7} f\left(\frac{10}{7} x-i+6\right)\right]$
-4.000000
-3.000000
-2.000000
-1.000000
0
1.000000
2.000000
3.000000
4.000000
Upper Curve: Beta density, $105x^4(1-x)^2$
Lower Curve: $\sum_{i=1}^{7} p_i[10f(10x-i)]$
0
200000
400000
600000
800000
1 000000

Figure 4

3. with probability p_3 put $X = U_1 + U_2 + U_3 + 2$

.
.
.

8. with probability p_8 put $X = U_1 + U_2 + U_3 + 7$
9. with probability p_9 generate X with density $r(x)$.

If p_9 is small this will be a fast and easy-to-program method for generating X with density $g(x)$. Furthermore, the procedure provides a standard pattern for generating many of the random variables occurring in Monte Carlo Theory, e.g. normal, beta, chi-square, F, gamma, log-exponential, and extreme-value distributions. The procedure is basically the same for all these distributions; one only needs a scale and location parameter and the eight probabilities $p_1, p_2, \ldots, p_8$. Papers giving these constants for many of the common distributions are in preparation. Marsaglia [2] also discusses some applications of this idea.

Figure 4 shows the fitted spline functions $\Sigma p_i f_i(x)$ for a beta, normal, and chi-square distribution.

Acknowledgement. I would like to thank David Walkup and Roger Wets for their advice on the linear programming aspects of this problem.

References

1. DANTZIG, G. Linear Programming and Extensions. Princeton, 1963.
2. MARSAGLIA, G. 'A general method for producing random variables in a computer'. American Federation of Information Processing Societies, Proceedings, Vol. 29, 1966, pp. 169-173.

APPROXIMATION OF NON LINEAR INEQUALITIES ON BANACH SPACES

M. Sibony

(University of Paris)

1. Introduction

Let X be a convex closed subset of a Banach space V, A an operator, not necessarily linear, from V to V' (the dual of V), and f given in V'. We seek a solution u ∈ X of the inequality:

$$(Au, v - u) \geq (f, v - u) \quad \forall v \in X \tag{1}$$

where (,) denotes the duality between V and V'.

If X = V the problem (1) becomes (cf. Sibony [6])

$$Au = f. \tag{2}$$

Let F be a functional on X. The problem of minimizing F on X, i.e. finding u ∈ X such that

$$F(u) \leq F(v) \quad \forall v \in X \tag{3}$$

can be written as (cf. [6])

$$(Gu, v - u) \geq 0 \quad \forall v \in X \tag{4}$$

where G is a non-linear monotone operator if F is a convex functional. We discuss first the existence and uniqueness of the solution of the general inequality (1) and give approximation methods for this solution. We then give examples.

2. Interpretation of some inequalities in Banach and Hilbert spaces

Let V be a Banach space on R and V' its dual. We indicate by $\| \;\|$ and $\| \;\|_*$ the norms in V and V'. The bilinear form (,) indicates the duality between V and V'. Let X be a convex closed subset of V.

Example 1.1

If V is a Hilbert space and P_X is the operator of projection onto X, the equation

$$u = P_X(v), \quad v \in V \tag{5}$$

is equivalent to

$$(u - v, w - u) \geq 0 \quad \forall w \in X. \tag{6}$$

Example 1.2

If V is a Hilbert space, let S be a linear operator in L(V,V') satisfying

(H1) $$(Su,v) = (u,Sv) \quad \forall u,v \in V.$$

There exists a constant $\sigma > 0$ such that

$$[u]^2 = (Su,u) \geq \sigma \|u\|^2.$$

Then [ ] is a norm equivalent to $\| \ \|$. The equation

$$u = P_X^S(v), \quad v \in V. \tag{7}$$

where P_X^S is the projection onto X with the norm [ ], is equivalent to

$$S(u - v, w - u) \geq 0 \quad \forall w \in X. \tag{8}$$

Theorem 1.1

If V is a Hilbert space and $S \in L(V,V')$ satisfies (H1), then the two following assertions are equivalent:

a) $u \in X$ is a solution of

$$u = P_X^S\,[u - \rho S^{-1}(Au - f)], \quad \rho \text{ constant} > 0, \tag{9}$$

b) $u \in X$ is a solution of

$$(Au, v - u) \geq (f, v - u) \quad \forall v \in X. \tag{10}$$

Proof. Put $g = \rho(Au - f)$, $\rho > 0$. Then (9) can be written as

$$u = P_X^S(u - S^{-1}g) \tag{11}$$

which is equivalent to

$$[-S^{-1}g, v - u] \leqslant 0 \quad \forall v \in X \tag{12}$$

where the scalar product $[u,v] = (Su,v)$. Then we have

$$(-g, v - u) \leqslant 0 \quad \forall v \in X \tag{13}$$

which gives (10).

Example 1.3

V is a Banach space. Let F be a functional on X which is convex and has Gateaux derivative F'. We want to characterize (cf. [6]) the solution $u \in X$ of

$$J(u) \leqslant J(v) \quad \forall v \in X, \text{ where } J(v) = F(v) - (f,v) \tag{14}$$

for f given in V'. We have

Theorem 1.2

$u \in X$ is a solution of (14) iff u is a solution in X of

$$(F'u, v - u) \geqslant (f, v - u) \quad \forall v \in X. \tag{15}$$

Proof. We shall need the lemma that if F' exists, F is convex iff the operator $u \to F'(u)$ is monotone on X, i.e.

$$(F'(u) - F'(v),\ u - v) \geqslant 0 \quad \forall u,v \in X.$$

To prove this, let $u,v \in X$, $t \in [0,1]$, $w = tv + (1-t)u$, and $\psi(t) = F(w)$. Then $\exists\ \psi'(t) = (F'(w), v - u)$, and

$$F \text{ convex} \leftrightarrow \psi \text{ convex} \leftrightarrow \psi'(t)\uparrow.$$

Also, (i) $\psi'(t)\uparrow \to \psi'(0) \leqslant \psi'(1) \to F'$ monotone,
and (ii) if $w_i = w(t_i)$, $i=1,2$,

$$F' \text{ monotone} \to 0 \leqslant (F'(w_1)-F'(w_2), w_1-w_2) = (t_1-t_2)(\psi'(t_1)-\psi'(t_2) \to \psi'(t)\uparrow,$$

whence the lemma follows.

Now let $u \in X$ be a solution of (14). Then if $v \in X$ and $w = u + t(v-u)$,

$$F(u) - (f,u) \leqslant F(w) - (f,w), \ \forall t \in [0,1]$$

and

$$\frac{F(w) - F(u)}{t} \geq (f, v - u).$$

Letting $t \to 0$ we obtain $(F'(u), v - u) \geq (f, v - u)$, which proves (15).

Conversely, let u be a solution of (15). Then by the lemma,

$$(F'(w), w - u) \geq (f, w - u), \ \forall w \in X.$$

Let $v \in X$, $w = u + t(v - u)$, and $h(t) = F(w) - t(f, v - u)$. Then for $t \in [0,1]$, $\exists h'(t) = (F'(w), v - u) - (f, v - u) \geq 0$, so that $h(t)\uparrow$. Thus $h(0) \leq h(1)$, which gives $F(u) \leq F(v) - (f, v - u)$, i.e. $J(u) \leq J(v)$, $\forall v \in X$. //

For existence and uniqueness of solutions $u \in X$ of (15) we have (cf. [6]):

Theorem 1.3

Let V be a reflexive Banach space, X a closed convex subset of V. Let $J : X \to (-\infty, +\infty]$ be lower-semi-continuous (l.s.c.) for the weak topology $\sigma(V, V')$. Suppose that J is not identically equal to $+\infty$, and

$$\lim_{\substack{\|u\| \to \infty \\ u \in X}} J(u) = +\infty . \tag{16}$$

Then

1) There exists $u \in X$ such that

$$J(u) \leq J(v) \quad \forall v \in X. \tag{17}$$

2) If J is strictly convex then u is unique.

<u>Proof</u>. 1) Let v_o be fixed in X. Put $K_{v_o} = \{u | u \in X; J(u) \leq J(v_o)\}$. Then (17) is equivalent to

$$J(u) \leq J(w) \quad \forall w \in K_{v_o}. \tag{18}$$

By (16) we can see that K_{v_o} is bounded in V, reflexive, and w-closed in V. The mapping $J : K_{v_o} \to \mathbb{R}$ is l.s.c. for the w-topology; thus there exists $u \in K_{v_o}$ satisfying (18).

2) If u_1 and u_2 are two different solutions of (17), we have $J(u_1) = J(u_2)$ and

$$J(tu_1 + (1-t)u_2) < t\, J(u_1) + (1-t)J(u_2) = J(u_1) \quad \forall t \in (0,1)$$

which contradicts (17). //

Remark 1.1. If J is strictly convex and l.s.c. then J is l.s.c. for the weak topology.

We can see now that problems (5), (7), (9), (14) are included in a large class of problems of the form: find $u \in X$ such that

$$(Au, v - u) \geq (f, v - u) \quad \forall v \in X, \quad f \text{ given in } V'. \tag{19}$$

If in Example 1.3 F' does not exist we can prove

Theorem 1.4

Suppose J is a convex functional on X. Then there exists an operator $A : X \to V'$ which is monotone (i.e. $(Au - Av, u - v) \geq 0$, $\forall u, v \in X$) and $\not\equiv 0$, and a functional $G : X \to (-\infty, +\infty]$; $G \not\equiv F$, $G \not\equiv +\infty$, G l.s.c. and convex, such that every solution $u \in X$ of (14) is a solution of

$$(-Au, v - u) \leq G(v) - G(u) \quad \forall v \in X. \tag{20}$$

The inequality (20) can be put in the form

$$(A_1 u_1, v_1 - u_1) \geq (f_1, v_1 - u_1) \quad \forall v_1 \in X_1 \tag{21}$$

where $X_1 = \{v_1 | v_1 = (v, \lambda) \in X \times R,\ G(v) \leq \lambda\}$, $A_1 u_1 = (Au, 0)$, $f_1 = (0, -1)$.

Proof. Let J_o be a convex functional on X which has Gateaux derivative, and is such that $G = J - J_o$ is also convex. (We can always take J_o linear.) Then every solution $u \in X$ of (14) is a solution of (20) with $A = J_o'$, and conversely. For a proof that (20) can be written as (21), see Sibony [6].

2. Methods of approximation in Banach spaces

We want first to assure the existence and uniqueness of the solution of inequality (10). After this, we give approximation theorems.

Let V be a reflexive Banach space, X a closed convex subset of V with $0 \in X$ (for simplicity).

Definition 2.1

a) $A : X \to V'$ is monotone if

$$(Au - Av, u - v) \geq 0 \quad \forall u, v \in X.$$

b) A is <u>strictly monotone</u> if

$$(Au - Av, u - v) > 0 \quad \forall u,v \in X,\ u \neq v.$$

Definition 2.2

$A : X \to V'$ is hemicontinuous if $\forall u,v \in X$ the mapping $t \in [0,1] \to (A[(1-t)u + tv], u-v)$ is continuous.

We formulate the following hypotheses:

(H2) A is a strictly monotone hemicontinuous operator such that

$$\lim_{\substack{\|u\| \to \infty \\ u \in X}} \frac{(Au,u)}{\|u\|} = +\infty . \tag{22}$$

(H3) V is uniformly convex and A is hemicontinuous and satisfies (22), and if $(Au - Av, u - v) = 0$ then $\|u\| = \|v\|$.

We have then (cf. [1], [2], [4], [6]):

Theorem 2.1

We suppose (H2) or (H3). Then $\exists$ a unique solution $u \in X$ of

$$(Au, v - u) \geq (f, v - u) \quad \forall v \in X, \text{ for f given in } V'. \tag{23}$$

Remark 2.1. If A is semicontinuous and satisfies

$$(Au - Av, u - v) \geq (\phi(\|u\|) - \phi(\|v\|))(\|u\| - \|v\|) \quad \forall u,v \in X$$

with $\phi: R_+ \to R$ strictly $\uparrow$ and $\lim_{r\to\infty} \phi(r) = +\infty$ then (22) holds, and also (H3) if V is uniformly convex.

If A is a monotone hemicontinuous operator and (23) has a solution (without supposing (H2) or (H3)) we can approximate this solution. More precisely let V be a uniformly convex Banach space, K a closed convex subset of V with $0 \in K$. We formulate the hypotheses:

(H4) $B : K \to V'$ is hemicontinuous and

$$(Bu - Bv, u - v) \geq (\phi(\|u\|) - \phi(\|v\|))(\|u\| - \|v\|)$$

where $\phi: R_+ \to R$ strictly $\uparrow$ and $\lim_{r\to\infty} \phi(r) = +\infty$.

(H5) $A : K \to V'$ is hemicontinuous monotone.

Let X be the set of solutions $u \in K$ of

$$(Au, v - u) \geq (f, v - u) \quad \forall v \in K, \tag{24}$$

and suppose $X \neq \emptyset$. Then X is a closed convex subset of K (cf. Brezis and Sibony [2]), and for g given in V', by Theorem 2.1 $\exists$ a unique solution $u_o \in X$ of

$$(Bu_o, v - u_o) \geq (g, v - u_o) \quad \forall v \in X. \tag{25}$$

Theorem 2.2

We suppose (H4) and (H5) hold. Then

1) $\forall \varepsilon > 0$ $\exists$ a unique solution $u_\varepsilon \in K$ of

$$(Au_\varepsilon + \varepsilon Bu_\varepsilon, v - u_\varepsilon) \geq (f + \varepsilon g, v - u_\varepsilon) \quad \forall v \in K. \tag{26}$$

for f and g given in V'.

2) $u_\varepsilon \to u_o$ strongly in V when $\varepsilon \to 0$, where $u_o \in X$ is the solution of (25) satisfying

$$(Au_o, v - u_o) \geq (f, v - u_o) \quad \forall v \in K. \tag{27}$$

<u>Proof</u>.

1) Existence and uniqueness of the solution $u_\varepsilon \in X$ of (26) result from Theorem 2.1 and Remark 2.1.

2) The proof is in three parts.

(a) <u>(u_ε) is bounded in V.</u> From (26) with $v = u_o$ and (27) we have

$$(Au_\varepsilon - Au_o, u_o - u_\varepsilon) + \varepsilon(Bu\ , u_o - u_\varepsilon) \geq \varepsilon(g, u_o - u_\varepsilon).$$

Thus

$$(g - Bu_\varepsilon, u_o - u_\varepsilon) \leq 0. \tag{28}$$

It follows that

$$(Bu_\varepsilon - Bu_o, u_\varepsilon - u_o) \leq (g - Bu_o, u_\varepsilon - u_o).$$

But we have

$$(\phi(\|u_\varepsilon\|) - \phi(\|u_o\|))(\|u_\varepsilon\| - \|u_o\|) \leq (Bu_\varepsilon - Bu_o, u_\varepsilon - u_o).$$

Hence

$$\left\{\phi(\|u_\varepsilon\|) - \phi(\|u_o\|)\right\} \left(1 - \frac{\|u_o\|}{\|u_\varepsilon\|}\right) \leq \left(g - Bu_o, \frac{u_\varepsilon - u_o}{\|u_\varepsilon\|}\right). \tag{29}$$

It follows from (29) that $||u|| \leqslant$ constant.

Thus there exists a subsequence, which we denote also by (u_ε), which converges weakly to ξ, say.

(b) <u>ξ belongs to X</u>. Since A and B are monotone, (26) gives

$$(Av + \varepsilon Bv, v - u_\varepsilon) \geqslant (f + \varepsilon g, v - u_\varepsilon) \quad \forall v \in K. \tag{30}$$

When $\varepsilon \to 0$ we get

$$(Av, v - \xi) \geqslant (f, v - \xi) \quad \forall v \in X$$

which is equivalent (cf. [2]) to

$$(A\xi, v - \xi) \geqslant (f, v - \xi) \quad \forall v \in X. \tag{31}$$

Thus $\xi \in X$.

(c) <u>$||u_\varepsilon|| \to ||\xi||$ when $\varepsilon \to 0$</u>. We put $v = \xi$ in (26), and in (24) we put $v = u_\varepsilon$ and $u = \xi$; by addition we get

$$(Au_\varepsilon - A\xi, \xi - u_\varepsilon) + \varepsilon(Bu_\varepsilon, \xi - u_\varepsilon) \geqslant \varepsilon(g, \xi - u_\varepsilon).$$

By monotonicity of A we have

$$\varepsilon(g - Bu_\varepsilon, \xi - u_\varepsilon) \leqslant (Au_\varepsilon - A\xi, \xi - u_\varepsilon) \leqslant 0. \tag{32}$$

Put $v = u_\varepsilon$ in (24); by addition with (30) where $v = u \in X$ we have:

$$(Bu, u - u_\varepsilon) \geqslant (g, u - u_\varepsilon) \quad \forall u \in X. \tag{33}$$

When $\varepsilon \to 0$ we get $(Bu, u - \xi) \geqslant (g, u - \xi)$ $\forall u \in X$, which is equivalent to: $(B\xi, u - \xi) \geqslant (g, u - \xi)$ $\forall u \in X$. Thus ξ is a solution of (25) and by uniqueness $\xi = u_o$. Then by (28), $(Bu_\varepsilon, u_\varepsilon - \xi) \leqslant (g, u_\varepsilon - \xi)$, and we have

$$0 \leqslant (\phi(||u_\varepsilon||) - \phi(||\xi||))(||u_\varepsilon|| - ||\xi||) \leqslant (Bu_\varepsilon - B\xi, u_\varepsilon - \xi)$$
$$\leqslant (g - B\xi, u_\varepsilon - \xi) \to 0$$

when $\varepsilon \to 0$. It follows by the strict monotonicity of ϕ that $||u_\varepsilon|| \to ||\xi||$. Thus $u_\varepsilon \to u_o$ strongly in V. //

We want now to approximate the inequality

$$(Au, v - u) \geqslant (f, v - u) \quad \forall v \in X, f \text{ given in } V' \tag{34}$$

by an equation of the form (cf. Courant [3], Sibony [6], [5])

$$Au_\varepsilon + \frac{1}{\varepsilon} Bu_\varepsilon = f. \tag{35}$$

Theorem 2.3

We suppose:

(H6) V is uniformly convex, and the convex closed subset X is of the form $X = \{v \in V \mid Bv = 0\}$ where B is a monotone hemicontinuous operator.

(H7) A is hemicontinuous and

$$(Au - Av, u - v) \geq (\phi(\|u\|) - \phi(\|v\|))(\|u\| - \|v\|) \quad \forall u,v \in V$$

where $\phi : R_+ \to R$ strictly ↑ and $\lim_{r\to\infty} \phi(r) = +\infty$. Then

1) ∃ a unique solution $u \in X$ of (34),

2) $\forall \varepsilon > 0$ ∃ a unique solution $u_\varepsilon \in V$ of (35),

3) $u_\varepsilon \to u$ strongly in V when $\varepsilon \to 0$.

<u>Proof</u>. The first two assertions are deduced from Theorem 2.1 and Remark 2.1.

3) The relation (35) is equivalent to

$$\varepsilon Au_\varepsilon + Bu_\varepsilon = \varepsilon f, \tag{36}$$

$$(Bu_\varepsilon + \varepsilon Au_\varepsilon, v - u_\varepsilon) \geq \varepsilon(f, v - u_\varepsilon) \quad \forall v \in V. \tag{37}$$

We apply then Theorem 2.2. //

Corollary 2.1

Let X be a closed convex subset for a Hilbert space V and P be the projector onto X. We suppose A satisfies (H7). Then

1) ∃ a unique solution $u \in X$ of

$$(Au, v - u) \geq (f, v - u) \quad \forall v \in X. \tag{38}$$

2) $\forall \varepsilon > 0$ ∃ unique solution $u_\varepsilon \in V$ of

$$Au_\varepsilon + \frac{1}{\varepsilon}(u_\varepsilon - Pu_\varepsilon) = 0. \tag{39}$$

3) $u_\varepsilon \to u$ strongly in V when $\varepsilon \to 0$.

Proof. Put $B = I - P$. B is a monotone hemicontinuous operator since $\| Pu - Pv \| \leq \|u - v\|$, and we have

$$X = \{u \in V \mid Pu = u\} = \{u \in V \mid Bu = 0\}. \tag{40}$$

The result now follows by Theorem 2.3.

Note that we have also proved that every convex closed subset in Hilbert space satisfies (H6).

Example 2.1

Let Ω be an open subset of R^n with boundary Γ sufficiently regular. We designate by $W^{1,p}(\Omega)$, $1 < p < \infty$ the space of functions $u \in L^p(\Omega)$ such that $D_i u \equiv \frac{\partial u}{\partial x_i} \in L^p(\Omega)$, $i = 1,\ldots,n$. The derivatives are in the sense of distributions. We take

$$V = W_0^{1,p}(\Omega) = \{u \mid u \in W^{1,p}(\Omega),\ u|\Gamma = 0\}.$$

Then

$$V' = W^{-1,q}(\Omega) = \{f \mid f = f_0 + \sum_{i=1}^{n} D_i f_i, \quad f_0, f_i \in L^q(\Omega)\},$$

with $\frac{1}{p} + \frac{1}{q} = 1$. On V we take the norm $\|u\| = \left(\sum_{i=1}^{n} \|D_i u\|_{L^p(\Omega)}^p \right)^{1/p}$. For this norm V is uniformly convex.

Let $X = \{v \in V \mid [v] = (\sum_{i=1}^{n} \|D_i v\|_{L^2}^2)^{1/2} \leq 1\}$. We want to find $u \in X$ such that

$$J(u) \leq J(v) \quad \forall v \in X, \tag{41}$$

$$J(v) = \frac{1}{p} \sum_{i=1}^{n} \|D_i v\|_{L^p}^p + \frac{\lambda}{2} \sum_{i=1}^{n} \|D_i v\|_{L^2}^2 - (f,v) \tag{42}$$

for $\lambda > 0$, $p \geq 2$, and f given in V'. We have:

Theorem 2.4

1) $\exists$ a unique solution $u \in X$ of (41), (42).
2) Any solution of (41), (42) is a solution of

$$(Au, v - u) \geq (f, v - u) \quad \forall v \in X \tag{43}$$

where

$$Au = J'u = - \sum_{i=1}^{n} D_i(|D_i u|^{p-2} D_i u) - \lambda \Delta u, \tag{44}$$

and conversely.

3) $\forall\varepsilon > 0$ $\exists$ a unique solution $u_\varepsilon \in V$ of

$$Au_\varepsilon + \frac{1}{\varepsilon} Bu_\varepsilon = f, \tag{45}$$

$$Bu = \begin{cases} 0 \text{ if } [u] \leqslant 1 \\ -4([u]^2 - 1)\Delta u \text{ if } [u] > 1. \end{cases} \tag{46}$$

4) When $\varepsilon \to 0$ the solution u_ε of (45), (46) converges strongly in V to the solution u of (43), (44).

5) When $\lambda \to 0$ the solution $u = u_\lambda$ of (43), (44) converges strongly in V to the solution of

$$(Cu, v - u) \geqslant (f, v - u) \quad \forall v \in X, \tag{47}$$

$$Cu = -\sum_{i=1}^{n} D_i(|D_i u|^{p-2} D_i u). \tag{48}$$

For proof and numerical results cf. Sibony [5].

Now let h be a parameter which tends to 0. Let V_h be a finite-dimensional space (associated with the step h) of norm $\| \ \|_h$ and V'_h its dual. We denote by $(,)_h$ the scalar product in the duality V_h, V'_h. Our purpose is now to approximate the solution of the general problem: find $u \in X$ such that

$$(Au, v - u) \geqslant (f, v - u) \quad \forall v \in X \tag{49}$$

by the solution $u_h \in X_h$ of

$$(A_h u_h, v_h - u_h)_h \geqslant (f_h, v_h - u_h)_h \quad \forall v_h \in X_h. \tag{50}$$

More precisely let $p_h \in L(V_h, V)$ be an injective extension from V_h to V. We denote by $\hat{r}_h$ its transpose. Put

$$\|u_h\|_h = \|p_h u_h\| \quad \forall u_h \in V_h, \text{ where } \| \ \| \text{ is the norm in } V,$$

and $A_h = \hat{r}_h A p_h$, $X_h = p_h^{-1}(X)$. Then we have the following scheme:

$$\begin{array}{ccc} V & \xrightarrow{A} & V' \\ {\scriptstyle p_h}\uparrow & & \uparrow{\scriptstyle \hat{r}_h} \\ V_h & \xrightarrow[A_h]{} & V'_h \end{array}$$

If $f_h \in V'_h$ we put

$$\|f_h\|_h^* = \sup_{v_h \in V_h} \frac{|(f_h,v_h)_h|}{\|v_h\|_h} .$$

<u>Definition 2.3</u>

$f_h \in V_h'$ is said (following J. P. Aubin) to converge <u>discretely</u> to $f \in V'$ if

$$\lim_{h \to 0} \|\hat{r}_h f - f_h\|_h^* = 0.$$

We formulate the hypotheses

(H8) The operator A transforms a bounded subset of V into a bounded subset of V'.

(H9) $\forall x \in X$ there exists $u_h \in X_h$ such that $p_h u_h \to x$ strongly in V.

Theorem 2.5

We suppose (H2), (H3), (H8) and (H9) hold. Then

1) $\exists$ a unique solution $u \in X$ of (49).

2) $\forall f_h \in V_h'$, $\exists$ a unique solution $u_h \in X_h$ of (50).

3) If f_h converges discretely to f then $p_h u_h \to u$ strongly in V when $h \to 0$.

<u>Proof</u>. For the first two assertions we apply Theorem 2.1. For 3) the proof is in three parts.

(a) <u>$\|p_h u_h\|$ is bounded.</u> We have

$$\frac{(A_h u_h,u_h)_h}{\|u_h\|_h} = \frac{(A\ p_h u_h,p_h u_h)}{\|p_h u_h\|} \leq \frac{(f_h,p_h u_h)}{\|p_h u_h\|} \leq \|f_h\|_h^* . \tag{51}$$

If f_h converges discretely to f then $\|f_h\|_h^*$ is bounded. From (51) and (H2) we deduce that $\|p_h u_h\| \leq$ constant.

(b) Thus a subsequence denoted also by $p_h u_h \to \xi \in X$, weakly. By (H8) $A\ p_h u_h \to \eta$ weakly in V'. Then from (H9) $\exists \xi_h \in X_h$ such that $p_h \xi_h \to \xi$ strongly in V. We have then

$$(Ap_h u_h,p_h u_h) = (A_p u_h,u_h)_h \leq (f_h,u_h - v_h)_h + (A_h u_h,v_h)_h . \tag{52}$$

Put $v_h = \xi_h$ in (52). Then

$$\lim\sup(Ap_h u_h,p_h u_h) \leq \lim\sup(f_h,u_h - \xi_h)_h + \lim\sup(Ap_h u_h,p_h \xi_h) .$$

As $\lim\sup(f_h, u_h - \xi)_h \to 0$, then $\lim\sup(A\, p_h u_h, p_h \xi_h) \leq (\eta, \xi)$. But if A is monotone hemicontinuous and if $x_i \to x$ weakly in V, $Ax_i \to y$ weakly in V', and $\lim\sup(Ax_i, x_i) \leq (y, x)$, then $Ax = y$. It follows that $A\xi = \eta$.

(c) $p_h u_h \to u$ strongly. Put $\alpha_h = (A\, p_h u_h - A\xi, p_h u_h - \xi)$. We have $\lim\sup \alpha_h \leq 0$. Then $(Ap_h u_h - A\xi, p_h u_h - \xi) \to 0$ when $h \to 0$. From (H3) we have $\|p_h u_h\| \to \|\xi\|$, and thus by uniform convexity of V, $p_h u_h \to \xi$ strongly in V. If $v \in X$ there exists $v_h \in X_h$ such that $p_h v_h \to v$ strongly when $h \to 0$. Then by letting $h \to 0$ in the inequality

$$(A_h u_h, v_h - u_h)_h \geq (f_h, v_h - u_h)_h \quad \forall v_h \in X$$

we obtain

$$(A\xi, v - \xi) \geq (f, v - \xi) \quad \forall v \in X.$$

By uniqueness of the solution we have $\xi = u$. So $p_h u_h \to u$ strongly in V.

Example 2.2. (cf. [2], [6])

We want to approximate the problem (43), (44) of Example 2.1. We put

$$W_i^{1,p}(\Omega) = \{\phi \mid \phi \in L^p(\Omega),\ D_i\, \phi \in L^p(\Omega)\}.$$

To the subset Ω we associate the net

$$R_h = \{M \mid M = (m_1 h_1, \ldots, m_n h_n),\ m_i \in Z,\ h = (h_1, \ldots, h_n), h_i \in R_+\}$$

and we write

$$\omega_{h,q}^M = \prod_{i=1}^{n} [(m_i - \frac{q_i+1}{2})h_i,\ (m_i + \frac{q_i+1}{2})h_i]; \quad \rho_h^M = \bigcup_{|q|\leq 1} \omega_{h,q}^M$$

where $q = (q_i)_1^n$, $q_i \geq 0$, $q_i \in N$, $|q| = \sum q_i$;

$$\Omega_h' = \{M \in R_h \mid \rho_h^M \subset \Omega\};\ \Omega_h = \bigcup_{M\in\Omega_h'} \omega_{h,0}^M$$

and

$$V_h = \{u_h \mid u_h = (u_h^M)_{M\in\Omega_h'}\}$$

where each u_h^M is associated with a point M and is in R^n.

The diagram illustrates the case n=2.

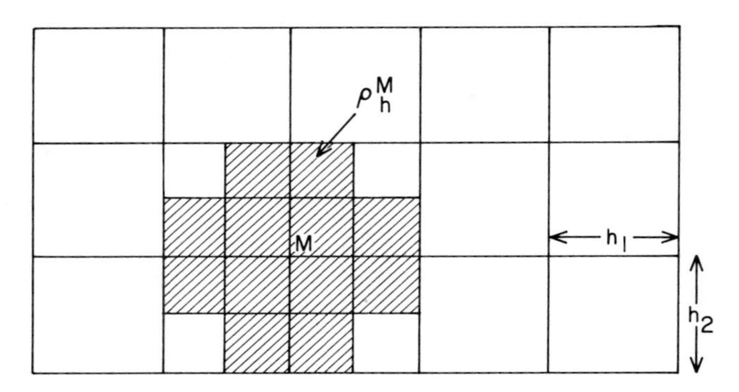

Let $x \in \Omega$, and write $u_h(x) = u_h^M$ if $x \in \omega_{h,0}^M$. Now writing $x + h_i$ for $(x_1,\ldots,x_i+h_i,\ldots,x_n)$, and so on, let

$$\nabla_i u_h(x) = \frac{1}{h_i}[u_h(x + \tfrac{1}{2}h_i) - u_h(x - \tfrac{1}{2}h_i)],$$

$$\nabla_i^2 u_h(x) = \frac{1}{h_i}[u_h(x + h_i) + u_h(x - h_i) - 2u_h(x)],$$

$$\theta_{h_i}^{m_i} = \text{characteristic function of } [(m_i - \tfrac{1}{2})h_i, (m_i + \tfrac{1}{2})h_i],$$

$$\chi_{h_i} = \frac{1}{h_i}\,\theta_{h_i}^0,$$

$$\theta_h^M = \text{characteristic function of } \omega_{h,0}^M = \prod_{i=1}^n \theta_{h_i}^{m_i},$$

$$\chi_h = \frac{1}{h_1\ldots h_n}\,\theta_h^0 = \prod_{i=1}^n \chi_{h_i},$$

$$p_h^i u_h = \sum_{M\in\Omega_h'} u_h^M \chi_{h_i} * \theta_{h_i}^M \quad (* \text{ is the convolution product}).$$

If $u_h \in V_h$ then $u_h = \sum_{M\in\Omega_h'} u_h^M \theta_h^M$; if $f \in V'$ then $f_h = \frac{1}{h_1\ldots h_n}\int_\Omega f\theta_h^M\,dx$.

$$X_h = \{u_h \in V_h \mid \sum_{i=1}^n \|\nabla_i u_h\|_{L^2}^2 \leq 1\}.$$

To the operator A we associate now the operator A_h by the formula:

$$\begin{aligned}(A_h u_h, v_h)_h &= (Ap_h u_h, p_h v_h)\\ &= \sum_{i=1}^n \int_\Omega |D_i p_h^i u_h|^{p-2} D_i p_h^i u_h D_i p_h v_h\,dx + \lambda \sum_{i=1}^n \int_\Omega D_i p_h^i u_h . D_i p_h^i v_h\,dx\\ &= \sum_{i=1}^n \int_\Omega |\nabla_i u_h|^{p-2} \nabla_i u_h \nabla_i v_h\,dx + \lambda \sum_{i=1}^n \int_\Omega \nabla_i u_h \nabla_i v_h\,dx .\end{aligned} \tag{53}$$

Then we get:

Theorem 2.6

1) $\exists\, u_h \in X_h$ such that

$$(A_h u_h, v_h - u_h)_h \geq (f_h, v_h - u_h)_h \quad \forall v_h \in X_h, \tag{54}$$

2) $p_h^i u_h \to$ solution u of problem (43), (44) strongly in $W_i^{1,p}$ for $i = 1,\ldots,n$.

3. An iterative method on Hilbert space.

Let V be a Hilbert space on R. We denote by (,) its scalar product and $\| \;\|$ its norm. Let A be a not necessarily linear operator from V to V'. We want to approximate the solution $u \in X$ of the inequality

$$(Au, v - u) \geq (f, v - u) \quad \forall v \in X \tag{55}$$

(for f given in V' and X a closed convex subset of V) by a sequence (u_n) given by an iterative method. Let S be a linear operator $S \in L(V,V')$ satisfying (H1) (cf. Example 1.2). We suppose the operator A satisfies:

(H10) (a) $(Au - Av, u - v) \geq k[u - v]^2 \quad \forall u,v \in X,\ k > 0,$

(b) $\forall$constant $N > 0$, $\exists$ a constant $C(N) > 0$ such that $\forall u,v \in X$ with $[u] \leq N$, $[v] \leq N$,

$$(Au - Av, w) \leq C(N)[u - v][w] \quad \forall w \in X.$$

(Hypothesis (b) means that A is Lipschitzian on bounded subsets of V.)

We have then:

Theorem 3.1

We suppose (H1) and (H10) to hold. Then

1) $\forall f \in V'$, $\exists$ a unique solution $u \in X$ of (55).

2) The sequence (u_n) defined by the algorithm:

$$u_{n+1} = P_X^S(u_n - \rho S^{-1}(Au_n - f)) \tag{56}$$

converges strongly to the solution u of (55) for any u_0 and $\rho = k/C^2(N)$.

<u>Proof</u>. 1) Existence and uniqueness of u result from Theorem 2.1.

2) Put $\varepsilon_{n+1} = u_{n+1} - u$. Then we have by Theorem 1.1:

$$\varepsilon_{n+1} = P_X^S(u_n - \rho S^{-1}(Au_n - f)) - P_X^S(u - \rho S^{-1}(Au - f)),$$

which gives, since $[P_X^S v - P_X^S w] \leq [v - w]$,

$$[\varepsilon_{n+1}]^2 \leq [\varepsilon_n - \rho S^{-1}(Au_n - Au)]^2 .$$

Let N_0 be such that $[u]$, $[u_0 - u] \leq \frac{1}{2}N_0$. We make the recurrence hypothesis: $[\varepsilon_n] = [u_n - u] \leq \frac{1}{2}N_0$; then $[u_n] \leq N_0$ and by (H10) $\exists$ $C(N_0) = C$ such that

$$(Au_n - Au, S^{-1}(Au_n - Au)) \leq C[\varepsilon_n][S^{-1}(Au_n - Au)],$$

and $(Au_n - Au, \varepsilon_n) \geq k[\varepsilon_n]^2$. Then we have:

$$[\varepsilon_{n+1}]^2 \leq (1 - 2\rho k + \rho^2 C^2)[\varepsilon_n]^2 = \theta[\varepsilon_n]^2.$$

If $\rho = k/C^2$, $\theta = 1 - k^2/C^2 < 1$ and $[\varepsilon_{n+1}] < [\varepsilon_n]$. Thus the hypothesis $[\varepsilon_n] \leq \frac{1}{2}N_0$ is confirmed, and the iterations (56) are contractive.

Remark 3.1. In particular we can take $u_0 = 0$, $N_0 = 2\,||f - A(0)||\,/k\sqrt{\sigma}$ (σ is a constant such that $[u]^2 \geq \sigma\,||u||^2$), $C = C(N_0)$ and $\rho_{opt} = k/C^2(N_0)$. Then we have

$$\sigma\,||u_n - u||^2 \leq [u_n - u]^2 \leq \theta_S^n[u]^2, \text{ with } \theta_S = 1 - k^2/C^2(N_0).$$

If $S = I$, we get: $||u_n - u|| \leq \theta_I^{n/2}\,||u||$.

Remark 3.2. If $X = V$ then (u_n) defined by

$$u_{n+1} = u_n - \rho S^{-1}(Au_n - f) \tag{57}$$

converges strongly in V to the solution u of

$$Au = f. \tag{58}$$

If we put $N_n = 2\,||f - Au_n||\,/k\sqrt{\sigma} + 2\sqrt{\sigma}\,||u_n||$ then $\lim_{n\to\infty} N_n = N_0 = 2[u]$ is the optimal constant N. Then we can prove that the sequence (u_n) given by

$$u_{n+1} = u_n - \rho_n S^{-1}(Au_n - f), \text{ with } \rho_n = k/C^2(N_n) \tag{59}$$

converges for any u_o to the solution u of (58).

Many examples and numerical results and choices of the parameter ρ and the operator S are given in Sibony [5], [6], [7].

Example 3.1

If $V = H_0^1(\Omega) = \{u \mid u \in L^2(\Omega); D_i u \in L^2(\Omega),\ i = 1,\dots,n;\ u|_\Gamma = 0\}$, $X = \{u \in V \mid \|u\|_{H_0^1(\Omega)} \leq 1\}$, $f \in V' = H^{-1}(\Omega)$, and

$A = -\Delta = -\sum_{i=1}^{n} \frac{\partial}{\partial x_i}$, we have $(Au,u) = \|u\|^2_{H_0^1}$, $(Au,v) \leq \|u\|_{H_0^1} \|v\|_{H_0^1}$,

and $\rho = 1$. Then, if we take $S = A$ the solution $u \in X$ of

$$(Au, v - u) \geq (f, v - u) \quad \forall v \in X \tag{60}$$

is given, by (56), without iterations by the formula:

$$u = P_X^S(A^{-1}f) = \begin{cases} A^{-1}f & \text{if } \|A^{-1}f\| \leq 1 \\ \dfrac{A^{-1}f}{\|A^{-1}f\|} & \text{if } \|A^{-1}f\| > 1 . \end{cases} \tag{61}$$

Example 3.2

With the notations of Example 2.2 we put in (56)

$$X = X_h = \{u_h \in V_h \mid (\sum_{i=1}^{n} \|\nabla_i u_h\|^2_{L^2}) \leq 1\},$$

$$S = S_h = -\sum_{i=1}^{n} \nabla_i^2,$$

$$A_h u_h = -\sum_{i=1}^{n} (|\nabla_i u_h|^{p-2} \nabla_i u_h) - \lambda \sum_{i=1}^{n} \nabla_i^2 u_h.$$

Then we have:

Theorem 3.2

The sequence (u_h^n) given by the algorithm

$$u_h^{n+1} = P_{X_h}^{S_h} (u_h^n - \rho S_h^{-1}(A_h u_h^n - f_h)) \tag{62}$$

converges to the solution u_h of (54), for $u_h^0 = 0$ and $\rho = \lambda / C^2(N_0)$;

where $N_0 = 2\|f_h\|_{L^2} / \lambda\sqrt{\sigma}$ (σ satisfies $[u_h] = \sum_{i=1}^{n} \|\nabla_i u_h\|^2_{L^2} \geq \sigma \|u_h\|^2_{L^2}$)

and $C(N_0) = (p-1) \dfrac{N_0^{p-2}}{(h_1 \dots h_n)^{(p-2)/2}} + \lambda.$

Remark 3.3. We can also prove that in the iterations (62) we can take $\rho = \lambda / C^2(N')$ with $C(N') = 2N' + \lambda$ and $\sup|\nabla_i u_h| \leq N'$. The parameter ρ does not now depend on the step h.

If we put $N_n' = \sup|\nabla_i u_h^{n-1}|$ then we get $\rho = \rho_n = \lambda / C^2(N_n')$ with $C(N_n') = 2N_n' + \lambda$.

We can also solve (54) by the algorithm

$$u^{n+1}_{h,\varepsilon} = u^{n}_{h,\varepsilon} - \rho' S_h^{-1}(A_h u^n_{h,\varepsilon} + \frac{1}{\varepsilon} B_h u^n_{h,\varepsilon} - f_h)$$

with $h \to 0$, $\varepsilon \to 0$ and $n \to \infty$ (cf. [5]).

Numerical results

1. If the dimension $n = 2$; $\Omega = (0,1) \times (0,1)$; $h_1 = h_1 = 1/10$, $\lambda = 10$, we have $||u^n_h - u||_{L^2(\Omega)} = 8.4.10^{-6}$ where u is the exact solution of (43) and u^n_h is the solution after 18 iterations given by (62) for the net Ω_h (121 points).

2. When $\lambda \to 0$ ($\lambda = 1/100$ numerically) then $||u^n_{h,\lambda} - u||_{L^2(\Omega)} = 1.10.10^{-5}$ for $h_1 = h_2 = 1/10$.

By these methods we have solved (cf. [5]) the following problem:

Example 3.3

Let $\Omega \subset R^n$, $t = (t_1,\ldots,t_n) \in \Omega$. We seek $u_1 = (u,x) = (u(t),x(t))$ such that

$$J(u_1) \leqslant J(v_1) \quad \forall v_1 \in X_1 \tag{63}$$

where

$$X_1 = \{v_1 = (v,y) \in H^1_0(\Omega) \times L^2(\Omega); \Delta y + f + v = 0; \Delta y \in L^2(\Omega); \; v \geqslant 0 \text{ a.e. in } \Omega\}$$

and

$$J(v_1) = ||\Delta y||^2_{L^2} + \sum_{i=1}^{n} ||D_i y||^2_{L^2} + ||y||^2_{L^2} + ||v||^2_{L^2}.$$

References

1. BREZIS, H. 'Equations et inéquations non linéaires dans les espaces vectoriels en dualité'. Ann. Inst. Fourier, 1969.

2. BREZIS, H. and SIBONY, M. 'Méthodes d'approximation et d'itération pour les opérateurs monotones'. Arch. Rat. Mech. Anal., 28 (1968), pp. 59-82.

3. COURANT, R. 'Variational methods for the solution of problems of equilibrium and vibration'. Bull. A.M.S., 49 (1943), pp. 1-23.

4. LIONS, J. L. and STAMPACCHIA, G. 'Variational inequalities'. Comm. Pure Appl. Math., 20 (1967), pp. 493-519.

5. SIBONY, M. 'Contrôle des systèmes gouvernés par des équations aux deriveés partielles'. (To appear.)

6. SIBONY, M. 'Sur l'approximation d'équations et inéquations aux deriveés partielles non linéaires de type monotone'. Fac. Sc. de Paris 1969. (To appear.)

7. SIBONY, M. 'Méthodes d'approximation d'une équation differentielle non linéaire'. (To appear.)

MINIMAL PROJECTIONS

E. W. Cheney and K. H. Price*

(University of Texas)

1. Introduction

[The role of projections in approximation theory; the classical examples; proximity maps; projections of norm 1; minimal projections; the existence and characterization of minimal projections.]

Our primary purpose here is to acquaint the interested reader with a particular branch of approximation theory, in which - despite current activity - much remains to be done. We hope that the problems discussed here will be found challenging to other workers and induce them to undertake researches in this area. In order to make this account most useful for the audience to which it is addressed, we have freely incorporated many known results. Furthermore, we have gone to some trouble to include an extensive bibliography and to pose explicitly a number of open problems. In most cases, the solution of these problems would illuminate long-standing mysteries in classical approximation theory and contribute new insights to the structure theory or normed linear spaces. An interesting feature of these problems is that many of them, although they are approximation problems within the broad interpretation of that term, concern the approximation of <u>operators</u> rather than <u>ordinary functions</u>. These operators are, in turn, of significance in the traditional branches of approximation theory.

We take this opportunity to summarize some notational conventions. The empty set is denoted by $\emptyset$. The difference of two sets is denoted by $A \setminus B = \{x : x \in A, x \notin B\}$. The restriction of a function f to a set A is denoted by $f|A$. The number of elements in a set A is denoted by card A. In describing mappings, a double arrow signifies a surjection; thus

* The authors were supported by the U.S. Air Force Office of Scientific Research. During the preparation of the manuscript the first author was a guest of Lund University, Sweden. The paper was presented by this author.

$f : A \twoheadrightarrow B$ means that f maps A onto B. The identity operator is denoted by I.

It is appropriate to begin with the definition of the term projection. That is taken to mean any bounded linear map P which carries a normed (linear) space X into a (linear) subspace Y in such a way that $Py = y$ for all $y \in Y$. It follows at once from the definition that Y is closed in X, P maps X onto Y, and P is idempotent ($P^2 = P$). Some examples from classical approximation theory will testify to the importance of projections.

Example 1. Let $X = C[0,1]$, the Banach space of all continuous real-valued functions on the interval $[0,1]$, normed by $\|x\| = \sup_t |x(t)|$. Let $Y = \Pi_{n-1}$, the subspace of polynomials of degree $< n$. If $t_1,\ldots,t_n$ are n distinct points in $[0,1]$, then there exist $y_1,\ldots,y_n \in Y$ such that $y_i(t_j) = \delta_{ij}$. The equation $Px = \sum x(t_i)y_i$ defines then a Lagrange interpolating projection P from X onto Y.

Example 2. Let X and Y be as in Example 1, and let w be a non-negative integrable function on $[0,1]$ such that $\int y^2 w > 0$ whenever $y \in Y \setminus 0$. The equation $(u,v) = \int_0^1 u(t)v(t)w(t)dt$ defines a pseudo-innerproduct on X and an innerproduct on Y. There corresponds a set of polynomials $y_1,\ldots,y_n$ in Y such that $(y_i,y_j) = \delta_{ij}$. The equation $Px = \sum (x,y_i)y_i$ defines then a projection P of X onto Y. It is termed the least squares projection with weight w. One can also describe Px as that element y of Y for which $\int (x-y)^2 w$ is a minimum.

Example 3. Let X and Y be as in Example 1, and let $t_0,\ldots,t_n$ be any n+1 distinct points in $[0,1]$. For each $x \in X$ let Px be that element $y \in Y$ for which the expression $\max_i |x(t_i) - y(t_i)|$ is a minimum. This operator P is a projection, the best-approximation operator on n+1 points. Note that P is linear - a consequence of the Tchebycheff theory.

Example 4. Let X be the space of those continuous functions on $[0,1]$ which satisfy the periodicity condition, $x(0) = x(1)$. Let points be prescribed as follows: $0 = t_0 < t_1 < \ldots < t_n = 1$. Let Y be the subspace of periodic cubic splines with knots $t_0,\ldots,t_n$. For each $x \in X$ let Px be the unique element $y \in Y$ such that $y(t_i) = x(t_i)$ for $i = 0,\ldots,n$. This is the familiar spline interpolation projection.

Of course, not all of the familiar operators in approximation theory are projections. The Bernstein-polynomial operator B_n is not a projection because it does not act like the identity operator on its range. The operators associated with the names of Fejér and de La Vallée Poussin are not projections for the same reason. The Tchebycheff map (best approximator) from $C[0,1]$ into Π_n is not a projection because it is nonlinear.

Closely related to the projections are the <u>proximity maps</u>. In order to define that term, first define the distance from a point x to a set Y by the equation

$$\text{dist }(x,Y) = \inf\{ \|x - y\| : y \in Y\}.$$

A <u>proximity map</u> for Y is a map $M : X \to Y$ such that $\|x - Mx\| = \text{dist }(x,Y)$ for all $x \in X$.* Occasionally, as in Hilbert space, the notions of proximity map and projection coincide, but proximity maps are usually nonlinear. A familiar nonlinear example is the map which associates with each element of $C[0,1]$ its best approximation in Π_n. It is clear that proximity maps are idempotent.

The quality of the approximations obtained from a projection is governed by the following elementary but fundamental inequality.

Lemma 1

If P is a projection of X onto Y then for all $x \in X$,

$$\|x - Px\| \leq \|I - P\| \text{ dist }(x,Y).$$

<u>Proof</u>. For any $y \in Y$, $Py = y$. Hence $\|x - Px\| = \|(x+y) - P(x+y)\|$ $= \|(I-P)(x+y)\| \leq \|I - P\| \|x + y\|$. Now take an infimum as y ranges over Y. //

This simple lemma focuses attention on the problem of discovering the projections P for which $\|I - P\|$ is small. There is, of course, a related problem of making $\|P\|$ small. We are therefore led to make the following definition.

<u>Definition</u>. Let $\mathbb{F}$ be a prescribed family of projections, all sharing the same domain and the same range. If $P_0 \in \mathbb{F}$ and $\|P_0\| \leq \|P\|$ for all $P \in \mathbb{F}$ then we say that P_0 is <u>minimal</u> in $\mathbb{F}$. If $\|I - P_0\| \leq \|I - P\|$ for all $P \in \mathbb{F}$ then we say that P_0 is <u>co-minimal</u> in $\mathbb{F}$.

---

* Such maps were employed by Aronszajn and Smith in [7] and termed "metric projections". The terminology has become confused by the later introduction of the terms "Tschebycheff map" and "metric selection". "Proximity map", as used in Goldstein and Cheney [33], seems more suggestive, and its use permits us to reserve the word "projection" for linear maps. A proximity map in a metric space can be defined as any map M with the property $d(x,Mx) \leq d(x,Mz)$ for all x and z.

Problem 1

In the family of all projections from $C[0,1]$ onto Π_n, what are the minimal elements? Are they unique? See Golomb [35]. (The minimal elements are identical with the co-minimal elements, as we prove below.)

Problem 2

In the family of all Lagrange interpolating projections from $C[0,1]$ onto Π_n what are the minimal elements? If the end-points of the interval are required to be nodes, is the minimal projection unique?

The earliest references to this problem known to us are Bernstein [10] 1931 and Fejér [24] 1932. See also [23, 21, 25, 62, 70], and Appendix 2 below.

Problem 3

Among the least-squares projections of $C[0,1]$ onto Π_n which ones are minimal? Is the minimal one unique?

In our search for projections which have favorable approximation properties we should also consider projections which are close to the proximity maps. There is one important case in which the minimal projections, the co-minimal projections, and the projections closest to the proximity map all coincide.

Theorem 1

Let T be a Tychonoff space* without isolated points. Let Let $X = C(T)$ and let Y be a finite-dimensional subspace of X with a homogeneous proximity map M. Let $\mathbb{F}$ be a family of projections from X onto Y. For an element P of $\mathbb{F}$ the following properties are equivalent:

(1) P is a best approximation to 0 in $\mathbb{F}$;
(2) P is a best approximation to I in $\mathbb{F}$;
(3) P is a best approximation to M in $\mathbb{F}$.

Proof. By Theorem 9, proved below in Sec. 3, the equation $\|I - P\| = 1 + \|P\|$ is valid for all $P \in \mathbb{F}$. From the inequality $\|x - Mx\| = \text{dist}(x,Y) \leq \|x\|$ we have $\|I - M\| \leq 1$. Hence $\|P\| = -1 + \|I - P\| \leq -1 + \|I - M\| + \|M - P\| \leq \|M - P\| = \|P(M - I)\| \leq \|P\| \|M - I\| \leq \|P\|$. Here we have used the fact that (nonlinear) operators satisfy

* In topological nomenclature we follow J. L. Kelley's "General Topology". Thus a Tychonoff space is one in which finite sets are closed, and for each point t and each neighbourhood U of t there corresponds a continuous function $\varphi: T \to [0,1]$ such that $\varphi(t) = 1$ and φ vanishes off U.

the inequality $\|A + B\| \leq \|A\| + \|B\|$. Also we have used the homogeneity of M and the fact that $\|LA\| \leq \|L\| \, \|A\|$ when L is a linear map and A is (possibly) nonlinear. The equivalence of (1), (2) and (3) now follows at once from the equations $\|P\| = \|M - P\| = -1 + \|I - P\|$.

<u>Remark</u>. The same argument shows the equivalence of (1) and (2) when Y is of finite codimension. We do not know, however, whether (3) is also equivalent in this case to (1) and (2).

Since every projection onto a nonzero subspace has norm at least 1, the projections of norm 1 are automatically minimal. The next result indicates that norm-1 projections are rare; also it shows that linear proximity maps are automatically co-minimal projections.

Lemma 2

If P is a linear proximity map then I - P is a projection of norm 1, and conversely.

<u>Proof</u>. If P is a linear proximity map of X onto Y then $\|x - Px\| = \text{dist}\,(x,Y) \leq \|x\|$. Thus $\|I - P\| \leq 1$. Conversely, if I - P is of norm 1 then by Lemma 1, $\|x - Px\| \leq \text{dist}\,(x,Y)$. Thus P is a linear proximity map.

In view of the above remarks, the minimal projections in Hilbert space can be characterized in an elementary way. To summarize, we state without proof a well-known result.

Lemma 3

Every nontrivial closed subspace in Hilbert space is the range of a unique norm-1 projection. This projection is also a proximity map.

Problem 4

For an arbitrary normal (topological) space T describe the subspaces of C(T) which are ranges of norm-1 projections defined on C(T).

For recent results on Problem 4, see Lindenstrauss and Wulbert [59] and Wulbert [92]. Under rather general circumstances, the subspaces described in Problem 4 are isometric to spaces C(Q), but the matter is not completely settled.

<u>Notation</u>. It is necessary to have a notation for operators which suppresses extraneous information. Let X be a normed space. If $x \in X$ and $f \in X^*$ we write fx in place of f(x) or (f,x). Likewise, if L is an operator we write Lx instead of L(x). If $x_i \in X$ and $f_i \in X^*$ then

$\sum_1^n x_i f_i$ denotes a linear operator whose value at $x \in X$ is $\sum x_i f_i x = \sum (f_i, x) x_i$.
No ambiguity arises from this notation, and indeed it is quite natural.

The existence problem for minimal and co-minimal projections has been studied in [47], [32] and [46]. The following theorem of Ikebe [46] is sufficiently general for most purposes. In the statement of the theorem, $\mathbb{B}(X,Z^*)$ denotes the space of all bounded linear maps from X into Z^*. The τ-topology in $\mathbb{B}(X,Z^*)$ is such that $L_\alpha \to 0 (\text{mod } \tau)$ if and only if $(L_\alpha x, z) \to 0$ for all $x \in X$ and $z \in Z$.

Theorem 2 (Ikebe)

> Let X and Z be two normed linear spaces. Any bounded map of X into Z^* has a best approximation in any τ-closed subset of $\mathbb{B}(X,Z^*)$.

The characterization of minimal or co-minimal projections can often be accomplished by using the general theorems of abstract approximation theory. The treatise [85] of Singer is the principal source of such theorems. As examples of the type of theorem obtained we give two corollaries of Proposition 3 from Wulbert and Cheney [93].

Theorem 3

> Let P be a projection of a normed space X onto a subspace Y. Let $\mathbb{B}$ denote the Banach space of all bounded linear maps from X into Y and let $\mathbb{B}_0$ denote the set $\{L \in \mathbb{B} : L|Y = 0\}$. Put $A(P) = \{\phi \in \mathbb{B}^* : ||\phi|| = 1 \text{ and } \phi P = \|P\|\}$ and $N_P(L) = \sup\{\phi(L) : \phi \in A(P)\}$. The following six assertions are equivalent:
>
> (1) P is minimal in the set of all projections from X onto Y.
>
> (2) $||P|| = \text{dist}\,(P, \mathbb{B}_0)$.
>
> (3) $A(P) \cap \mathbb{B}_0^\perp \neq \emptyset$.
>
> (4) To each $L \in \mathbb{B}_0$ there correspond $\phi_i \in \text{ext}\, A(P)$ and positive scalars λ_i such that $|\sum_1^n \lambda_i \phi_i L| < 1 = \sum_1^n \lambda_i$.
>
> (5) $N_P(P) \leqslant N_P(P - L)$ for all $L \in \mathbb{B}_0$.
>
> (6) $N_{P-L}(P) \leqslant N_{P-L}(P - L)$ for all $L \in \mathbb{B}_0$.

Theorem 4

> Let Y be an n-dimensional subspace in a normed space X. Let $P \equiv \sum_1^n y_i f_i$ be a projection of X onto $Y (y_i \in Y,\ f_i \in X^*)$. In order that P be minimal in the set of all projections from X onto Y it is

necessary and sufficient that there exist n functionals $F_i \in X^{**}$ such that

(1) $\sum_1^n F_i g_i = 0$ when $g_i \in Y$; and

(2) $\sum_1^n F_i g_i \leq \| \sum y_i g_i \|$ when $g_i \in X^*$; and

(3) $\sum_1^n F_i f_i = \|P\|$.

2. Projection constants

[The lemmas of Auerbach and John; elementary bounds on projection constants; boundaries of subspaces; a table of known values.]

If Y is a subspace of a normed space X, the relative projection constant of Y is the quantity

$$p(Y,X) = \inf \{\|P\| : P \text{ is a projection of } X \text{ onto } Y\}.$$

The absolute projection constant or simply the projection constant of Y is then

$$p(Y) = \sup \{p(Y,X) : X \text{ is a normed space containing } Y\}.$$

These concepts were introduced by Murray in [65]. We shall establish some coarse estimates of p(Y,X) in terms of simple properties of Y.

Problem 5

Is the inequality $p(Y) \leq \sqrt{n}$ true for every normed space Y of dimension n?

(See [37, 39, 42, 72, 86].)

If X is a normed space, we define SX to be its unit sphere: $SX = \{x : x \in X, \|x\| \leq 1\}$. A boundary for X is any set $B \subset SX^*$ such that $\|x\| = \sup\{|fx| : f \in B\}$ for all $x \in X$. The following lemma, in the case $B = SX^*$, is ascribed to Auerbach by Banach in his "Théorie des Opérations Linéaires" p. 238. Proofs were later given in [18, 89, 94, 71]. Here we follow Ruston [71]. Observe that the theorem has an obvious dual form.

Lemma 4 (Auerbach)

If X is an n-dimensional normed space and B is a closed boundary for X then there exist $x_1,\ldots,x_n \in SX$ and $f_1,\ldots,f_n \in B$ such that $f_i x_j = \delta_{ij}$.

Proof. Let $\{z_1,\ldots,z_n\}$ be any basis for X. By continuity and compactness there exist $f_1,\ldots,f_n \in B$ which make $|\det(f_i z_j)|$ a maximum. Let A be the matrix with entries $A_{ij} = f_i z_j$ and let λ be its determinant. Observe that B contains a basis for X*. Indeed, if this were not so then B would lie on a hyperplane of the form $\{f : fx_0 = 0\}$ with $x_0 \in X \setminus 0$, and this would be incompatible with the equation $\|x_0\| = \sup\{|fx_0| : f \in B\}$. We conclude therefore that $\lambda \neq 0$. Let $\bar{A}$ denote the matrix inverse of A, and define $x_j = \sum_\nu \bar{A}_{\nu j} z_\nu$. Then $f_i x_j = \sum_\nu \bar{A}_{\nu j} f_i z_\nu = \sum_\nu \bar{A}_{\nu j} A_{i\nu} = \delta_{ij}$. Now write $\lambda = \lambda \sum_\nu A_{i\nu}\bar{A}_{\nu i} = \sum_\nu f_i z_\nu \lambda \bar{A}_{\nu i}$, and interpret this equation as the expansion of the determinant of A by means of the elements in the i-th row. The cofactor of $f_i z_\nu$ is $\lambda \bar{A}_{\nu i}$. By the choice of $f_1,\ldots,f_n$, the modulus of the determinant is not increased if we replace f_i by any other element f of B. Consequently, $|\sum_\nu f z_\nu \lambda \bar{A}_{\nu i}| \leq |\lambda|$. It follows that $|f \sum_\nu \bar{A}_{\nu i} z_\nu| \leq 1$ and $|fx_i| \leq 1$ for all $f \in B$. This implies that $x_i \in SX$. //

Theorem 5

For every n-dimensional normed space Y, $p(Y) \leq n$.

Proof (Ruston [71]). By Auerbach's Lemma, there exist $y_1,\ldots,y_n \in SY$ and $f_1,\ldots,f_n \in SY^*$ such that $f_i y_j = \delta_{ij}$. If X is any normed space containing Y as a subspace, each f_i has an extension $F_i \in SX^*$, by the Hahn-Banach Theorem. The operator $P = \sum y_i F_i$, defined by the equation $Px = \sum F_i(x) y_i$, is immediately seen to be a projection of norm at most n from X onto Y. //

Grünbaum [39] has improved this upper bound to $\sqrt{2/\pi}\, n + O(1/n)$. Within the same circle of ideas there occurs an important lemma of John [48].

Lemma 5 (F. John)

If Y is an n-dimensional normed linear space then there exists in Y a quadratic norm $\|.\|_2$ such that $\|y\|_2 \leq \|y\| \leq \sqrt{n}\,\|y\|_2$.

From this lemma one can derive the preceding theorem in the following way. The quadratic norm must be of the form $\|y\|_2 = (\sum f_i^2 y)^{\frac{1}{2}}$ for an appropriate set of functionals $f_1,\ldots,f_n \in Y^*$. It follows that $f_i \in SY^*$ because $|f_i y| \leq (f_1^2 y + \ldots + f_n^2 y)^{\frac{1}{2}} = \|y\|_2 \leq \|y\|$. Each f_i therefore has an extension $F_i \in SX^*$, X again being any normed space containing Y. The quadratic norm on Y can be extended to a quadratic seminorm on X by writing $\|x\|_2 = (\sum F_i^2 x)^{\frac{1}{2}}$. Since $\|F_i\| \leq 1$, we have $\|x\|_2 \leq (\sum \|x\|^2)^{\frac{1}{2}} = \sqrt{n}\,\|x\|$. Let P be the orthogonal projection of X onto Y associated with the quadratic seminorm. Since such a projection is norm-decreasing, we have $\|Px\| \leq \sqrt{n}\,\|Px\|_2 \leq \sqrt{n}\,\|x\|_2 \leq n\,\|x\|$.

Problem 6

> If Y is an n-dimensional subspace of a normed space X, does there necessarily exist a quadratic seminorm $\|\cdot\|_2$ on X such that $\|y\| \leq \sqrt{n}\,\|y\|_2$ for $y \in Y$ and $\|x\|_2 \leq \|x\|$ for $x \in X$? Do there exist $f_1,\ldots,f_n \in SY^*$ such that $\|y\| \leq \sqrt{\sum f_i^2 y}$?

In connection with Problem 6 the following theorem of Sobczyk [87] is of interest: A seminorm N defined on a subspace Y in a normed space X and satisfying $N(y) \leq \|y\|$ can be extended to a seminorm N' on X in such a way that $N'(x) \leq \|x\|$. There is, of course, no assurance that N' will enjoy other characteristics of N, such as quadratic behavior. A relation between projections and quadratic seminorms also exists in the following form: every projection onto a finite-dimensional subspace is an orthogonal projection relative to an appropriate quadratic seminorm. Indeed, if the projection is $P = \sum y_i f_i$, one can define a pseudo inner-product by putting $(x,z) = \sum f_i x \cdot f_i z$. Then $\{y_1,\ldots,y_n\}$ is an orthonormal set and P is the associated orthogonal projection.

A subspace Y in a normed space X is termed an E-space or existence space if there corresponds to each $x \in X$ a closest point $y \in Y$. This is the terminology of Garkavi [29]. In other terms, an E-space is a subspace which has a proximity map. Recall also that in a quotient space X/Y, the norm of a coset (equivalence class) is defined by $|x + Y| = \text{dist}\,(x,Y)$. The <u>codimension</u> of Y is the dimension of X/Y.

Theorem 6

> If Y is a closed subspace of codimension n in a normed space X then for each $\varepsilon > 0$ there exists a projection of norm $\leq n + 1 + \varepsilon$ from X onto Y. If Y is an E-space then there is a projection of norm n+1.

<u>Proof</u>. Let $Z = X/Y$. By Auerbach's Lemma, there exist $z_1,\ldots,z_n \in SZ$ and $f_1,\ldots,f_n \in SZ^*$ such that $f_i z_j = \delta_{ij}$. For each i there is an $x_i \in X$ such that $z_i = x_i + Y$. Thus $1 = |z_i| = |x_i + Y| = \text{dist}\,(x_i,Y)$. Corresponding to each x_i there exists a point $y_i \in Y$ such that $\|x_i - y_i\| \leq 1 + \varepsilon/n$. (If Y is an E-space then ε can be 0.) Put $u_i = x_i - y_i$ so that $z_i = u_i + Y$ and $\|u_i\| \leq 1 + \varepsilon/n$. Define g_i on X by the equation $g_i x = f_i(x + Y)$. Then $g_i \in Y^\perp$ (i.e., $g_i y = 0$ for all $y \in Y$). Furthermore, $\|g_i\| \leq 1$ because $|g_i x| = |f_i(x + Y)| \leq \|f_i\|\,|x + Y| \leq \|f_i\|\,\|x\| \leq \|x\|$. Also, $g_i u_j = f_i(u_j + Y) = f_i z_j = \delta_{ij}$.

Define $P = I - \sum u_i g_i$. Now $g_i \cdot P = 0$ for $i = 1,\ldots,n$. Hence $f_i(Px + Y) = 0$ for all x, and $Px + Y = 0$ in Z. Thus $Px \in Y$. If $y \in Y$ then $g_i y = f_i(y + Y) = 0$, and consequently $Py = y$. This establishes that P is a projection of X onto Y. Finally, we have $\|P\| = \|I - \sum u_i g_i\| \leq 1 + \sum \|u_i\| \|g_i\| = 1 + n(1 + \varepsilon/n) = 1 + n + \varepsilon$. //

Problem 7

Is the relative projection constant of an E-space Y of finite codimension in a normed space X "exact"? That is, does a minimal projection exist from X onto Y?

For a subspace of codimension 1 the existence of a cominimal projection is easily seen to be equivalent to the E-property.

Problem 8

Let $c_n = \sup \{p(X) : \dim X = n\}$. Is it true, for any subspace Y of codimension n in any space X, that $p(Y,X) \leq 1 + c_n$?

Theorem 7

Let X be a normed space, and let $f_1,\ldots,f_n \in SX^*$.

(1) If $\|x\| \leq \lambda\sqrt{\Sigma_i f_i^2 x}$ for all x, then $p(X) \leq \lambda\sqrt{n}$.

(2) If $\dim X = n$ and $\|x\| \leq \lambda \max_i |f_i x|$ then $p(X) \leq \lambda$. [72]

(3) If $\|x\| \leq \lambda \max_i |f_i x|$ then $p(X) \leq \frac{1}{2}\lambda(1 + \sqrt{n})$.

<u>Proof</u>. Let $Z \supset X$. Extend each f_i to become an element of SZ^*. For Assertion (1), let $|z| = \lambda\sqrt{\Sigma f_i^2 z}$ and let P be the orthogonal projection of Z onto X associated with this quadratic seminorm. Then for all $z \in Z$, $\|Pz\| \leq |Pz| \leq |z| \leq \lambda\sqrt{\Sigma \|z\|^2} \leq \lambda\sqrt{n}\,\|z\|$.

For Assertion (2), define $|z| = \max_i |f_i z|$. For $z \in Z$ we have $|z| \leq \|z\|$, and for $x \in X$ we have $\|x\| \leq \lambda\|x\|$. Select $x_1,\ldots,x_n \in X$ such that $f_i x_j = \delta_{ij}$, and put $P = \sum x_i f_i$. Since $f_i \cdot P = f_i$, we have $|z| = |Pz|$. Consequently $\|Pz\| \leq \lambda\,|Pz| = \lambda\|z\| \leq \lambda\|z\|$.

For Assertion (3), we associate with each $x \in X$ an element $Hx \in \ell_n^\infty$ by putting $Hx = (f_1 x \ldots f_n x)$. Then H is an isomorphism between X and a certain subspace HX in ℓ_n^∞. For such a subspace we have $p(HX) = p(HX,\ell_n^\infty)$, as is well-known. (See Day [19].) By the following lemma, $p(HX) \leq \frac{1}{2}(1 + \sqrt{n})$. Now $\|H\| \leq 1$ because $\|Hx\| = \max |f_i x| \leq \|x\|$. Also $\|H^{-1}\| \leq \lambda$ because if $u = H^{-1}x$ then $\|x\| = \|Hu\| = \max|f_i u| \geq \lambda^{-1}\|u\| = \lambda^{-1}\|H^{-1}x\|$. Now it is well-known that for any isomorphism H, $p(X) \leq \|H\|\,\|H^{-1}\|\,p(HX)$. Hence in this case $p(X) \leq \lambda\frac{1}{2}(1 + \sqrt{n})$. //

Lemma 6

$$p(Y,X) \leq \tfrac{1}{2}(1 + \sqrt{\dim X}).$$

Proof. If dim X = n then by John's lemma, there exists a quadratic norm $|\ |$ on X such that $|x| \leq \|x\| \leq \sqrt{n}\,|x|$. Let P be the orthogonal projection of X onto Y associated with this quadratic norm. Following Sobczyk [86], define $U = 2P - I$. Since $Px \perp Px - x$, the Pythagorean Law yields $|Ux|^2 = |Px + (Px - x)|^2 = |Px - (Px - x)|^2 = |x|^2$. Hence $\|Ux\| \leq \sqrt{n}\,|Ux| = \sqrt{n}\,|x| \leq \sqrt{n}\,\|x\|$. Thus $\|U\| \leq \sqrt{n}$ and $\|P\| = \|\tfrac{1}{2}(U + I)\| \leq \tfrac{1}{2}(1 + \sqrt{n})$. //

Problem 9

Is it true, for each finite-dimensional space X, that

$$p(X) = \lim_{n\to\infty} \sup \{p(X,Z) : X \subset Z,\ \dim Z = n\}?$$

Problem 10

Do there exist constants α and β with the following property? To each finite-dimensional space X there corresponds a set $B \subset SX^*$ such that $\|x\| \leq \alpha \max \{|fx| : f \in B\}$ and the number of elements in B does not exceed $\beta \dim X$.

There are rather few situations in which minimal projections are known explicitly or are characterized by some interesting property. Still rarer is the situation in which the minimal projection is known to be unique. One such case occurs in projecting $C_{2\pi}$ upon the n-th order trigonometric polynomials, Hobby et al. [45]. Further examples and counterexamples of this type (i.e., in topological groups) have been given in the dissertation of Pol Lambert. See [53, 52, 54]. Another such situation is Hilbert space. The unicity of minimal projections here has been generalized by Wulbert [92] as follows. Call a subspace Y in a normed space X weakly separating if each extreme point† of SY* has a unique (Hahn-Banach) extension in SX*. An elementary argument shows that closed subspaces of Hilbert space are weakly separating.

Theorem 8 (Wulbert)

A weakly separating subspace can be the range of at most one norm-1 projection.

---

† We shall use ext K to denote the set of extreme points of a set K; thus $\text{ext } K = \{x \in K : \text{if } y \in K,\ z \in K, \text{ and } x = (y + z)/2, \text{then } y = z\}$.

Proof. Let Y be weakly separating in X, and let P be a projection of norm 1 from X onto Y. Put $B = \{f \in \text{ext } SX^* : f|Y \in \text{ext } SY^*\}$. (This defines the Choquet boundary of Y in X^*.) If $f \in B$ then f and $f \cdot P$ are both Hahn-Banach extensions of $f|Y$. Since Y is weakly separating, $f = f \cdot P$. If there exist two such projections, P_i, we infer that $f = f \cdot P_1 = f \cdot P_2$, whence $f \cdot (P_1 - P_2) = 0$. Once we know that B is a boundary for Y, it will follow at once that $P_1 - P_2 = 0$. So let $z \in Y \setminus 0$. On the 1-dimensional subspace Z spanned by z define $f(\lambda z) = \lambda \|z\|$. Then $f \in \text{ext } SZ^*$. By Singer's Lemma (below), f can be extended first to become an element of ext SY^* and then to become an element of ext SX^*. The result is an element f of B for which $fz = \|z\|$. //

Lemma 7 (Singer, [82, 84])

Each $f \in \text{ext } SY^*$ has an extension in ext SX^*.

Proof. The set $K = \{g \in SX^* : g|Y = f\}$ is compact in the $w(X^*,X)$-topology and is convex. It is nonvoid, by the Hahn-Banach Theorem. By the Krein-Milman Theorem, K has an extreme point, g. Actually, $g \in \text{ext } SX^*$ because if $g = \frac{1}{2}(g_1 + g_2)$ with $g_i \in SX^*$ then $\frac{1}{2}(g_1 + g_2)|Y = f$. Since $g_i|Y \in SY^*$ and $f \in \text{ext } SY^*$ we infer that $g_i|Y = f$. Hence $g_i \in K$. Since $g \in \text{ext } K$, $g_i = g$. //

We conclude this section with Table 1 showing known values of projection constants, or bounds on these.

X	Y	$\lambda = p(Y,X)$	Remarks
Hilbert space	arbitrary	$\lambda = 1$	
$C_{2\pi}$ (1)	trigonometric polynomials of order n	$\lambda = \rho_n$ (2)	[61, 45]
$C[0,1]$	Π_n	$\frac{1}{2}(\rho_n - 1) \leq \lambda \leq \rho_n$	[35,14]
arbitrary	$\ell_n^p \quad 1 \leq p \leq 2$ (3)	$\sqrt{n}/\sinh\frac{\pi}{2} \leq \lambda \leq (1+\sqrt{2})\sqrt{n}$ $\lambda \leq \sqrt{n} + O(1)$	[42,37] [37]
arbitrary	ℓ_n^1	$\lambda = (2k-1)\Gamma(k-\frac{1}{2})/\sqrt{\pi}\Gamma(k)$	n=2k or 2k-1. [39]
arbitrary	$\ell_n^p \quad 2 \leq p \leq \infty$	$\sqrt{2/\pi}\, n^{1/p} \leq \lambda \leq n^{1/p}$	[72] $\sqrt{2/\pi} \approx 0.8$
arbitrary	ℓ_n^2	$\lambda = n\Gamma(\frac{n}{2})/\sqrt{\pi}\ \Gamma(\frac{n+1}{2})$	[39,37,72]
arbitrary	dim Y = n	$1 \leq \lambda \leq \sqrt{2/\pi}\ n + O(1/n)$	[39]
arbitrary	codim Y = n	$1 \leq \lambda \leq 1 + n$	this paper
dim X = n	arbitrary	$1 \leq \lambda \leq (1 + \sqrt{n})/2$	[86]
C(T), T metric	$\mathbb{I}(Q)$ (4)	$1 \leq \lambda \leq 2$	[36]
$C_0[0,1]$ (5)	cubic splines, n equally-spaced knots	$1 \leq \lambda \leq 1.548$	[78]
$C_0[0,1]$ (5)	quintic splines, n equally-spaced knots	$1 \leq \lambda \leq 1.8161$	[79]
arbitrary	C(T), T Stonian (6)	$\lambda = 1$	[66,50]
C(T), T a T_4-space	functions constant on Q, Q a closed set whose boundary contains n points	$3 - (2/n) \leq \lambda$	[6,8]

Table 1. Known values of projection constants.

(1) $C_{2\pi}$ denotes the space of continuous, 2π-periodic functions.

(2) ρ_n is the classical Lebesgue constant. See Appendix 1 of this paper.

(3) ℓ_n^p is n-space with norm $\|x\| = (\sum_1^n |x_i|^p)^{1/p}$.

(4) If Q is a closed set in a topological space T, $\mathbb{I}(Q)$ denotes the ideal of all functions in C(T) which vanish throughout Q.

(5) $C_0[0,1]$ denotes the space of continuous x on [0,1] such that x(0) = x(1).

(6) A topological space T is <u>Stonian</u> if it is compact, Hausdorff, and extremally disconnected (the closure of each open set is open).

3. Projections in the space C

[The equation $\|I - P\| = 1 + \|P\|$; projections onto the polynomials; minimal projections which interpolate; projections of norm 1 onto hyperplanes; projection constants and moduli of continuity.]

In this section we consider mainly the space C[0,1], although some of the results remain valid when [0,1] is replaced by a more general topological space. The first result states that the equation $\|I - P\| = 1 + \|P\|$ is valid in many important situations. Such a theorem for compact operators on C[0,1] was first proved by Daugavet [16]. Arens, in his review of that paper [MR 28-461] noticed that the result should hold true in a wider setting. See also Krasnoselski [51].

Theorem 9

Let T be a Tychonoff space without isolated points, and $X = C(T)$. If $x_1,\ldots,x_n \in X$ and $f_1,\ldots,f_n \in X^*$ then the operator $L = \sum x_i f_i$ obeys the equation $\|I + L\| = 1 + \|L\|$.

Proof. There is no loss of generality in supposing that $\|x_i\| = 1$. Given $\varepsilon > 0$, select $y \in SX$ so that $\|Ly\| > \|L\| - \varepsilon$. Put $u = Ly$. Since we can replace y by -y if necessary, there is no loss of generality in supposing that the open set $U = \{t \in T : u(t) > \|L\| - \varepsilon\}$ is nonvoid. If we apply the following lemma to the functionals $2n\varepsilon^{-1}f_1,\ldots,2n\varepsilon^{-1}f_n$ in turn, we obtain a nonvoid open set $V \subset U$ with the property that $|f_i x| < \varepsilon\|x\|/2n$ whenever $x \in X$ and $x|(T \setminus V) = 0$. Select $t_0 \in V$. Since $t_0 \in U$, $u(t_0) > \|L\| - \varepsilon$. By the complete regularity of T, $\exists m \in X$ such that $0 \leq m \leq 1$, $m(t_0) = 0$, and $m|(T \setminus V) = 1$. Put $z = 1 + m(y - 1)$. Then $z \in SX$, $z(t_0) = 1$, and $(z - y)|(T \setminus V) = 0$. Put $v = Lz$. Since $z - y$ vanishes on $T \setminus V$, we have $|f_i(z - y)| < \varepsilon\|z - y\|/2n \leq \varepsilon/n$. Hence $\|v - u\| = \|L(z - y)\| = \|\sum f_i(z - y)x_i\| \leq \sum \varepsilon/n = \varepsilon$. The proof is completed by writing $1 + \|L\| \geq \|I + L\| \geq \|(I + L)z\| = \|z + v\| \geq z(t_0) + v(t_0) = 1 + u(t_0) + [v(t_0) - u(t_0)] > 1 + \|L\| - \varepsilon - \|v - u\| > 1 + \|L\| - 2\varepsilon$. Since ε was arbitrary, $1 + \|L\| = \|I + L\|$. //

Lemma 8

If T is a Hausdorff space without isolated points, if $X = C(T)$, and if $f \in X^*$, then every nonvoid open set U contains a nonvoid open set V with the property that $|fx| \leq \|x\|$ whenever $x \in X$ and $x|(T \setminus V) = 0$.

Proof. Select $n > \|f\|$. Since T is a Hausdorff space and has no isolated points, it is possible to divide U into n disjoint nonvoid open sets, $U_1,\ldots,U_n$. If none of the sets U_i has the property required of V then for each i there is an $x_i \in X$ such that $x_i|(T \setminus U_i) = 0$ and $|fx_i| > \|x_i\|$. By homogeneity we can assume $fx_i > 1 = \|x_i\|$. The function $x = \sum x_i$ is of norm 1 because the x_i have disjoint supports. Thus $\|f\| \geq fx = \sum fx_i > n > \|f\|$, a contradiction. Hence one of the U_i is a suitable choice for V. //

Corollary A

Let T be a Tychonoff space without isolated points. For a projection P of C(T) onto a subspace of finite codimension, the property of being a proximity map is equivalent to the property $\|P\| = 2$.

Proof. The projection I - P satisfies the conditions of the preceding theorem. Hence $\|P\| = \|I - (I - P)\| = 1 + \|I - P\|$. If P is a proximity map, then $\|I - P\| = 1$, so $\|P\| = 2$. If $\|P\| = 2$ then $\|I - P\| = 1$, and P is a proximity map. //

Corollary B

If T is a Tychonoff space without isolated points, then no non-zero finite-dimensional subspace in C(T) can have a linear proximity map.

Proof. If P is a linear proximity map with a finite-dimensional range, then (see Section 1) $\|I - P\| = 1$. But by the above theorem, $\|I - P\| = 1 + \|P\|$. Hence P = 0. //

Corollary C

If T is a Tychonoff space without isolated points, no proper subspace of finite codimension in C(T) can be the range of a norm-1 projection.

Proof. If P is a norm-1 projection onto a subspace of finite codimension then I - P is a linear proximity map onto a finite-dimensional subspace. By the preceding corollary, I - P = 0. //

Example 5. If the space T contains isolated points, the previous results fail. Thus if T is a 2-point space, $\{t_1,t_2\}$ and if L is defined by putting $\hat{t}_1 \cdot L = -\hat{t}_1 + \hat{t}_2$ and $\hat{t}_2 \cdot L = 0$, then $\|L\| = 2$ and $\|I + L\| = 1$.

Example 6. Let T be the real line, with open sets defined to be intervals of the form $(-\infty,b)$, $(-\infty \leq b \leq \infty)$. This space is normal but not T_1. Every element of C(T) is constant and thus C(T) has dimension 1. The assertion of Theorem 9 is not true for this space. (Let L = -I.) Thus the T_1-hypothesis in Theorem 9 is necessary.

Some work by Wulbert [92] is related. He has proved that if $C(T)$ is the domain of a norm-1 projection with a range of codimension n then T contains n isolated points.

Problem 11

Characterize the projections P defined on $C[0,1]$ for which the inequality $\|P\| - 1 < \|P - I\| < \|P\| + 1$ holds.

Lemma 9

Let T be a normal space, and let $X = C(T)$, $f_i \in X^*$, $x_i \in X$, $\|f_i\| = 1$, and $L = \sum_{i=1}^{n} x_i f_i$. If the functionals f_i have disjoint carriers† then $\|L\| = \|\sum |x_i|\,\|$.

<u>Proof</u>. Let $c = \|\sum |x_i|\,\|$. If $x \in SX$ then $|Lx| = |\sum x_i f_i x| \leqslant \sum |x_i|\,|f_i x| \leqslant \sum |x_i| \leqslant c$. Hence $\|Lx\| \leqslant c$ and $\|L\| \leqslant c$. On the other hand, if $\varepsilon > 0$ then there exists a point $s \in T$ such that $\sum |x_i(s)| > c - \varepsilon$. For each i select an open neighborhood U_i for the carrier of f_i in such a way that the collection of sets $\{U_1, \ldots, U_n\}$ is disjoint. Select $y_i \in SX$ so that y_i vanishes on $T \setminus U_i$ and $f_i y_i > 1 - \varepsilon$. This is possible by the Tietze Lemma. Define $\sigma_i = \operatorname{sgn} x_i(s)$ and $y = \sum \sigma_i y_i$. Then $\|y\| \leqslant 1$ and $f_i y = \sigma_i f_i y_i$. Hence $\|L\| \geqslant \|Ly\| \geqslant \hat{s}Ly = \sum x_i(s) f_i y = \sum |x_i(s)| f_i y_i > (1 - \varepsilon) \sum |x_i(s)| > (1 - \varepsilon)(c - \varepsilon)$. Since ε was arbitrary, $\|L\| \geqslant c$. //

Among the operators described in the preceding lemma, one finds the <u>interpolating projections</u>. These are projections in $C(T)$ of the form $P = \sum_{i=1}^{n} y_i \hat{t}_i$, where $y_i(t_j) = \delta_{ij}$. Here $\hat{t}$ denotes the point-evaluation functional. Observe the interpolating property of Px : $(Px)(t_i) = x(t_i)$. Otherwise expressed, $\hat{t}_i \cdot P = \hat{t}_i$. By the Auerbach Lemma, each n-dimensional subspace in $C(T)$ has an interpolating projection of norm $\leqslant n$. In the case of the subspace Π_n in $C[-1,1]$, interpolating projections of norm $\sim \frac{2}{\pi} \log n$ exist, and Erdös has established that this is the optimal order of growth [22]. Let ρ_n denote the (classical) Lebesgue constant. (See the Appendices below.) Summarizing results of Golomb [35], Erdös [22], Luttmann-Rivlin [62], Ehlich-Zeller [21], and Powell [69], we have:

† The carrier of the functional f is the smallest closed set Q with the property $x|Q = 0 \Rightarrow fx = 0$.

Theorem 10

The norms of the minimal projections of $C[-1,1]$ onto Π_n lie in the interval $[\frac{1}{2}(\rho_n-1),\rho_n]$. The minimal interpolating projections have norms $\frac{1}{2}\pi\rho_n + O(1)$. Interpolation at the roots of the Tchebycheff polynomial T_{n+1} yields norm $\frac{1}{2}\pi\rho_n - 1.0329 + o(1)$. The latter is never minimal in the set of all interpolating projections. For all large n the minimal interpolating projections are not minimal in the class of all projections.

Problem 12

Does there exist (for each n) a projection of $C[-1,1]$ onto Π_n with norm $< \rho_n$?

A curious special property of the spaces Π_n was discovered by Fejér [24, 25]. In order to arrive quickly at his result, consider Auerbach's Lemma with $X = C[0,1]$, $Y = \Pi_{n-1}$, and B the set of all evaluation functionals. That lemma guarantees the existence of $y_1,\ldots,y_n \in Y$ and $t_1,\ldots,t_n \in [0,1]$ such that $\|y_i\| = 1$ and $y_i(t_j) = \delta_{ij}$. We will prove, in fact, that $\sum y_i^2 \leqslant 1$. From the proof of Auerbach's Lemma, we see that $t_1,\ldots,t_n$ must maximize the Vandermonde determinant $\prod_{1\leqslant j\leqslant i\leqslant n} |t_i - t_j|$. If the t_i are arranged in order $0 \leqslant t_1 < \ldots < t_n \leqslant 1$, then clearly $t_1 = 0$ and $t_n = 1$. Since the nodes $t_2,\ldots,t_{n-1}$ are interior to the interval and are relative maxima of the corresponding polynomials $y_2,\ldots,y_{n-1}$, we have $y_i'(t_i) = 0$ for $2 \leqslant i \leqslant n-1$. A sketch of y_1 and y_n reveals that $y_1'(t_1) < 0 < y_n'(t_n)$. Now define the polynomial $q(t) = \sum y_i^2(t) - 2ty_1'(0)y_1^2(t) - 2(t-1)y_n'(t_n)y_n^2(t)$. Note that $q \in \Pi_{2n-1}$, that $q(t_i) = 1$, and that $q'(t_i) = 0$ for $i = 1,\ldots,n$. Since 1 is the only function having these three properties, we conclude that $q = 1$. Consequently, $\sum y_i^2(t) = 1 + 2ty_1'(0)y_1^2(t) + 2(t-1)y_n'(t_n)y_n^2(t) \leqslant 1$. This establishes Fejér's theorem:

Theorem 11

In $\Pi_{n-1} \subset C[0,1]$ there exists a basis $\{y_1,\ldots,y_n\}$ such that $\|y_i\| = 1 \geqslant \sum y_i^2$.

Fejér also proved that the nodes t_i described above are unique. They are relative extrema of the (n-1)-st Legendre polynomial (including the endpoints of the interval). (The Legendre polynomial required here can be defined as a nonzero element $q \in \Pi_{n-1}$ such that $q \perp \Pi_{n-2}$, the inner-product being $\int_0^1 x(t)y(t)dt$.)

Corollary

Π_{2n} contains an isometric copy of ℓ^{∞}_{n+1}.

Proof. If $\{y_0,\ldots,y_n\}$ is a basis for Π_n in $C[0,1]$ such that $1 = \|y_i\| \geq \sum y_i^2$ then with each $\lambda = (\lambda_0,\ldots,\lambda_n) \in \ell^{\infty}_{n+1}$ we associate the element $\sum\lambda_i y_i^2 \in \Pi_{2n}$. For each i select $t_i \in [0,1]$ such that $|y_i(t_i)| = 1$. Then $y_j(t_i) = 0$ for $i \neq j$. Hence $\|\lambda\| = \max_j|\lambda_j| = \max_j|\sum_i \lambda_i y_i^2(t_j)|$ $\leq \max_t |\sum\lambda_i y_i^2(t)| \leq \|\lambda\| \, \|\sum y_i^2\| = \|\lambda\|$. //

Problem 13

Characterize the subspaces Y in C(T) which possess bases $\{y_1,\ldots,y_n\}$ such that $\|y_i\| = 1 \geq \sum y_i^2$.

Subspaces such as those in Problem 13 have projections of norm $\leq\sqrt{n}$. Indeed, there exist points $t_1,\ldots,t_n$ such that $y_i(t_j) = \delta_{ij}$. (Change y_i to $-y_i$ if necessary.) Then the projection $P = \sum y_i t_i$ has norm $\leq \sqrt{n}$ by the Cauchy-Schwarz inequality: $|\hat{t}Px| = |\sum x(t_i)y_i(t)|$ $\leq (\sum x^2(t_i))^{\frac{1}{2}}(\sum y_i^2(t))^{\frac{1}{2}} \leq \sqrt{n}\,\|x\|$.

Problem 14

If $P = \sum_{i=1}^{n} y_i\hat{t}_i$ is an interpolating projection of C[0,1] onto Π_{n-1} such that the function $z = \sum|y_i|$ attains its norm at n+1 points, then does it follow that P is minimal in the class of interpolating projections?

See Bernstein [10], Erdős [22], [23].

Problem 15

For what subspaces Y in C[0,1] is it true that at least one of the minimal projections of C onto Y is an interpolating projection?

Problem 16

What is the absolute projection constant of the space Π_n normed by $\|x\| = \max_{0\leq t\leq 1} |x(t)|$?

It is possible to obtain some information about interpolating projections which are minimal among all projections. Unfortunately these theorems do not apply if <u>none</u> of the interpolating projections are minimal.

Theorem 12

Let $X = C(T)$, T being compact Hausdorff. Let Y be a finite-dimensional subspace of X, and P an interpolating projection from X onto Y. In order that P be minimal in the class of all projections from X onto Y it is necessary and sufficient that there exist no bounded linear map $L : X \to Y$ with the properties $L|Y = 0$ and $0 < \inf \{\hat{t}Lx : t \in T, x \in X, \|x\| = 1, \hat{t}Px = \|P\|\}$.

Corollary

Let Y be an n-dimensional Haar subspace in $X = C[0,1]$. Let $P = \sum_1^n y_i \hat{t}_i$ be an interpolating projection of X onto Y. If P is minimal in the class of all projections from X onto Y then either $\| P \| = 1$ or the function $\sum_1^n |y_i|$ has at least $n+1$ critical points.*

The proofs of these theorems appear in [70].

Theorem 13

In $C(T)$, every 2-dimensional subspace containing 1 is the range of a projection of norm 1.

Proof. Let Y be such a subspace. Select $y_1, y_2 \in Y$ and $t_1, t_2 \in T$ so that $y_i(t_j) = \delta_{ij}$ and $\|y_i\| = 1$. Put $P = \sum y_i \hat{t}_i$. Since $1 \in Y$, $1 = \sum y_i$. Since $|y_2| \leq 1$, $y_1 = 1 - y_2 \geq 0$. Similarly $y_2 \geq 0$. Thus $\|P\| = \| \sum |y_i| \| = \| \sum y_i \| = \|1\| = 1$. //

This simple technique of proof does not, of course, extend to subspaces of higher dimension. For example, let Y be spanned by the three functions:

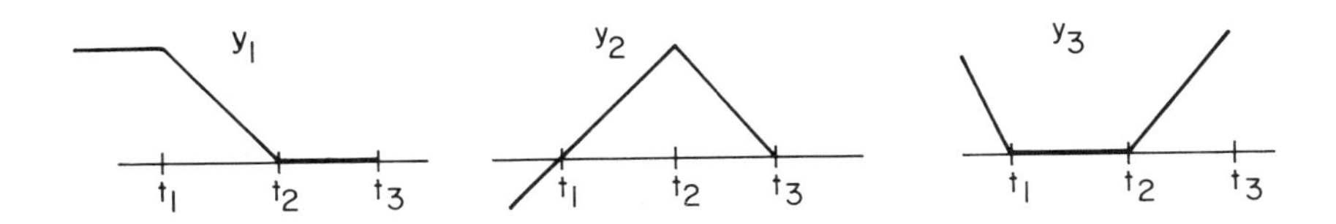

Then we have $\|y_i\| = 1$ and $y_i(t_j) = \delta_{ij}$. However, $\| \sum |y_i| \| = 3$. Note that $\sum y_i = 1$, also. Since the subspace Y has a boundary consisting of four points (viz., the joints in the polygonal lines) a previous theorem implies the existence of a projection onto Y of norm $\leq \frac{1}{2}(1 + \sqrt{4}) = 3/2$.

---

* The critical points of a function x are those t such that $|x(t)| = \|x\|$.

This example also disproves the conjecture that for any n-dimensional subspace of C[0,1] there exist a basis $\{y_1,\ldots,y_n\}$ and points $t_1,\ldots,t_n$ such that $y_i(t_j) = \delta_{ij}$ and $\sum y_i^2 \leq 1$. The verification of this statement is, however, tedious and is therefore omitted. By a theorem of Bohnenblust [12], every n-dimensional space Y imbedded as a hyperplane in a space X has the property $p(Y,X) \leq 2n(n+1)^{-1}$. This estimate, applied to the above example, gives the bound 3/2 again. In fact, here $p(Y,X) = 3/2$.

We have noted above (see Theorem 10) that the projection constant of the polynomial space Π_n in C(T) is at least $\frac{1}{2}(\rho_n - 1)$, and $\frac{1}{2}(\rho_n - 1) \geq \frac{2}{\pi^2}\log n$. By the Uniform Boundedness Principle, one obtains the Lozinski-Kharshiladze Theorem: There do not exist projections P_n such that

$$\text{(i)} \quad P_n : C[0,1] \twoheadrightarrow \Pi_n$$

$$\text{(ii)} \quad \|P_n x - x\| \to 0 \text{ for all } x \in C[0,1].$$

It is natural to ask what can be done if some of these conditions are relaxed. If, for example, we replace Π_n in (i) by Π (the space of <u>all</u> polynomials) then we obtain the following theorem.

Theorem 14

For any sequence $\varepsilon_n \downarrow 0$ there exist projections P_n of C[0,1] into Π such that $\|P_n\| \leq 1 + \varepsilon_n$ and such that $\|P_n x - x\| \to 0$ for all $x \in C[0,1]$.

<u>Proof</u>. By a classical result of Schauder, there exist $z_1, z_2, \ldots \in SX$, $X = C[0,1]$, and $f_1, f_2, \ldots \in SX^*$ such that $f_i(z_j) = \delta_{ij}$,

$$x = \sum_{i=1}^{\infty} f_i(x) z_i \text{ for all } x \in X, \text{ and } \Big\|\sum_{i=1}^{n} f_i(x) z_i\Big\| \leq \|x\| \text{ for all } x \text{ and } n.$$

Put $J_n = \sum_{i=1}^{n} z_i f_i$. Select $\delta_n \in (0,1)$ such that $(1+\delta_n)/(1-\delta_n) < 1 + \varepsilon_n$.

For each n, select a sequence of polynomials $y_{n1}, y_{n2}, \ldots$ with the aid of Weierstrass' Theorem so that $\sum_{i=1}^{\infty} \|y_{ni} - z_i\| < \delta_n$. Put $K_n = \sum_{i=1}^{\infty} y_{ni} f_i$.

This series converges by the Cauchy Criterion:

$$\Big\|\sum_{i=k}^{m} f_i(x) y_{ni}\Big\| \leq \Big\|\sum_{i=k}^{m} f_i(x)(y_{ni} - z_i)\Big\| + \Big\|\sum_{i=k}^{n} f_i(x) z_i\Big\| .$$

Since $\|x - K_n x\| = \|\sum f_i(x)(z_i - y_{ni})\| \leq \|x\| \sum \|z_i - y_{ni}\| \leq \|x\|\,\delta_n$, we have $\|I - K_n\| \leq \delta_n < 1$. Consequently K_n^{-1} exists and is bounded by $\|K_n^{-1}\| \leq (1-\delta_n)^{-1}$. Also, $\|K_n\| \leq 1 + \delta_n$. Define $P_n = K_n J_n K_n^{-1}$.

Then $P_n^2 = P_n$ since $J_n^2 = J_n$. The range of J_n is $[z_1,\ldots,z_n]$, and so the range of P_n is $[y_{n1},\ldots,y_{nn}]$. Furthermore, $\|P_n\| \le \|K_n\|\,\|J_n\|\,\|K_n^{-1}\| \le (1+\delta_n)(1-\delta_n)^{-1} < 1+\varepsilon_n$. Finally, $\|P_nx - x\| = \|K_n(J_nx - x)K_n^{-1}\| < (1+\varepsilon_n)\|J_nx - x\| \to 0$. //

Theorem 15

Let $X = C(T)$, where T is a compact metric space, and let Y be a finite-dimensional subspace of X. Let ω be a common modulus of continuity for SY. Let δ be a positive number such that $\omega(\delta) \le 1/2$, and let B be a finite subset of T such that* $\Delta(B) \le \delta$. Then $p(Y,X) \le 1 + \sqrt{m}$, where m is the number of elements in B.

Proof. This follows readily from Theorem 7. Let $y \in Y$ and $\|y\| = 1$. Let $t \in T$ and $|y(t)| = \|y\|$. Select $s \in B$ such that $d(s,t) \le \delta$. Define $\|x\|_B = \max\{|x(p)| : p \in B\}$. Then

$$1 = \|y\| = |y(t)| \le |y(t) - y(s)| + |y(s)| \le \omega(\delta) + \|y\|_B \le \tfrac{1}{2} + \|y\|_B.$$

Hence $\|y\|_B \ge 1/2$. By homogeneity, $\|y\|_B \ge \frac{1}{2}\|y\|$ for all $y \in Y$. Now use Theorem 7, part (3) with $\lambda = 2$. //

Example 7. We apply Theorem 15 to the space $Y = \Pi_n$ in $C(T)$, where T is the interval $[-1,1]$ with metric $d(t,s) = |\cos^{-1}t - \cos^{-1}s|$. If $y \in Y$, define $z(t) = y(\cos t)$. Then z is a trigonometric polynomial, to which Bernstein's Inequality can be applied. Thus $|y(t) - y(s)| = |y(\cos\alpha) - y(\cos\beta)| = |z(\alpha) - z(\beta)| = |z'(\gamma)|\,|\alpha - \beta| \le n\|z\|\,|\alpha - \beta| = n\|y\|\,|\cos^{-1}t - \cos^{-1}s| = n\|y\|\,d(t,s)$. The function ω can therefore be defined by $\omega(\delta) = n\delta$. In order to achieve $\omega(\delta) \le 1/2$ we take $\delta = 1/2n$. Let $B = \{t_1,\ldots,t_m\}$ with $t_i = \cos\frac{2i-1}{2m}\pi$. Then $\Delta(B) = \frac{\pi}{2m}$. Thus m in the theorem can be πn and we obtain $p(Y,X) \le 1 + \sqrt{\pi n}$.

Although we have emphasized the problem of investigating minimal projections onto the space Π_n of polynomials, the very same questions can be posed for spaces of spline functions. Here there is more variety because many different types of spline functions can be defined. Thus we must be content to cite a few examples of open questions.

Problem 17

Fixing the knots $0 = x_0 < \ldots < x_n = 1$, we ask for the minimal projection of the periodic part of $C[0,1]$ onto the periodic cubic splines with the given knots.

* $\Delta(B) = \sup_{t\in T}\inf_{s\in B} d(s,t)$. This is sometimes called the "mesh" of B.

Results of Schurer and Cheney [77] show that if the knots are equally-distributed, then the operator L of interpolation at the knots is nearly minimal, since its norm is close to 1. If the knots are ill-distributed, then L is certainly not minimal, because results of [77] yield a large value for the norm of L, while an operator discussed by de Boor [13] has norm ≈ 15 no matter how the knots are distributed.

Problem 18

Allowing the knots $0 = x_0 < \ldots < x_n = 1$ to vary, we seek that distribution of knots for which the interpolation operator just described has minimum norm.

It should be noted that Problem 18 is of a somewhat different character from the problem previously discussed, because here the subspace changes as the knots change.

APPENDICES

Appendix 1. On the Lebesgue Constants

Theorem

The Lebesgue constants obey the equation

$$\rho_n = \frac{4}{\pi^2} \log n + 1.27033 + \varepsilon_n$$

in which $0.166 > \varepsilon_n \downarrow 0$.

Proof. We take the above equation as the definition of ε_n. It has been known for many years that $\varepsilon_n \to 0$, and here we only wish to establish the slightly more precise result. What we want to prove first is that $\varepsilon_{n+1} < \varepsilon_n$, or

$$\rho_{n+1} - \frac{4}{\pi^2} \log (n+1) < \rho_n - \frac{4}{\pi^2} \log n.$$

Equivalently, we want to prove

$$\rho_{n+1} - \rho_n < \frac{4}{\pi^2} \log \frac{n+1}{n}.$$

Using a formula of Szegö [88] to express the left hand side, we get

$$\frac{16}{\pi^2} \sum_{\nu=1}^{\infty} (4\nu^2-1)^{-1} [(4n\nu+2\nu+1)^{-1} + (4n\nu+2\nu+3)^{-1} + \ldots + (4n\nu+6\nu-1)^{-1}] < \frac{4}{\pi^2} \log \frac{n+1}{n}.$$

It will be sufficient to establish the stronger inequality

$$4\sum_{\nu=1}^{\infty}(4\nu^2-1)^{-1}[(4n\nu+2\nu)^{-1}+(4n\nu+2\nu)^{-1}+\ldots+(4n\nu+2\nu)^{-1}] < \log\frac{n+1}{n}.$$

Within the brackets there are 2ν terms. The left-hand side is therefore

$$\frac{4}{2n+1}\sum_{\nu=1}^{\infty}\frac{1}{4\nu^2-1} = \frac{2}{2n+1}\sum_{\nu=1}^{\infty}\left(\frac{1}{2\nu-1}-\frac{1}{2\nu+1}\right) = \frac{2}{2n+1}.$$

Thus, writing $x = 2/(2n+1)$, we have to prove

$$e^x < \frac{2+x}{2-x} = 1 + x\sum_{\nu=0}^{\infty}\left(\frac{x}{2}\right)^{\nu},$$

which follows at once on expanding e^x and comparing coefficients.

Finally, $\varepsilon_1 = \rho_1 - 1.27033 = 0.166$. //

Appendix 2. The Lagrange Operator

We wish to summarize what is known about the problem of optimizing the Lagrange interpolation operator. In order to establish the notation, let $-1 \leqslant t_n < t_{n-1} < \ldots < t_1 \leqslant 1$. Put

$$\ell_i(t) = \prod_{\substack{j=1\\ j\neq i}}^{n}\frac{t-t_j}{t_i-t_j},\quad Lx = \sum_{i=1}^{n}x(t_i)\ell_i,\quad z(t) = \sum_{i=1}^{n}|\ell_i(t)|.$$

It is known that the norm of L, considered as an operator defined on and taking values in $C[-1,1]$, is given by $||L|| = ||z|| = \max_t z(t)$. The problem is to select nodes $t_1,\ldots,t_n$ so that $||L||$ is a minimum.

1. Erdős proved in [22] the existence of a constant c_1 such that $||L|| \geqslant (2/\pi)\log n - c_1$ for all n.

2. If $t_i = \cos[(2i-1)\pi/2n]$ - these are the roots of the Tchebycheff polynomial T_n - then $||L|| \leqslant (2/\pi)\log n + c_2$. This was known to Bernstein. In [21] Ehlich and Zeller gave the exact expression $||L|| = n^{-1}\sum_{i=1}^{n}\cot(2i-1)\pi/4n$. In [62] Luttmann and Rivlin prove a result which implies

$$||L|| = (2/\pi)\log n + c_3 + \delta_n$$

in which $c_3 = (2/\pi)[\log(8/\pi)+\gamma] = 0.9625\ldots$, γ is Euler's constant, and $\{\delta_n\}$ is a sequence tending to zero. See also Powell [69]. Thus Erdős' result mentioned above is (asymptotically) best possible, and interpolation at the roots of T_n is (asymptotically) best possible.

3. By taking the nodes to be the roots of $(x^2 - 1)P_n'(x)$, where P_n is the n-th Legendre polynomial, Luttmann and Rivlin [62] obtained lower values of $||L||$ than were obtained using the roots of T_n. This they verified only for $n \leq 40$.

4. By taking the nodes $t_i = \sec(\pi/2n) \cos(2i - 1)\pi/2n$, Luttmann and Rivlin obtained still lower values of $||L||$. This was verified for $n \leq 40$.

5. Luttmann and Rivlin prove that the optimal nodes are not unique for any value of $n \geq 1$. This was also known to Ehlich and Zeller. If the nodes are subjected to an affine transformation such that $t_n = 1$ and $t_1 = -1$ then $||L||$ does not change. It is conjectured that the optimal nodes are unique if the conditions $t_n = -1$, $t_1 = 1$ are imposed.

6. By taking the nodes to be the extrema of T_{n-1}, Ehlich and Zeller obtained $||L|| = A_{n-1}$ for even n and $A_{n-1} - (n - 1)^{-2} < ||L|| < A_{n-1}$ for odd n. Here A_n is the operator-norm described above in (2).

Appendix 3. <u>On a Theorem of Sobczyk</u>.

Here we prove a theorem of Sobczyk in a form slightly stronger than the original. The importance of the theorem is that it gives a lower bound on $p(Y,X)$ when $\dim X \lesssim 2 \dim Y$.

Theorem (Sobczyk)

For each n of the form 2^k there exist complementary subspaces Y_1 and Y_2 in ℓ_n^∞ such that $p(Y_i) \geq \sqrt{n}/2$.

<u>Proof</u>. Define matrices $B^1,\dots,B^k$ as follows. $B^1 = \begin{pmatrix} 1 & 1 \\ 1 & -1 \end{pmatrix}$. Then $B^{\nu+1}$ is obtained from B^ν by replacing each ± 1 in B^ν by $\pm B^1$. We assert that $B^\nu B^\nu = 2^\nu I$. For $\nu = 1$ this is quickly verified. If it is true for an index ν then let the elements of B^ν be b_{ij} so that $\sum_\alpha b_{i\alpha} b_{\alpha j} = 2^\nu \delta_{ij}$. The matrix $B^{\nu+1}$ is composed of 2×2 blocks, $b_{ij}B^1$. The 2×2 block components of $B^{\nu+1} B^{\nu+1}$ are therefore given by $C_{ij} = \sum_\alpha b_{i\alpha} B^1 b_{\alpha j} B^1 = 2^\nu \delta_{ij} \begin{pmatrix} 2 & 0 \\ 0 & 2 \end{pmatrix}$. Hence $B^{\nu+1} B^{\nu+1} = 2^{\nu+1} I$. Let $U = B^k/\sqrt{n}$. Then $U^2 = I$. By induction we see that $\mathrm{tr}\, U = 0$ (tr = trace). Put $Y_1 = \{x : Ux = x\}$, and $Y_2 = \{x : Ux = -x\}$. One easily verifies that the operator $Q_1 = \frac{1}{2}(I + U)$ is a projection of ℓ_n^∞ onto Y_1 and that $Q_2 = I - Q_1$ is a projection onto Y_2. Thus $\ell_n^\infty = Y_1 \oplus Y_2$. For the rest of the proof we consider Y_1. The argument for Y_2 is the same, mutatis mutandis.

Let P be any projection of ℓ_n^∞ onto Y_1. Put $A = 2P - I - U$. Then $UA = 2UP - U - I = 2P - U - I = A$. Note that $UP = P$ because P projects into the space where U acts like the identity. Since P and Q_1 are both projections onto Y_1, we have $PQ_1 = Q_1$. Thus $\frac{1}{2}(A + I + U)\frac{1}{2}(I + U) = \frac{1}{2}(I + U)$. After expanding and setting $U^2 = I$ we obtain $AU + A = 0$. Thus $UA = -AU = A$.

From this last equation, it follows that tr A = 0 because $\text{tr } A = \text{tr } UA = \sum_i \sum_\nu U_{i\nu} A_{\nu i} = \text{tr } AU = -\text{tr } A$. Hence $\text{tr } PU = \text{tr } \frac{1}{2}(A + I + U)U =$

$\frac{1}{2}\text{tr}(-A + U + I) = \frac{1}{2}\text{tr } I = n/2$. We infer that at least one diagonal element of PU is $\geq 1/2$. For some index j, then, $1/2 \leq (PU)_{jj} = \sum_\nu P_{j\nu} U_{\nu j} \leq$

$\max_\nu |U_{\nu j}| \sum_\nu |P_{j\nu}| \leq \|P\| /\sqrt{n}$. This establishes that $p(Y_1, \ell_n^\infty) \geq \sqrt{n}/2$. //

References

1. AMIR, D. 'Continuous function spaces with the bounded extension property'. Israel J. Math., 10F (1962), pp. 133-138.

2. AMIR, D. 'Continuous function spaces with the separable projection property'. Israel J. Math., 10F (1962), pp. 163-164.

3. AMIR, D. 'Projections into continuous function spaces'. Proc. Amer. Math. Soc., 15 (1964), pp. 396-402.

4. ANDO, T. 'Contractive projections in L_p-spaces'. Pacific J. Math., 17 (1966), pp. 391-405.

5. ANDO, T. and AMEMIYA, I. 'Almost everywhere convergence of prediction sequence in L_p $(1 < p < \infty)$'. Z. Wahrscheinlichkeitstheorie und Verw. Gebiete, 4 (1965), pp. 113-120.

6. ARENS, R. 'Projections on continuous function spaces'. Duke Math. J., 32 (1965), pp. 469-478.

7. ARONSZAJN, N. and SMITH, K. T. 'Invariant subspaces of completely continuous operators'. Ann. of Math., 60 (1954), pp. 345-350.

8. BAKER, J. W. 'Some uncompleted subspaces of C(X) of the type C(Y)'. Studia Math., 36 (1969), No. 2.

9. BERMAN, D. L. A series of papers on linear polynomial operators in various Russian journals; we give only the citations in Math. Reviews: 20-5387, 24-A962, 24-A2835, 24-A3463, 25-2367, 26-4180, 27-1827, 28-473, 28-5143, 27-516, 29-3810, 30-3332, 31-3784.

10. BERNSTEIN, S. N. 'Sur la limitation des valeurs d'un polynome...'. Izv. Akad. Nauk SSSR Ser. Mat. (1931), pp. 1025-1050. Collected Works, Moscow 1955, vol. II, pp. 107-129.

11. BLUMENTHAL, R. M., LINDENSTRAUSS, J. and PHELPS, R. R. 'Extreme operators into C(K)'. Pacific J. Math., 15 (1965), pp. 747-756.

12. BOHNENBLUST, F. 'Convex regions and projections in Minkowski spaces'. Ann. of Math., 39 (1938), pp. 301-308.

13. BOOR, C. de. 'On uniform approximation by splines'. J. Approx. Th., 1 (1968), pp. 219-235.

14. CHENEY, E. W. Introduction to Approximation Theory. McGraw-Hill, 1966.

15. CLENSHAW, C. W. 'Comparison of 'best'polynomial approximations with truncated Chebyshev series expansions'. SIAM J. Numer. Anal., 1 (1964), pp. 26-37.

16. DAUGAVET, I. K. 'A property of compact operators in the space C'. Uspehi Mat. Nauk SSSR, 18 (1963), pp. 157-158, Math. Reviews 28-461.

17. DAVIS, W. J. , DEAN, D. W. and SINGER, I. 'Complemented subspaces and Λ-systems in Banach spaces'. Israel J. Math., 6 (1968), pp. 303-309.

18. DAY, M. M. 'Polynomials circumscribed about closed convex curves'. Trans. Amer. Math. Soc., 62 (1947), pp. 315-319.

19. DAY, M. M. Normed Linear Spaces. Springer, 1962.

20. DOUGLAS, R. G. 'Contractive projections on an L^1-space'. Pacific J. Math., 15 (1965), pp. 443-462.

21. EHLICH, H. and ZELLER, K. 'Auswertung der Normen von Interpolationsoperatoren'. Math. Ann., 164 (1966), pp. 105-112.

22. ERDOS, P. 'Problems and results...'. Acta Math. Acad. Sci. Hung., 12 (1961), pp. 235-244.

23. ERDOS, P. 'Problems and results...'. Mathematica (Cluj), 10 (1968), pp. 65-73.

24. FEJER, L. 'Bestimmung derjenigen Abszissen...'. Ann. Scuola Norm. Sup. Pisa, 2 (1932), pp. 263-276.

25. FEJER, L. 'Lagrangesche Interpolation...'. Math. Ann., 106 (1932), pp. 1-55.

26. FEJER, L. 'Lebesguesche Konstanten...'. J. Reine Angew. Math., 138 (1910), pp. 22-53.

27. FEKETE, M. 'Uber die Verteilung...'. Math. Z., 17 (1923), pp. 228-249.

28. FREY, T. 'Conditions of convergence...'. Mat. Sb., 54 (1961), pp. 137-176; Math. Reviews, 26-6651.

29. GARKAVI, A. L. 'On best approximation by elements of infinite-dimensional subspaces'. Mat. Sb., 62 (1963), pp. 104-120.

30. GARKAVI, A. L. 'On Cebyshev and almost Cebyshev subspaces'. Dokl. Akad. Nauk SSSR, 149 (1963), pp. 1250-1255.

31. GARSIA, A. M. 'Some bounds on best uniform linear approximation'. Numer. Math., 7 (1965), pp. 197-205.

32. GOLDSTEIN, A. A. and CHENEY, E. W. 'Tchebycheff approximation and related extremal problems'. J. Math. Mech., 14 (1965), pp. 87-98.

33. GOLDSTEIN, A. A. and CHENEY, E. W. 'Proximity maps for convex sets'. Proc. Amer. Math. Soc., 10 (1959), pp. 448-450.

34. GOLOMB, M. Lectures on Theory of Approximation. Argonne Nat. Lab., Argonne, Ill., USA, 1962.

35. GOLOMB, M. 'Optimal and nearly optimal linear approximation', in Garabedian, H. L. (Ed.), Approximation of Functions, pp. 83-100. Elsevier, 1965.

36. GOODNER, D. B. 'Projections in normed linear spaces'. Trans. Amer. Math. Soc., 69 (1950), pp. 89-108.

37. GORDAN, Y. 'On the projection and MacPhail constants of ℓ_n^p-spaces'. Israel J. Math., 6 (1968), pp. 295-302.

38. GRUNBAUM, B. 'On some covering and intersection properties...'. Pacific J. Math., 9 (1959), pp. 487-494.

39. GRUNBAUM, B. 'Projection constants'. Trans. Amer. Math. Soc., 95 (1960), pp. 451-465.

40. GRUNBAUM, B. 'Some applications of expansion constants'. Pacific J. Math., 10 (1960), pp. 193-201.

41. GRUNBAUM, B. 'Projections into function spaces'. Proc. Amer. Math. Soc., 13 (1962), pp. 316-324.

42. GURARII, V. I., KADEC, M. I. and MACAEV, V. I. 'On distances between finite-dimensional analogues of L^p-spaces'. Mat. Sb., 70 (1966), pp. 481-489. Transl.: Math. USSR-Sb. Ser. II, 76, pp. 207-216.

43. HANNER, O. 'Intersections of translates of convex bodies'. Math. Scand., 4 (1956), pp. 65-87.

44. HARDY, G. H. 'Note on Lebesgue's constants...'. J. London Math. Soc., 17 (1942), pp. 4-13.

45. HOBBY, C., CHENEY, E. W., MORRIS, P. D., SCHURER, F. and WULBERT, D. E. 'On the minimal property of the Fourier projection'. Bull. Amer. Math. Soc., 75 (1969), pp. 51-52; Trans. Amer. Math. Soc., to appear.

46. IKEBE, Y. 'Generalizations of the Alaoglu theorem with applications to approximation theory', Part II. Proc. Japan Acad., 44 (1968), pp. 442-444.

47. ISBELL, J. R. and SEMADENI, Z. 'Projection constants and spaces of continuous functions'. Trans. Amer. Math. Soc., 107 (1963), pp. 38-48.

48. JOHN, F. 'Extremum problems with inequalities...'. Courant Anniversary Volume, Interscience, 1948.

49. KADEC, M. I. 'On the systems of Lozinski-Kharshiladze'. Uspehi Mat. Nauk, 18 (1963), pp. 167-170.

50. KELLEY, J. L. 'Banach spaces with the extension property'. Trans. Amer. Math. Soc., 72 (1952), pp. 323-326.

51. KRASNOSELSKI, A. 'A class of operators in the space of abstract continuous functions'. Mat. Zametki, 2 (1967), pp. 599-604 = Math. Notes USSR, 2 (1967), pp. 600-605.

52. LAMBERT, P. V. 'Realité des projecteurs de norme minimum...'. Bull. Acad. Royale Belgique Classe de Sciences, 5e Serie, 53 (1967), pp. 91-100.

53. LAMBERT, P. V. Minimum norm projectors on the linear spaces of finite sets of characters. Dissertation, University of Brussels, 1968.

54. LAMBERT, P. V. 'On the minimum norm property of the Fourier projection...'. Bull. Soc. Math. Belg., to appear.

55. LAZAR, A. J., WULBERT, D. E. and MORRIS, P. D. 'Continuous selections for metric projections'. J. Functional Anal., 3 (1969), pp. 193-216.

56. LINDENSTRAUSS, J. 'On operators which attain their norm'. Israel J. Math., 1 (1963), pp. 139-148.

57. LINDENSTRAUSS, J. 'On projections with norm 1...'. Proc. Amer. Math. Soc., 15 (1964), pp. 403-406.

58. LINDENSTRAUSS, J. 'Extension of Compact Operators'. Amer. Math. Soc. Memoir 48 (1964).

59. LINDENSTRAUSS, J. and WULBERT, D. E. 'Classificationof Banach spaces whose duals are L_1-spaces'. J. Functional Anal., to appear.

60. LLOYD, S. P. 'On certain projections in spaces of continuous functions'. Pacific J. Math., 13 (1963), pp. 171-175.

61. LOZINSKI, S. 'On a class of linear operators'. Dokl. Akad. Nauk SSSR, 61 (1948), pp. 193-196.

62. LUTTMANN, F. W. and RIVLIN, T. J. 'Some numerical experiments in the theory of polynomial interpolation'. IBM J. Develop., 9 (1965), pp. 187-191.

63. MICHAEL, E. and PELCZYNSKI, A. 'Separable Banach spaces which admit ℓ_n^∞ approximations'. Israel J. Math., 4 (1966), pp. 189-198.

64. MOTZKIN, T. S. and SHARMA, A. 'Next-to-interpolatory approximation'. Canad. Math. J., 18 (1966), pp. 1196-1211.

65. MURRAY, F. J. 'On complementary manifolds and projections...'. Trans. Amer. Math. Soc., 41 (1937), pp. 138-152.

66. NACHBIN, L. 'A theorem of Hahn-Banach type for linear transformations'. Trans. Amer. Math. Soc., 68 (1950), pp. 28-46.

67. NEUMANN, J. von. 'Some matrix inequalities and metrization of matrix space'. Tomsk Univ. Review, 1 (1937), pp. 286-300. Collected works, vol. 4, pp. 205-219.

68. PELCZYNSKI, A. 'Projections in certain Banach spaces'. Studia Math., 19 (1960), pp. 209-228.

69. POWELL, M. J. D.'On the maximum errors of polynomial approximation...'. Computer J., 9 (1967), pp. 404-407.

70. PRICE, K. and CHENEY, E. W. 'Minimal interpolating projections'. To appear in Proceedings of Conference on Approximation Theory, Oberwolfach, Germany, June 1969. Birkhauser-Verlag.

71. RUSTON, A. F. 'Auerbach's theorem...'. Proc. Camb. Phil. Soc., 58 (1964), pp. 476-480.

72. RUTOVITZ, D. 'Some parameters associated with finite-dimensional Banach spaces'. J. London Math. Soc., 40 (1965), pp. 241-255.

73. SAPOGOV, N. A. 'Norms of linear polynomial operators'. Sov. Math. Dokl., 3 (1962), pp. 602-604.

74. SCHATTEN, R. 'On projections with bound 1'. Ann. of Math., 48 (1947), pp. 321-325.

75. SCHATTEN, R. 'The greatest cross-norm'. J. Res. Nat. Bur. Standards 68B (1964), pp. 185-193.

76. SCHONHAGE, A. 'Fehlerfortpflanzung bei Interpolation'. Numer. Math., 3 (1961), pp. 62-71.

77. SCHURER, F. and CHENEY, E. W. 'A note on the operators arising in splin approximation'. J. Approx. Th., 1 (1968), pp. 94-102.

78. SCHURER, F. and CHENEY, E. W. 'On interpolating cubic splines with equally-spaced nodes'. Indag. Math., 30 (1968), pp. 517-524.

79. SCHURER, F. 'On interpolating periodic quintic spline functions with equally-spaced nodes'. These Proceedings, pp. 71-81.

80. SEEVER, G. L. 'Nonnegative projections on $C_0(X)$'. Pacific J. Math., 17 (1966), pp. 159-166.

81. SEMADENI, Z. 'Simultaneous extensions and projections in spaces of continuous functions'. Lecture Notes, Aarhus University, 1965.

82. SINGER, I. 'Sur l'extension des fonctionelles linéaires'. Rev. Roumaine Math. Pures Appl., 1 (1956), pp. 99-106.

83. SINGER, I. 'Sur l'approximation uniform des operateurs...'. Arch. Math., 11 (1960), pp. 289-293.

84. SINGER, I. 'On the extension of continuous linear functionals...'. Math. Ann., 159 (1965), pp. 344-355.

85. SINGER, I. Best Approximation in Normed Spaces by Elements of Subspaces. Ed. Acad. Repub. Social. Romania, Bucarest 1967 (Rumanian).

86. SOBCZYK, A. 'Projections in Minkowski and Banach spaces'. Duke Math. J., 8 (1941), pp. 78-106.

87. SOBCZYK, A. 'On the extension of linear transformations'. Trans. Amer. Math. Soc., 55 (1944), pp. 153-169.

88. SZEGO, G. 'Uber die Lebesgueschen Konstanten...'. Math. Z., 9 (1921), pp. 163-166.

89. TAYLOR, A. 'A geometric theorem and its application to biorthogonal systems'. Bull. Amer. Math. Soc., 53 (1947), pp. 614-616.

90. TIKHOMIROV, V. 'Diameter of sets in function spaces and the theory of best approximation'. Uspehi Mat. Nauk, 15 (1960) = Russian Math. Surveys, 15 (1960), pp. 75-111.

91. WULBERT, D. E. 'Convergence of operators and Korovkin's theorem'. J. Approx. Th., 1 (1968), pp. 381-390.

92. WULBERT, D. E. 'Some complemented function spaces in C(X)'. Pacific J. Math., 24 (1968), pp. 589-602.

93. WULBERT, D. E. and CHENEY, E. W. 'Existence and unicity of best approximations'. Scand. Math., 24 (1969), pp. 113-140.

94. YAMABE, H. and YUJOBO, Z. 'On the continuous function defined on a sphere'. Osaka Math. J., 2 (1950), pp. 19-22. Also, Collected Works of H. Yamabe. Gordon and Breach, 1967.

INTERPOLATING SUBSPACES IN APPROXIMATION THEORY

D. A. Ault, F. R. Deutsch*†, P. D. Morris† and J. E. Olson

(Pennsylvania State University)

1. Introduction

There is a very beautiful, now classical, theory associated with the problem of best approximation in $C[a,b]$ by elements of an n-dimensional Haar subspace. In particular (cf. e.g. Cheney [4]): best approximations are always unique and are characterized by an alternation property; a de la Vallée Poussin theorem provides lower bounds on the error of approximation; best approximations are strongly unique (in the sense of Newman and Shapiro [18]); the metric projection or best approximation operator is pointwise Lipschitz continuous; and the so-called "first and second algorithms" of Remez provide effective means for the actual computation of best approximations.

It is natural to ask whether one can extend the notion of a Haar subspace so as to be valid in an <u>arbitrary</u> normed linear space, and at the same time preserve as much of the $C[a,b]$-theory as possible. In this paper we introduce the notion of an <u>interpolating subspace</u> of a normed linear space. In the particular space $C(T)$, T compact Hausdorff, the interpolating subspaces turn out to be precisely the Haar subspaces. (Recall that an n-dimensional subspace M of $C(T)$ is called a <u>Haar subspace</u> if every function in $M \sim \{0\}$ has at most $n-1$ zeros in T.) We shall verify that <u>corresponding to each one of the classical results mentioned in the preceding paragraph for Haar subspaces in $C[a,b]$, there is a strictly analogous result valid for interpolating subspaces in an arbitrary normed linear space</u>.

---

* Paper presented by this author.

† These authors were supported by grants from the National Science Foundation.

Because the richness of the classical Haar subspace theory carries over in toto to the more general case of interpolating subspaces, it might be suspected that interpolating subspaces are rather rare in general normed linear spaces. Indeed, interpolating subspaces do not exist in those spaces having strictly convex dual spaces (theorem 3.1). On the other hand, theorem 3.2 says that in $C_o(T)$, T locally compact Hausdorff, the interpolating subspaces are precisely the Haar subspaces again. (The definition of Haar subspace in $C_o(T)$ is the same as given for C(T) above.) Also, if (T,Σ,μ) is a σ-finite measure space, then (theorem 3.3) $L_1(T,\Sigma,\mu)$ contains an interpolating subspace of dimension $n > 1$ if and only if T is the union of at least n atoms. Also, $L_1(T,\Sigma,\mu)$ contains a one-dimensional interpolating subspace if and only if T contains an atom. In particular, (corollary 3.5) the space ℓ_1 has interpolating subspaces of every finite dimension.

In this paper, we will for the most part simply state some of the main results concerning interpolating subspaces. Detailed proofs, along with related material, will appear elsewhere.

2. Definitions, notation, and two basic results

Let X be a real normed linear space and X* its dual space. We denote the norm-closed unit balls in each of these spaces by S(X) and S(X*) respectively. If K is any subset of X, ext K denotes the set of extreme points of K. If $x_1,\ldots,x_n$ are n independent vectors in X, then $[x_1,\ldots,x_n]$ denotes the n-dimensional linear subspace of X generated by these vectors. By subspace we always mean linear subspace. If K is a subset of X and $x \in X$, an element $x_o \in K$ is called a <u>best approximation</u> to x from K if

$$\|x - x_o\| = \inf\{\|x - y\| : y \in K\} \equiv d(x,K).$$

If each $x \in X$ has a unique best approximation in K, then K is called a <u>Tchebycheff</u> set. If M is a subspace of X, then

$$M^{\perp} \equiv \{x^* \in X^*: x^*(y) = 0 \text{ for every } y \in M\}.$$

All other notation or terminology is defined in Dunford and Schwartz [8].

<u>Definition</u>. An n-dimensional subspace M of X is called an <u>interpolating subspace</u> if, for each set of n independent functionals $x_1^*,\ldots,x_n^*$ in ext S(X*) and each set of n real scalars $c_1,\ldots,c_n$, there is a unique

element $y \in M$ such that $x_i^*(y) = c_i$ for $i = 1,\ldots,n$.

Theorem 2.1

Let $M = [x_1,\ldots,x_n]$ be an n-dimensional subspace of X. The following statements are equivalent.

(1) M is an interpolating subspace.

(2) For each set of n independent functionals $x_1^*,\ldots,x_n^*$ in ext $S(X^*)$, $\det [x_i^*(x_j)] \neq 0$.

(3) If $x_1^*,\ldots,x_n^*$ are n independent functionals in ext $S(X^*)$, $y \in M$, and $x_i^*(y) = 0$ for $i = 1,\ldots,n$, then $y = 0$.

(4) $M^\perp \cap (\cup\{[x_1^*,\ldots,x_n^*] : x_1^*,\ldots,x_n^*$ are independent in ext $S(X^*)\}) = \{0\}$.

(5) $M^\perp \cap [x_1^*,\ldots,x_n^*] = \{0\}$ for every set of n independent functionals $x_1^*,\ldots,x_n^*$ in ext $S(X^*)$.

(6) $X^* = M^\perp \oplus [x_1^*,\ldots,x_n^*]$ for every set of independent functionals $x_1^*,\ldots,x_n^*$ in ext $S(X^*)$.

Each interpolating subspace is a Tchebycheff subspace, although the converse is false in general. The first part of this statement can be deduced, for example, with the aid of the following result of Singer [21] (or cf. [7] for somewhat more general result), together with (3) and (5) of Theorem 2.1.

Theorem A

An n-dimensional subspace M of X is Tchebycheff if and only if there do not exist $m \leq n+1$ independent functionals $x_1^*,\ldots,x_n^*$ in ext $S(X^*)$, m positive numbers $\lambda_1,\ldots,\lambda_m$, and distinct elements y_1 and y_2 with $y_1 - y_2 \in M$, such that $\sum_1^m \lambda_i x_i^* \in M^\perp$ and $x_i^*(y_j) = \|y_j\|$ for $i = 1,\ldots,m$; $j = 1,2$.

Theorem 2.2

Every interpolating subspace is a Tchebycheff subspace.

To see that the converse of theorem 2.2 is false in general, let $X = \ell_1$ and $M = [e_1,\ldots,e_n]$ where e_i is the ith unit vector: $e_i = (\delta_{1i},\delta_{2i},\ldots)$. It is easy to verify that M is Tchebycheff. Indeed, if $x = (\xi_1,\xi_2,\ldots) \in \ell_1$, then its unique best approximation $B_M(x) \in M$ is given by $B_M(x) = (\xi_1,\ldots,\xi_n,0,\ldots)$. We identify ℓ_1^* with ℓ_∞ in the usual way. Then each functional $x^* \in$ ext $S(\ell_1^*)$ is of the form $x^* = (\sigma_1,\sigma_2,\ldots)$ where $\sigma_i = \pm 1$ for each i. Let $x_1^*,\ldots,x_n^*$ be any n independent elements of ext $S(\ell_1^*)$ each of whose first n coordinates is +1.

Then $x_i^*(e_j) = 1$ for $i,j = 1,\dots,n$ so that $\det [x_i^*(e_j)] = 0$. By Theorem 2.1, M is not an interpolating subspace.

3. Existence of interpolating subspaces in concrete spaces

We begin this section by first observing a "nonexistence" theorem. (Recall that a normed linear space X is called strictly convex if $\text{ext } S(X) = \{x \in X: \|x\| = 1\}$.) A proof uses the Hahn-Banach theorem and (4) of Theorem 2.1.

Theorem 3.1

If X is a normed linear space whose dual X* is strictly convex, then X has no proper interpolating subspace.

Corollary 3.1

In an inner product space or any $L_p(T,\Sigma,\mu)$ space, $1 < p < \infty$, there are no proper interpolating subspaces.

Remark. If X is n-dimensional and M = X, then M is trivially an interpolating subspace. Indeed, $\det [x_i^*(x_j)] \neq 0$ for any set of n independent functionals $x_1^*,\dots,x_n^*$ in X* and any basis $x_1,\dots,x_n$ of X (cf. e.g. Davis [6, p. 26]).

If T is a locally compact Hausdorff space, let $C_0(T)$ denote the space of all real-valued continuous functions on T which vanish at infinity, and with the supremum norm. That is, $x \in C_0(T)$ if and only if x is continuous and for each $\varepsilon > 0$ the set $\{t \in T: |x(t)| \geq \varepsilon\}$ is compact.

Theorem 3.2

Let M be a finite-dimensional subspace of $C_0(T)$. The following statements are equivalent.

(1) M is an interpolating subspace.

(2) M is a Tchebycheff subspace.

(3) M is a Haar subspace.

Proof. The equivalence of (1) and (3) follows from part (3) of Theorem 2.1 and the known result that the extreme points of $S(C_0(T)^*)$ are (plus or minus) the point evaluation functionals. The equivalence of (2) and (3) is due to Phelps [19, p. 250].

Corollary 3.2a

A subspace of c_0 is a Tchebycheff subspace if and only if it is an interpolating subspace.

This corollary follows by first recalling (Garkavi [11]) that c_0 has no infinite-dimensional Tchebycheff subspaces, and then applying Theorem 3.2.

In the particular case when T is actually compact, then $C_o(T) = C(T)$, the continuous functions on T, and we immediately obtain the following corollary of Theorem 3.2.

Corollary 3.2b

Let M be a finite-dimensional subspace of C(T). The following statements are equivalent.

(1) M is an interpolating subspace.

(2) M is a Tchebycheff subspace.

(3) M is a Haar subspace.

The equivalence of (2) and (3) in this corollary constitutes the well-known Haar theorem (cf. e.g. Singer [22, p. 200]).

Clearly, the constant 1 function spans a one-dimensional Tchebycheff subspace in C(T) for any compact Hausdorff space T. On the other hand, the following important theorem - due essentially to the combined efforts of Mairhuber [17], Sieklucki [20], and Curtis [5] - shows that the question of the existence of Haar subspaces of dimension > 1 in C(T) depends on the topological nature of T.

Theorem B

The space C(T) contains a Haar, i.e. interpolating, subspace of dimension $n > 1$ (if and) only if T is homeomorphic to a subset of the circumference of the unit circle.

Lutts [16] has verified that Theorem B is also valid for the space $C_o(T)$, where T is locally compact Hausdorff.

Recently Ikebe [12] has shown that a finite-dimensional subspace M of $X \equiv C[a,b]$ is a Haar subspace if and only if the following property holds:

(I) For each nonzero $x \in X$ and each best approximation $x_o \in M$ to x, $\|x_o\| < 2\|x\|$.

Property (I) obviously makes sense in any normed linear space X. Since the interpolating subspaces in C[a,b] are precisely the Haar subspaces, it might be conjectured that property (I) is equivalent to M being an interpolating subspace. However, the example given at the end of Section 2 (of an n-dimensional Tchebycheff subspace M of ℓ_1 which was <u>not</u> an interpolating subspace) affords a simple counterexample. In fact, for that example it is obvious that $\|x_o\| \leq \|x\|$ for every $x \in \ell_1$ and, in particular, property (I) holds for M.

Let (T,Σ,μ) be a σ-finite measure space. An <u>atom</u> is a set $A \in \Sigma$ with $0 < \mu(A) < \infty$, and such that $B \in \Sigma$, $B \subset A$ implies that either $\mu(B) = 0$ or $\mu(B) = \mu(A)$. It is well-known (and easy to prove) that T can have at most countably many atoms. The measure space (T,Σ,μ), or the measure μ itself, is called <u>non-atomic</u> if T has no atoms. R. R. Phelps and Henry Dye [19] have shown that <u>if T has no atoms then $L_1(T,\Sigma,\mu)$ has no finite-dimensional Tchebycheff subspaces</u> (and, a fortiori, no interpolating subspaces). Sharpening this result, Garkavi [10] established that <u>$L_1(T,\Sigma,\mu)$ has an n-dimensional Tchebycheff subspace if and only if T contains at least n atoms</u>.

The main result on the existence of interpolating subspaces in $L_1(T,\Sigma,\mu)$ is the following.

Theorem 3.3

The space $L_1(T,\Sigma,\mu)$ contains an interpolating subspace of dimension $n > 1$ if and only if T is the union of at least n atoms. Also, $L_1(T,\Sigma,\mu)$ contains a one-dimensional interpolating subspace if and only if T contains an atom.

As an immediate consequence of this fact, we obtain the following two corollaries, the first of which is the L_1-analogue of Theorem B.

Corollary 3.3a

The space $L_1(T,\Sigma,\mu)$ contains an interpolating subspace of dimension $n > 1$ only if T is purely atomic.

Corollary 3.3b

The space ℓ_1 has interpolating subspaces of every (finite) dimension.

We remark that if (T,Σ,μ) is σ-finite the condition that T be the union of atoms is equivalent to the condition that $L_1(T,\Sigma,\mu)$ be isometrically isomorphic to ℓ_1 or ℓ_1^m depending on whether T is a countable union of atoms or a finite union of m atoms respectively.

In contrast to Theorem 3.2, the example given at the end of Section 2 showed that <u>not</u> every finite-dimensional Tchebycheff subspace in ℓ_1 is an interpolating subspace.

Our proof of Theorem 3.3 is rather lengthy, involves arguments using infinite matrices, and is non-constructive in nature. In this regard, it would be of some practical value to have a <u>constructive</u> proof of the existence of interpolating subspaces in ℓ_1. With respect to this problem we make the following conjecture:

The vectors $x_i = (1, r_i, r_i^2, r_i^3, \dots) \in \ell_1$ $(i=1,\dots,n)$ span an n-dimensional interpolating subspace if $0 < r_1 < r_2 < \dots < r_n < \frac{1}{2}$ and the ration r_j/r_{j+1} is "sufficiently" small $(j=1,\dots,n-1)$.

We have thus far verified the truth of this conjecture for $n \leq 4$. In the absence of a complete proof of the conjecture, the following results might be useful in recognizing interpolating subspaces in ℓ_1.

Proposition 3.1

Let $M = [x_1,\dots,x_n]$, $n \geq 2$, be an n-dimensional interpolating subspace in ℓ_1. Then the x_i have no common zero coordinates.

Proposition 3.2

Let M be an interpolating subspace of dimension $n > 2$ in ℓ_1. Then every pair of independent vectors in M have at most $n - 2$ common zero coordinates.

4. Characterization of best approximations

Let $x, x_1, \dots, x_n \in X$, $x_1^*, \dots, x_{n+1}^* \in X^*$, and define the determinant $\Delta = \Delta(x, x_1, \dots, x_n; x_1^*, \dots, x_{n+1}^*)$ by

$$\Delta = \begin{vmatrix} x_1^*(x) & \dots & x_{n+1}^*(x) \\ x_1^*(x_1) & \dots & x_{n+1}^*(x_1) \\ \dots & & \\ x_1^*(x_n) & \dots & x_{n+1}^*(x_n) \end{vmatrix} \tag{1}$$

The cofactor of $x_i^*(x)$ in Δ will be denoted by $\Delta_i \equiv \Delta_i(x_1,\dots,x_n; x_1^*,\dots,x_{n+1}^*)$, i.e.

$$\Delta_i = (-1)^{i+1} \begin{vmatrix} x_1^*(x_1) & \dots & x_{i-1}^*(x_1) x_{i+1}^*(x_1) & \dots & x_{n+1}^*(x_1) \\ \dots & & & & \\ x_1^*(x_n) & \dots & x_{i-1}^*(x_n) x_{i+1}^*(x_n) & \dots & x_{n+1}^*(x_n) \end{vmatrix} \tag{2}$$

It is worth emphasizing that cofactors Δ_i do not depend on x.

Lemma 4.1

Assume $M = [x_1,\dots,x_n]$ is an n-dimensional interpolating subspace in X, $x_1^*,\dots,x_m^*$ are $m \leq n+1$ independent functionals in ext $S(X^*)$, and $\alpha_1,\dots,\alpha_m$ are nonzero scalars. Then $\sum_1^m \alpha_i x_i^* \in M^\perp$ if and only if

i) $m = n+1$, and

ii) $\alpha_i = \alpha_{n+1} \Delta_i/\Delta_{n+1}$ $(i=1,\dots,n+1)$ where Δ_i are given by (2).

In particular, $\sum_{1}^{n+1} \Delta_i x_i^* \in M^{\perp}$.

The necessity of i) follows since if $m < n+1$, $\exists y \in M$ such that $x_i^*(y) = \alpha_i$ $(i=1,\ldots,m)$, and $\Sigma\alpha_i x_i^*(y) > 0$. The remainder of the proof is straightforward.

The following "alternation" theorem characterizes best approximations from interpolating subspaces.

Theorem 4.1

Let $M = [x_1,\ldots,x_n]$ be an n-dimensional interpolating subspace in X, let $x \in X \sim M$, and let $x_o \in M$. Then the following statements are equivalent.

(1) x_o is a best approximation to x from M.

(2) There exist n+1 independent functionals $x_1^*,\ldots,x_{n+1}^*$ in ext $S(X^*)$ such that

(a) $x_i^*(x-x_o) = \|x-x_o\|$ $(i=1,\ldots,n+1)$

(b) The determinants Δ_i, defined by eq. (2), all have the same sign.

(3) There exist n+1 independent functionals $x_1^*,\ldots,x_{n+1}^*$ in ext $S(X^*)$ such that

(a) $x_i^*(x-x_o) = \|x-x_o\|$ $(i=1,\ldots,n+1)$

(b) $\operatorname{sgn}(\Delta_i\Delta) = 1$ $(i=1,\ldots,n+1)$ where Δ and Δ_i are as defined in eqs. (1) and (2).

(4) There exist n+1 independent functionals $x_1^*,\ldots,x_{n+1}^*$ in ext $S(X^*)$ and n+1 nonzero scalars $\alpha_1,\ldots,\alpha_{n+1}$ such that

(a) $|x_i^*(x-x_o)| = \|x-x_o\|$ $(i=1,\ldots,n+1)$

(b) $\sum_{1}^{n+1} \alpha_i x_i^* \in M^{\perp}$

(c) $\operatorname{sgn}[\alpha_1 x_1^*(x-x_o)] = \ldots = \operatorname{sgn}[\alpha_{n+1} x_{n+1}^*(x-x_o)]$.

(5) The zero n-tuple $(0,\ldots,0)$ is in the convex hull of the set of n-tuples

$\{(x^*(x_1),\ldots,x^*(x_n)): x^* \in \text{ext } S(X^*),\ x^*(x-x_o) = \|x-x_o\|\}$.

The equivalences can be proved via the implications $(1)\to(2)\to(3)\to(4)\to$

$\to$ (5) $\to$ (1), using a characterization theorem of Singer [21] for the first and last.

As our first application of Theorem 4.1, we consider the space $X = C_0(T)$, T locally compact Hausdorff.

Theorem 4.2

Let $M = [x_1,\dots,x_n]$ be an n-dimensional interpolating subspace in $C_0(T)$, let $x \in C_0(T) \sim M$, and let $x_0 \in M$. Then x_0 is a best approximation to x from M if and only if there exist n+1 distinct points $t_1,\dots,t_{n+1} \in T$ such that

$$x(t_i) - x_0(t_i) = \operatorname{sgn}(D_iD)\,||x-x_0|| \qquad (i=1,\dots,n+1)$$

where

$$D \equiv \begin{vmatrix} x(t_1) & \dots & x(t_{n+1}) \\ x_1(t_1) & \dots & x_1(t_{n+1}) \\ \dots & & \\ x_n(t_1) & \dots & x_n(t_{n+1}) \end{vmatrix} \neq 0$$

and D_i is the cofactor of $x(t_i)$ in D.

Necessity follows from (3) of Theorem 4.1, using the extreme functionals in $S(C_0(T)^*)$; sufficiency follows from (4) of Theorem 4.1.

Theorem 4.2 was, in essence, established by Bram [2] who gave a direct proof. In the particular case when T is compact (so that $C_0(T) = C(T)$), Theorem 4.2 was proved by Zuhovitki [23]. If we further specialize and take T to be an (infinite or finite) interval on the real line, we obtain

Corollary 4.2

Let M be an n-dimensional interpolating subspace in $C_0(T)$, $x \in C_0(T) \sim M$, and $x_0 \in M$. Then x_0 is a best approximation to x from M if and only if there exist n+1 points $t_1 < \dots < t_{n+1}$ in T such that

$$x(t_i) - x_0(t_i) = (-1)^i\sigma\,||x-x_0|| \qquad (i=1,\dots,n+1)$$

where $\sigma = \pm 1$.

Proof. We need only observe that since T is an interval on the real line, the determinants D_i as defined in Theorem 4.2 alternate in sign (cf. e.g. [4, p. 74] or [22, p. 171]), and then apply Theorem 4.2. //

Of course if $T = [a,b]$, where $-\infty < a < b < \infty$, then $C_o(T) = C[a,b]$ and Corollary 4.1 is just the classical Tchebycheff alternation theorem. We note that the "alternation" Corollary 4.2 is false in general if T is not an interval. For example, let $T = [0,1] \cup [2,3]$ and let $x_1(t) = 1$ if $t \in [0,1]$, $x_1(t) = -1$ if $t \in [2,3]$. Then $M = [x_1]$ is a 1-dimensional interpolating subspace of C(T) and the best approximation from M to the constant function $x(t) \equiv 1$ is $x_o = 0$. But $x - x_o$ has no sign changes in T.

As another application of Theorem 4.1, we consider the space $L_1 \equiv L_1(T,\Sigma,\mu)$ where T is the union of (at most) countably many atoms, say $T = \bigcap_{i\in I} A_i$. Since each measurable function x must be constant almost everywhere (a.e.) on an atom and since $L_1^* = L_\infty$, it is easy to verify that each $x^* \in \text{ext } S(L_1^*)$ has the representation

$$x^*(x) = \sum_{i\in I} x(A_i)\sigma(A_i)\mu(A_i), \quad x \in L_1$$

where $|\sigma(A_i)| = 1$ and $x(A_i)$ denotes the constant value which x has a.e. on A_i. For any $x \in L_1$, we denote the set $\{i \in I: x(A_i) = 0\}$ by $Z(x)$. If S is a set, then card S will denote the cardinality of S. In this situation we have the following characterization theorem.

Theorem 4.3

Let $M = [x_1,\ldots,x_n]$ be an n-dimensional interpolating subspace in L_1, let $x \in L_1 \sim M$, and let $x_o \in M$. The following statements are equivalent.

(1) x_o is a best approximation to x from M.

(2) There exist n+1 independent measurable functions $\sigma_1,\ldots,\sigma_{n+1}$ with $|\sigma_i| = 1$ $(i=1,\ldots,n+1)$ such that

(a) $\sigma_1(A_i) = \ldots = \sigma_{n+1}(A_i) = \text{sgn}\,[x(A_i) - x_o(A_i)]$ for each $i \in I \sim Z(x-x_o)$

(b) card $Z(x-x_o) \geq n$

(c) The n-tuple

$$\Big(\sum_{i\in I} \text{sgn}[x(A_i)-x_o(A_i)]\,x_1(A_i)\mu(A_i),\ldots,\sum_{i\in I} \text{sgn}[x(A_i)-x_o(A_i)]\,x_n(A_i)\mu(A_i)\Big)$$

is in the convex hull of the set of n-tuples

$$\Big\{\Big(\sum_{i\in Z(x-x_o)} \sigma_j(A_i)x_1(A_i)\mu(A_i),\ldots,\sum_{i\in Z(x-x_o)} \sigma_j(A_i)x_n(A_i)\mu(A_i)\Big) : j=1,\ldots,n+1\Big\}.$$

(3) Card $Z(x-x_o) \geq n$ and

$$\left|\sum_{i\in I} \operatorname{sgn}[x(A_i)-x_o(A_i)]y(A_i)\mu(A_i)\right| \leq \sum_{i\in Z(x-x_o)} |y(A_i)|\mu(A_i) \tag{3}$$

for every $y \in M$.

(4) Eq. (3) is valid for every $y \in M$.

The proof uses the cycle of implications (1) → (2) → (3) → (4) → (1), the last one following by an application of a result of H. S. Shapiro (cf. e.g. [13, Corollary 1.4]).

In particular, the space ℓ_1 is the most important example of the type we have been considering. (In fact, $\ell_1 = L_1(T,\Sigma,\mu)$ where $T = \{1,2,3,\ldots\}$, Σ is the collection of all subsets of T, and μ is "counting" measure: $\mu(B) = \text{card}(B)$.) Thus we immediately deduce from Theorem 4.3 the following corollary.

Corollary 4.3

Let $M = [x_1,\ldots,x_n]$ be an n-dimensional interpolating subspace in ℓ_1, let $x = (\xi_1,\xi_2,\ldots) \in \ell_1 \sim M$, and let $x_o \in M$ where $x_i = (\xi_{i1},\xi_{i2},\ldots)$ $(i=0,1,\ldots,n)$. The following statements are equivalent.

(1) x_o is a best approximation to x from M.

(2) There exist n+1 independent vectors $\sigma_i = (\sigma_{i1},\sigma_{i2},\ldots) \in \ell_\infty$ with $|\sigma_{ij}| = 1$ such that

(a) For each $i=1,\ldots,n+1$, $\sigma_{ij} = \operatorname{sgn}[\xi_j - \xi_{0j}]$ whenever $j \in k:\{\xi_k \neq \xi_{0k}\}$

(b) Card $Z(x-x_o) \geq n$ $(Z(x-x_o) \equiv \{k: \xi_k = \xi_{0k}\})$

(c) The n-tuple

$$\left(\sum_1^\infty \operatorname{sgn}(\xi_i - \xi_{0i})\xi_{1i},\ldots,\sum_1^\infty \operatorname{sgn}(\xi_i - \xi_{0i})\xi_{ni}\right)$$

is in the convex hull of the set of n-tuples

$$\left\{\left(\sum_{i\in Z(x-x_o)} \sigma_{ji}\xi_{1i},\ldots,\sum_{i\in Z(x-x_o)} \sigma_{ji}\xi_{ni}\right): j=1,\ldots,n+1\right\}.$$

(3) Card $Z(x-x_o) \geq n$ and

$$\left|\sum_1^\infty \operatorname{sgn}(\xi_i - \xi_{0i})\eta_i\right| \leq \sum_{i\in Z(x-x_o)} |\eta_i| \tag{4}$$

for every $y = (\eta_1,\eta_2,\ldots) \in M$.

(4) Eq. (4) is valid for every $y = (\eta_1,\eta_2,\ldots) \in M$.

5. Error of approximation

The first result of this section provides a useful relation for obtaining the error of approximation of a vector by elements of an interpolating subspace, and in particular, for obtaining lower bounds on this approximation error.

Theorem 5.1

Let M be an n-dimensional interpolating subspace in X and $x \in X$. Then

$$d(x,M) = \max \left| \sum_{1}^{n+1} \lambda_i x_i^*(x) \right|$$

where the maximum is taken over all sets of n+1 independent functionals $x_1^*,\ldots,x_{n+1}^*$ in ext $S(X^*)$ and $\lambda_i \equiv \lambda_i(x_1^*,\ldots,x_{n+1}^*) = \Delta_i / \sum_{1}^{n+1} \Delta_k$, where the determinants $\Delta_i \equiv \Delta_i(x_1^*,\ldots,x_{n+1}^*)$ are defined by eq. (2) and all have the same sign.

Proof. It is a well-known consequence of the Hahn-Banach theorem that (for an arbitrary subspace M)

$$d(x,M) = \max\{|x^*(x)|: x^* \in S(X^*) \cap M^{\perp}\}.$$

Moreover, when M is n-dimensional, we may restrict the search for a maximum to those x^* of the form $x^* = \sum_{1}^{m} \lambda_i x_i^*$, where $x_i^* \in$ ext $S(X^*)$, $\lambda_i > 0$, $\sum_{1}^{m} \lambda_i = 1$, and $m \leq n+1$ (cf. [22]). Our conclusion now follows immediately from lemma 4.1. //

With the help of Theorem 5.1, we can deduce the following generalized "de la Vallée Poussin" theorem.

Theorem 5.2

Let M be an n-dimensional interpolating subspace of X and let $x \in X$. Suppose there exists a $y \in M$ and n+1 independent functionals $x_1^*,\ldots,x_{n+1}^*$ in ext $S(X^*)$ such that

$$[\Delta_i x_i^*(x-y)][\Delta_{i+1} x_{i+1}^*(x-y)] > 0 \quad (i=1,\ldots,n)$$

where the determinants Δ_i are defined by eq. (2) Then

$$\min_i |x_i^*(x-y)| \leq d(x,M).$$

Also, if this inequality is actually an equality, then $|x_i^*(x-y)| = d(x,M)$ for every i.

In the particular case when $X = C_o(T)$ and T is a (finite or infinite) interval on the real line, Theorem 5.2 reduces to the following.

Corollary 5.2

Let M be an n-dimensional interpolating subspace of $C_o(T)$ and let $x \in C_o(T)$. Suppose there exist $y \in M$ and n+1 points $t_1 < t_2 < \dots < t_{n+1}$ in T such that

$$[x(t_i) - y(t_i)][x(t_{i+1}) - y(t_{i+1})] < 0 \quad (i=1,\dots,n).$$

Then

$$\min_i |x(t_i) - y(t_i)| \leq d(x,M).$$

Moreover, if $\min_i |x(t_i) - y(t_i)| = d(x,M)$, then $|x(t_i) - y(t_i)| = d(x,M)$ for every i.

In the special case when T is the finite interval [a,b], then Corollary 5.2 is just the classical de la Vallée Poussin theorem.

6. Continuity of best approximations

We now state a "strong uniqueness" theorem which generalizes a result of Newman and Shapiro [18]. If M is an interpolating subspace in X, we denote the unique best approximation in M to any $x \in X$ by $B_M(x)$. The operator B_M is called the metric projection onto M.

Theorem 6.1

Let M be an interpolating subspace in X. Then for each $x \in X$ there exists a constant $\gamma = \gamma(x)$ with $0 < \gamma \leq 1$ such that

$$||x-y|| \geq ||x-B_M(x)|| + \gamma ||B_M(x)-y||$$

for every $y \in M$.

Cheney and Wulbert (unpublished, 1967) have obtained a result slightly stronger than Theorem 6.1. Their proof, as well as ours, is an obvious modification of the proof of the Newman-Shapiro Theorem as given by Cheney [3], [4].

Freud [9], in essence, showed that the metric projection onto a Haar subspace in C[a,b] is pointwise Lipschitz continuous. Cheney [4, p. 82] observed that this fact is a consequence only of the strong uniqueness theorem, so that it is equally valid for our situation. Thus Theorem 6.1 yields the following:

Theorem 6.2

Let M be an interpolating subspace of X. Then for each $x \in X$ there exists a constant $\lambda = \lambda(x) > 0$ such that

$$\|B_M(x) - B_M(z)\| \leqslant \lambda \|x - z\|$$

for every $z \in X$.

7. Algorithms for constructing best approximations

We shall consider two algorithms for the construction of best approximations from interpolating subspaces.

Let M be an n-dimensional subspace of X, let $x \in X \sim M$, and let Γ be any set of functionals in X^* of norm 1 such that for each $z \in M \oplus [x]$, there is an $x^* \in \Gamma$ such that $x^*(z) = \|z\|$. In [1], Akilov and Rubinov have described an algorithm - a generalization of the "first algorithm" of Remez - for the construction of a best approximation to x from M. If we specialize their result to the case where M is an interpolating subspace and where $\Gamma = \text{ext } S(X^*)$, the algorithm may be described as follows.

Let $x_1^*,\ldots,x_n^* \in \Gamma$. For each $m \geqslant n$ select $y_m \in M$ and $x_{n+1}^* \in \Gamma$ so that

$$\max_{k\leqslant m} |x_k^*(x-y_m)| = \min_{y\in M} \max_{k\leqslant m} |x_k^*(x-y)|$$

and

$$|x_{m+1}^*(x-y_m)| = \|x-y_m\| .$$

Introducing the notation $e_m = \|x - y_m\|$, $\|z\|_m = \max_{k\leqslant m} |x_k^*(z)|$, and $\lambda_m = \|x - y_m\|_m$, the effectiveness of this algorithm can be summarized in the following theorem.

Theorem

(i) $\lambda_n \leqslant \lambda_{n+1} \leqslant \cdots \leqslant d(x,M) \leqslant e_m$ for all $m \geqslant n$, and $\lim \lambda_m = d(x,M) = \lim e_m$.

(ii) The sequence $\{y_m\}$ converges to the unique best approximation of x from M.

There has also been a generalization of the "second algorithm" of Remez which was established recently by Laurent [14], and valid for n-dimensional subspaces $M = [x_1,\ldots,x_n]$ of a normed linear space X which also satisfy the condition:

(L) For each set of n independent functionals $x_1^*,\ldots,x_n^*$ in the weak* closure of ext S(X*), $\det [x_i^*(x_j)] \neq 0$.

In particular, any subspace with property (L) is necessarily an interpolating subspace. In the special cases when X = C(T), T compact Hausdorff, or when $X = L_1(T,\Sigma,\mu)$, where T is (at most) a countable union of atoms, it can be shown that ext S(X*) is weak* closed. Hence in <u>these special cases</u> property (L) is <u>equivalent</u> to the condition that M be an interpolating subspace. However, in the space c_o, for example, there are interpolating subspaces of every finite dimension. But since 0 is in the weak* closure of ext $S(c_o^*)$, it follows that <u>no</u> subspace of c_o has property (L). We do not know whether this algorithm is still valid for interpolating subspaces in X for which ext S(X*) is not weak* closed.

A detailed description of the algorithm of Laurent would take us too far astray here. It suffices to say that it is a convergent scheme.

We conclude this section by observing that if the n+1 functionals $x_1^*,\ldots,x_{n+1}^*$ in the characterization Theorem 4.1 are known, then it is possible to determine the best approximation, as well as the error of approximation, by simply solving a <u>linear</u> system of n+1 equations. Indeed, suppose $M = [x_1,\ldots,x_n]$ is an n-dimensional interpolating subspace in X, $x \in X \sim M$, and $x_o = \sum_1^n \alpha_i x_i$ is the best approximation to x from M. Suppose that $x_1^*,\ldots,x_{n+1}$ are any n+1 independent functionals in ext S(X*) whose existence is guaranteed by Theorem 4.1. Then in particular

$$x_i^*(x_o) + d = x_i^*(x) \quad (i=1,\ldots,n+1)$$

where d = d(x,M). Substituting for x_o into these equations, we get

$$\sum_{j=1}^n \alpha_j x_i^*(x_j) + d = x_i^*(x) \quad (i=1,\ldots,n+1).$$

This system can now be solved by Cramer's rule to determine the unknowns α_i (and hence x_o) and d.

We remark that the Laurent algorithm involves the solving of a sequence of such (n+1)-st order linear systems.

References

1. AKILOV, G. P. and RUBINOV, A. M. 'The method of successive approximation for determining the polynomial of best approximation'. Sov. Math. Dokl. 5 (1964), pp. 951-953.

2. BRAM, J. 'Chebychev approximation in locally compact spaces'. Proc. Amer. Math. Soc., 9 (1958), pp. 133-136.

3. CHENEY, E. W. 'Some relationships between the Tchebycheff approximations on an interval and on a discrete subset of that interval'. Math. Note no. 262, Boeing Scientific Research Labs.,Seattle, Wash.

4. CHENEY, E. W. Introduction to Approximation Theory. McGraw-Hill, 1966.

5. CURTIS, P. C. 'n-parameter families and best approximation'. Pac. J. Math., 9 (1959), pp. 1013-1027.

6. DAVIS, P. J. Interpolation and Approximation. Blaisdell, 1963.

7. DEUTSCH, F. R. and MASERICK, P. H. 'Applications of the Hahn-Banach theorem in approximation theory'. SIAM Review, 9 (1967), pp. 516-530.

8. DUNFORD, N. and SCHWARTZ, J. T. Linear Operators.I. Interscience, 1958.

9. FREUD, G. 'Eine ungleichung für Tschebyscheffsche approximationspolynome Acta Sci. Math. Szeged, 19 (1958), pp. 162-164.

10. GARKAVI, A. L. 'On uniqueness of the solutions of the L-problem of moments' (Russian), Izv. Akad. Nauk S.S.S.R., 28 (1964), pp. 553-570.

11. GARKAVI, A. L. On Čebyšev and almost-Čebyšev subspaces (Russian), Izv. Akad. Nauk S.S.S.R., 28 (1964), pp. 799-818.

12. IKEBE, Y. 'A characterization of Haar subspaces in C[a,b]'. Proc. Japan Acad., 44 (1968), pp. 219-220.

13. KRIPKE, B. R. and RIVLIN, T. J. 'Approximation in the metric of $L^1(X,\mu)$'. Trans. Amer. Math. Soc., 119 (1965), pp. 101-122.

14. LAURENT, P. J. 'Théorèmes de caractérisation d'une meilleure approximation dans un espace normé et généralisation de l'algorithme de Rémès'. Num. Math., 10 (1967), pp. 190-208.

15. LIAPOUNOFF, A. A. 'On completely additive vector-functions'. Izv. Akad. Nauk S.S.S.R., 4 (1940), pp. 465-478.

16. LUTTS, J. A. 'Topological spaces which admit unisolvent systems'. Trans. Amer. Math. Soc., 111 (1964), pp. 440-448.

17. MAIRHUBER, J. C. 'On Haar's theorem concerning Chebychev approximation problems having unique solution'. Proc. Amer. Math. Soc., 7 (1956), pp. 609-615.

18. NEWMAN, D. J. and SHAPIRO, H. S. 'Some theorems on Čebyšev approximation' Duke Math. J., 30 (1963), pp. 673-682.

19. PHELPS, R. R. 'Uniqueness of Hahn-Banach extensions and unique best approximation'. Trans. Amer. Math. Soc., 95 (1960), pp. 238-255.

20. SIEKLUCKI, K. 'Topological properties of sets admitting the Tschebycheff systems'. Bull Acad. Polonaise Sci., 6 (1958), pp. 603-606.

21. SINGER, I. 'Caractérisation des éléments de meilleure approximation dans un espace de Banach quelconque'. Acta. Sci. Math., 17 (1956), pp. 181-189.

22. SINGER, I. 'On best approximation in normed vector spaces by elements of vector subspaces' (Roumanian), Bucharest, 1967.

23. ZUHOVITKI, S. I. 'On the approximation of real functions in the sense of P. L. Chebychev' (Russian), Uspehi Mat. Nauk, 11 (1956), pp. 125-159.

SIMULTANEOUS APPROXIMATION AND INTERPOLATION WITH PRESERVATION OF NORM

F. Deutsch* and P.D. Morris*,†

(Pennsylvania State University)

1. Introduction

In [1], W. Wolibner proved the following:

Theorem

Let $a \leq t_1 < t_2 < \ldots < t_n \leq b$ be real numbers and let $\mathbb{P}$ be the set of all real polynomials on $[a,b]$. For each f in $C([a,b])$ and each $\varepsilon > 0$, there exists p in $\mathbb{P}$ such that

a) $\|f-p\| < \varepsilon$ (uniform norm)

b) $p(t_i) = f(t_i)$, $i=1,2,\ldots,n$

and c) $\|p\| = \|f\|$.

We were led by this result to make the following:

Definition. Let X be a real normed vector space, let M be a dense subspace of X, and let $\{x_1^*,x_2^*,\ldots,x_n^*\}$ be a finite subset of the dual space X^*. Then $(X,M,\{x_i^*\})$ has property SAIN (simultaneous approximation and interpolation with norm-preservation) if, whenever x is in X and $\varepsilon > 0$, there exists m in M with (i) $\|x-m\| < \varepsilon$, (ii) $x_i^*(m) = x_i^*(x)$, $i=1,2,\ldots,n$, and (iii) $\|m\| = \|x\|$.

Thus Wolibner's Theorem asserts that $(C([a,b]),\mathbb{P},\{\hat{t}_1,\ldots,\hat{t}_n\})$ has SAIN for any choice of points $t_1,t_2,\ldots,t_n$ in $[a,b]$. (Here $\hat{t}$ in $C([a,b])^*$ denotes the point-evaluation functional at t in $[a,b]$).

If either of the requirements (ii) or (iii) is dropped from the definition of SAIN, then the remaining two can always be satisfied. This follows from the following two results, of which the first is due to Yamabe.

* Supported in part by the National Science Foundation (U.S.A).

† Paper presented by this author.

Theorem ([2])

Let D be a dense convex subset of the real normed linear space X and let $x_1^*, x_2^*, \ldots, x_n^*$ be in X^*. For each x in X and for each $\varepsilon > 0$, there exists d in D such that $\|x-d\| < \varepsilon$ and $x_i^*(d) = x_i^*(x)$, for all $i=1,2,\ldots,n$.

This shows that (i) and (ii) can always be satisfied. That (i) and (iii) can always be satisfied is shown by:

Proposition.

If M is a dense subspace of the normed space X and if x is in X and $\varepsilon > 0$, then there exists m in M with $\|x-m\| < \varepsilon$ and $\|m\| = \|x\|$.

The proof is easy and is omitted.

We shall now investigate SAIN in two classes of spaces: Hilbert space and spaces of type C(T), where T is a compact Hausdorff space.

2. SAIN in Hilbert space

The situation can be completely described:

Theorem

Let X be a real Hilbert space, and let M be a dense subspace of X, and let $\{x_1^*, \ldots, x_n^*\} \subset X^*$. Then $(X, M, \{x_i^*\})$ has SAIN if, and only if, each x_i^* attains its norm on the unit ball of M.

Proof. Since X is a Hilbert space, it is self-dual and therefore there exist uniquely $y_1, y_2, \ldots, y_n$ in X such that $x_i^*(x) = \langle y_i, x \rangle$, for all x in X. (Here, $\langle \cdot, \cdot \rangle$ denotes the inner product in X.)

Suppose $(X, M, \{x_i^*\})$ has SAIN. Our assertion is clearly equivalent to the assertion that each y_i is in M. Suppose, on the contrary, that y_i is not in M. By SAIN, there exists m in M with $\|m\| = \|y_i\|$ and $\langle y_i, m \rangle = \langle y_i, y_i \rangle = \|y_i\|^2$. On the other hand, by Schwartz's inequality,

$$|\langle y_i, m \rangle| \leq \|y_i\| \; \|m\| = \|y_i\|^2.$$

Thus equality is achieved in Schwartz's inequality, and therefore y_i is a scalar multiple of m. Since m is in the subspace M, so is y_i, which is a contradiction.

Now suppose each x_i^* attains its norm on the unit ball of M. As before, this is the same as saying that each y_i is in M. By replacing, if necessary, $\{y_i\}$ by an orthonormal basis for $Y = [\{y_i\}]$, we can assume that $\{y_i\}$ is an orthonormal set. Let x be in X and let $\varepsilon > 0$. Then

$X = Y \oplus Y^{\perp}$, where $Y^{\perp}$ is the orthogonal complement of Y. We can write

$$x = \sum_{1}^{n} a_i y_i + z,$$

where z is in $Y^{\perp}$. By an easy application of Yamabe's theorem, quoted earlier, the subspace $M \cap Y^{\perp}$ is dense in $Y^{\perp}$. By the Proposition in §1, there exists w in $M \cap Y^{\perp}$ such that $\|z-w\| < \varepsilon$ and $\|w\| = \|z\|$. Now let $y = w + \sum_{1}^{n} a_i y_i$. Clearly y is in M. We check that it satisfies (i), (ii), and (iii) of the definition of SAIN. (i) $\|x-y\| = \|z-w\| < \varepsilon$;
(ii) $x_i^*(y) = \langle y_i, y\rangle = \langle y_i, w\rangle + \langle y_i, \sum_{1}^{n} a_i y_i\rangle = 0 + a_i = a_i = \langle y_i, x\rangle$;
(iii) $\|y\|^2 = \|w\|^2 + \sum_{1}^{n} |a_i|^2 = \|z\|^2 + \sum_{1}^{n} |a_i|^2 = \|x\|^2$.

This completes the proof.

3. SAIN in the spaces C(T)

We are able to generalize Wolibner's theorem:

Theorem

Let T be a compact Hausdorff space, let M be a dense subalgebra of real C(T), and let $t_1, t_2, \ldots, t_n$ be in T. Then $(C(T), M, \{\hat{t}_i\})$ has property SAIN.

The proof is rather long and we omit it. An example will be given later to show that "dense subalgebra" cannot be replaced by "dense subspace" in the preceding result. However, we can prove the following:

Theorem

Let T be a compact Hausdorff space and let M be a dense linear sublattice of real C(T) which contains the constant functions. If $t_1, t_2, \ldots, t_n$ are in T, then $(C(T), M, \{\hat{t}_i\})$ has SAIN.

Proof. Let f be in C(T), $\varepsilon > 0$. Without loss of generality, we may assume that $\|f\| = 1$. Let t_{n+1} in T be such that $|f(t_{n+1})| = 1$. By Yamabe's theorem, there exists m_1 in M such that $\|m_1 - f\| < \varepsilon$ and $m_1(t_i) = f(t_i)$, $i=1,2,\ldots,n+1$. Let e denote the function identically equal to 1 on T. Then, by hypothesis, e is in M, and therefore $m = (m_1 \wedge e) \vee (-e)$ is in M, since M is a sublattice. We now verify that m satisfies the SAIN conditions. Since m agrees with m_1 except when $|m_1(t)| > 1$, $\|f-m\| \leq \|f-m_1\| < \varepsilon$. Since $-e \leq m \leq e$, $\|m\| < 1$. But $|m(t_{n+1})| = 1$ and so $\|m\| = 1 = \|f\|$. Finally, $|m_1(t_i)| \leq 1$, $i=1,2,\ldots,n$, so that

$m(t_i) = m_1(t_i) = f(t_i)$.

This completes the proof.

Some counterexamples.

1) $(C(T), M, \{\hat{t}_i\})$ may not have SAIN when M is merely a dense subspace. Let $T = [0,1]$ and let $M = \{f \text{ in } C(T): f'(\frac{1}{2}) \text{ exists and } f'(\frac{1}{2}) = f(0)-f(1)\}$. It is easily checked that M is a dense subspace containing the constant functions. Let g in C(T) be such that $g(0) = g(\frac{1}{2}) = 1$, $g(1) = 0$, and $\|g\| = 1$. Suppose m in M is such that $\|m-g\| < \frac{1}{2}$ and $m(\frac{1}{2}) = g(\frac{1}{2}) = 1$. Then $m(0) > \frac{1}{2}$, $m(1) < \frac{1}{2}$, and so

$$m'(\tfrac{1}{2}) = m(0) - m(1) > 0.$$

Hence there exists $t > \frac{1}{2}$ such that $m(t) > m(\frac{1}{2}) = 1$. Thus $\|m\| > 1 = \|g\|$. This shows that $(C[0,1],M,\{\frac{1}{2}\})$ does not have SAIN.

2) In C(T), it is difficult to replace point evaluations by other functionals. Let $T = [0,1]$, let M be the polynomials on T, and define x^* in $C([0,1])^*$ by:

$$x^*(f) = \int_0^{1/2} f(t)\,dt.$$

Let g be the piecewise-linear continuous function defined as follows: $g(0) = g(\frac{1}{2}) = 1$, $g(1) = 0$, g linear elsewhere. Suppose there is a polynomial p such that $\|g-p\| < 1$, $\|p\| = \|g\| = 1$, and $x^*(p) = x^*(g) = \frac{1}{2}$. Since $-1 \leq p(t) \leq 1$, for t in $[0,\frac{1}{2}]$ and since $\int_0^{1/2} p(t)dt = \frac{1}{2}$, we conclude that $p(t) = 1$ for all t in $[0,\frac{1}{2}]$. But the only polynomial with this property is the constant 1. Thus $\|g-p\| \geq |g(1)-p(1)| = 1$, which is a contradiction. Thus $(C[0,1]),\mathbb{P},\{x^*\})$ does not have SAIN.

3) For a linear sublattice M of C(T), the condition that M contain constants cannot be dropped (in distinction to the subalgebra case). Let $T = [0,1]$ and let

$$M = \{f \text{ in } C([0,1]): f'(0) \text{ exists and } f'(0) = f(0)\}.$$

It is routine but tedious to check that M is a dense sublattice. Let e be the function identically 1. Certainly, e is not in M. Suppose there exists m in M such that $\|m\| = \|e\| = 1$ and $m(0) = e(0) = 1$. Then $m'(0) = 1$ and hence there is $t > 0$ such that $m(t) > 1$, contradicting the assumption that $\|m\| = 1$.

Other results on property SAIN, as well as a proof of our generalization of Wolibner's theorem will appear in a paper to be published in the Journal of Approximation Theory.

References

1. WOLIBNER, W. 'Sur un polynôme d'interpolation'. Colloq. Math., 2 (1951), pp. 136-137.

2. YAMABE, H. 'On an extension of the Helly's theorem'. Osaka Math. J., 2 (1950), pp. 15-17.

ON ASYMPTOTIC APPROXIMATION THEOREMS
FOR SEQUENCES OF LINEAR POSITIVE OPERATORS

M. W. Müller

(University of Stuttgart)

1. A generalisation of a theorem of Mamedov

Let Ω denote a nonvoid (bounded or unbounded) domain of the real line, $D(\Omega)$ the linear space of all complex-valued functions f defined on Ω and $D_{2p}(\Omega;x)$ the linear subspace of those functions $f \in D(\Omega)$ having derivatives up to and including the 2p-th order ($p=1,2,\ldots$) at the fixed point $x \in \Omega$.

In 1959 R. G. Mamedov [9] published without proof the following remarkable result:

Let $\{L_n\}_{n=1}^{\infty}$ be a sequence of linear positive operators mapping $D(\Omega)$ into $D(\Omega)$. For the three special functions $e_i : t \to t^i$, $t \in \Omega$ $(i=0,1,2)$ we assume that the relations

$$\left.\begin{aligned} (L_n e_0)(x) &= 1 + o\left(\frac{1}{\phi(n)}\right) \\ (L_n e_i)(x) &= x^i + \frac{\psi_i(x)}{\phi(n)} + o\left(\frac{1}{\phi(n)}\right), \ i = 1,2, \end{aligned}\right\} \qquad \text{(M1)}$$

hold at a fixed point $x \in \Omega$, where $\phi(n) > 0$ and $\phi(n) \to \infty$ for $n \to \infty$. If there exists a natural number m such that

$$\tau_n^{[2m+2]}(x) := (L_n(t-x)^{2m+2})(x) = o\left(\frac{1}{\phi(n)}\right) \qquad \text{(M2)}$$

for $n \to \infty$, then we have for any <u>bounded</u> function $f \in D_2(\Omega;x)$ and $n \to \infty$

$$(L_n f)(x) - f(x) = \frac{2\psi_1(x)f'(x) + [\psi_2(x) - 2x\psi_1(x)]f''(x)}{2\phi(n)} + o\left(\frac{1}{\phi(n)}\right). \quad (1)$$

A local test of the operator-sequence $\{L_n\}_{n=1}^{\infty}$ with the three functions e_i yields, roughly speaking, information on the speed with which the bounded elements of the linear space $D_2(\Omega;x)$ are locally approximated by the sequence of their L_n-images.

In the case of an unbounded domain Ω the identity e_0 is the only one of the three test-functions which belongs to this class. In 1965 in his thesis F. Schurer [14] removed this defect by proving that the assertion of Mamedov's theorem is still valid for the larger class of those functions $f \in D_2(\Omega;x)$ which are at most of order $O(t^2)$ as $|t| \to \infty$. His method of proof fails for functions increasing faster than this. Therefore we propose for our theorem 1 another method. We do not make any direct assumption on the order of growth of f, but a local assumption on the L_n-images of $|f|^r$, which can be easily verified in applications and which on the other hand always holds trivially for bounded functions. This assumption (W) is used for the first time by H. Walk [17] in proving theorems of the type of the well-known theorem of P. P. Korovkin for sequences of linear positive operators.

Theorem 1

Let $f \in D_2(\Omega;x)$ and let $\{L_n\}_{n=1}^{\infty}$ be a sequence of linear positive operators mapping $D(\Omega)$ into $D(\Omega)$ which satisfies the conditions (M1) and

$$\overline{\lim_{n\to\infty}}\,(L_n\,|f|^r)(x) < \infty \quad (r > 1 \text{ a real constant}). \quad \text{(W)}$$

If there exists a natural number m such that

$$\tau_n^{[2m+2]}(x) = o\left(\frac{1}{[\phi(n)]^{r'}}\right), \quad \frac{1}{r} + \frac{1}{r'} = 1 \qquad \text{(M2')}$$

for $n \to \infty$, then the local degree of approximation to f by the sequence $\{L_n f\}_{n=1}^{\infty}$ is given by the asymptotic formula (1).

Proof. Since $f \in D_2(\Omega;x)$ we have for $t \in \Omega$

$$f(t) = f(x) + f'(x)(t-x) + [\tfrac{1}{2} f''(x) + g(t)]\,(t-x)^2 \qquad (2)$$

with $\lim_{t\to x} g(t) = 0$, i.e. for all $\varepsilon > 0$ $\exists \delta(\varepsilon) > 0$ such that $|g(t)| \leq \varepsilon$ for $t \in I := (x-\delta, x+\delta)$. Let λ_I be the characteristic function of the open interval I and $\mu_I := e_0 - \lambda_I$. Applying to (2) the operator L_n for fixed n and using the conditions (M1) and the fact that L_n is linear, we obtain after some elementary calculations

$$(L_n f)(x) - f(x) = \tau_n^{[2]}(x) + (L_n \mu_I g(e_1 - x)^2)\,(x) + o\left(\frac{1}{\phi(n)}\right)$$

with

$$\tau_n^{[2]}(x) = \frac{2\psi_1(x)f'(x) + [\psi_2(x) - 2x\psi_1(x)]f''(x)}{2\phi(n)} + o(\frac{1}{\phi(n)}).$$

Thus we have still only to show that

$$(L_n\mu_I\ g(e_1 - x)^2)(x) = o(\frac{1}{\phi(n)})$$

for $n \to \infty$.

In view of (2) and the monotonicity of L_n we can write

$$|(L_n\mu_I\ g(e_1 - x)^2)(x)| \leqslant (L_n\mu_I|g|(e_1 - x)^2)(x)$$
$$\leqslant (L_n\mu_I|f|)(x) + \sum_{k=0}^{2} \frac{|f^{(k)}(x)|}{k!}(L_n\mu_I|e_1 - x|^k)(x), \qquad (3)$$

and in view of the monotonicity alone it follows that

$$(L_n\mu_I|e_1 - x|^k)(x) \leqslant \frac{\tau_n^{[2m+2]}(x)}{\delta^{2m+2-k}} \qquad (k = 0,1,\dots,2m+2). \qquad (4)$$

From now on we suppose that n has been chosen so large that $(L_m|f|^r)(x)$ is finite for all $m \geqslant n$.

The first term on the right-hand side of (3) is estimated at this stage with the aid of the Hölder-inequality for linear positive operators by

$$(L_n\mu_I|f|)(x) \leqslant [(L_n|f|^r)(x)]^{1/r}[(L_n\mu_I)(x)]^{1/r'}$$

(cf. also Walk [17]). Observing moreover (4), (W) and (M2'), we obtain

$$(L_n\mu_I|f|)(x) \leqslant [(L_n|f|^r)(x)]^{1/r}\left\{\frac{\tau_n^{[2m+2]}(x)}{\delta^{2m+2}}\right\}^{1/r'} \qquad (5)$$
$$= o(\frac{1}{\phi(n)}) \qquad (n \to \infty).$$

The second term on the right-hand side of (3) can be estimated in view of (4) and (M2') by $o(\frac{1}{[\phi(n)]^{r'}})$ and thus likewise by $o(\frac{1}{\phi(n)})$.

2. <u>A property of the Taylor series remainder</u>

Let $f \in D_{2m+2}(\Omega;x)$ and let

$$R_{2m+1}(t) := f(t) - \sum_{k=0}^{2m+1} \frac{f^{(k)}(x)}{k!}(t - x)^k,\ t \in \Omega \qquad (6)$$

by the error in replacing the function f(t) by the first 2m+2 terms of its Taylor-series expansion around the point t = x. On account of l'Hospital's rule and the existence of the (2m+2)-th order derivative of f at the point t = x we have

$$\lim_{t\to x} \frac{R_{2m+1}(t)}{(t-x)^{2m+2}} = \frac{f^{(2m+2)}(x)}{(2m+2)!} =: A, \tag{7}$$

i.e. $R_{2m+1}(t)$ behaves locally like $A(t - x)^{2m+2}$. Our next theorem shows that for large n the same holds again locally (i.e. at the point $t = x$) for the respective L_n-images.

Theorem 2

Let $f \in D_{2m+2}(\Omega;x)$ and let $\{L_n\}_{n=1}^{\infty}$ be a sequence of linear positive operators mapping $D(\Omega)$ into $D(\Omega)$ and satisfying the condition (W) with a real constant $r > 1$. If there exists a natural number j such that

$$\lim_{n\to\infty} \frac{\{\tau_n^{[2m+2j+2]}(x)\}^{1/r'}}{\tau_n^{[2m+2]}(x)} = 0, \quad \frac{1}{r} + \frac{1}{r'} = 1 \tag{M3}$$

for $n \to \infty$, then

$$\lim_{n\to\infty} \frac{(L_n R_{2m+1})(x)}{\tau_n^{[2m+2]}(x)} = \frac{f^{(2m+2)}(x)}{(2m+2)!}. \tag{8}$$

(Note: For the subspace of $D_{2m+2}(\Omega;x)$ consisting of those $f \in D_{2m+2}(\Omega;x)$ which for $|t| \to \infty$ are at most of the order $O(t^{2m+2})$ Mamedov [10] proves a similar theorem.)

<u>Proof</u>. For all $\varepsilon > 0$ $\exists\delta(\varepsilon) > 0$ (without loss of generality $\delta < x$) such that

$$(A - \varepsilon)(t - x)^{2m+2} \leq R_{2m+1}(t) \leq (A + \varepsilon)(t - x)^{2m+2} \tag{9}$$

for $t \in I := (x - \delta, x + \delta)$. We split up the function $R_{2m+1}(t)$ into

$$R_{2m+1}(t) = \lambda_I(t)R_{2m+1}(t) + \mu_I(t)R_{2m+1}(t). \tag{10}$$

Since the operators L_n are linear, it follows from this that

$$(L_n R_{2m+1})(x) = (L_n\lambda_I R_{2m+1})(x) + (L_n\mu_I R_{2m+1})(x). \tag{11}$$

In view of (9) and the monotonicity of the operators L_n we obtain

$$(A - \varepsilon)\tau_n^{[2m+2]}(x) \leq (L_n\mu_I|R_{2m+1}|)(x)$$
$$\leq (A + \varepsilon)\tau_n^{[2m+2]}(x). \tag{12}$$

From now on we suppose that the index n has been chosen so large that $(L_m|f|^r)(x)$ is finite for $m \geq n$. With the aid of (5) and an inequality corresponding to (4) we have then

$$\begin{aligned}|(L_n\mu_I R_{2m+1})(x)| &\leq (L_n\mu_I|R_{2m+1}|)(x)\\ &\leq (L_n\mu_I|f|)(x) + \sum_{k=0}^{2m+1} \frac{|f^{(k)}(x)|}{k!}(L_n\mu_I|e_1 - x|^k)(x)\\ &= \{\overline{\lim_{n\to\infty}}(L_n|f|^r)(x)\}^{1/r}\left\{\frac{\tau_n^{[2m+2j+2]}(x)}{\delta^{2m+2j+2}}\right\}^{1/r'} + \\ &\quad + \sum_{k=0}^{2m+1}\frac{|f^{(k)}(x)|}{k!}\frac{\tau_n^{[2m+2j+2]}(x)}{\delta^{2m+2j+2-k}},\end{aligned}$$

and from this together with (11) and the assumption (M3), it follows that for sufficiently large n

$$\left|\frac{(L_n R_{2m+1})(x)}{\tau_n^{[2m+2]}(x)} - A\right| \leq 2\varepsilon.$$

3. Further remarks

For the sequence of Gammaoperators introduced by the author in his thesis, Müller [12], (W) and (M2') can be verified immediately. Therefore theorem 5.3 in Lupas and Müller [8] follows directly from our theorem 1 without the use of a pair of localization theorems necessary in the cited paper.

Probably the best known asymptotic approximation theorem for a special sequence of linear positive operators is Voronovskaya's theorem for Bernstein polynomials published in 1932. Voronovskaya assumes boundedness of the functions. But it can be easily shown that in the case of Bernstein polynomials the condition (W) is still satisfied by those functions $f \in D([0,1];x)$ behaving like x^{-a} or $(1 - x)^{-b}$ ($a > 1$ and $b > 1$ real constants) in the neighbourhood of the two endpoints of the interval [0,1] respectively. (We assume finite values of f for x=0 and x=1.) For a great number of further special sequences of linear positive operators asymptotic theorems are known which can be generalized considerably in the above mentioned sense. Without claiming completeness we mention results in papers of Baskakov [1], Butzer [2,3], Jakimovski and Leviatan [4,5], Leviatan [7], Stancu [15] and Szasz [16].

In a forthcoming paper we will establish generalizations of further asymptotic approximation theorems of Mamedov [11] for sequences of linear positive operators.

References

1. BASKAKOV, V. A. 'An example of a sequence of linear positive operators in the space of continuous functions'. Dokl. Akad. Nauk SSSR, 113 (1957), pp. 249-251 (in Russian).

2. BUTZER, P. L. 'Linear combinations of Bernstein polynomials'. Canad. J. Math., 5 (1953), pp. 559-567.

3. BUTZER, P. L. 'Zur Frage der Saturationsklassen singularer Integraloperatoren'. Math. Z., 70 (1958), pp. 93-112.

4. JAKIMOVSKI, A. and LEVIATAN, D. 'Generalized Bernstein polynomials'. Math. Z., 93 (1966), pp. 416-426.

5. JAKIMOVSKI, A. and LEVIATAN, D. 'Generalized Bernstein power series'. Math. Z., 96 (1967), pp. 333-342.

6. KOROVKIN, P. P. Linear operators and approximation theory. Hindustan Publ. Corp., 1960. (English translation).

7. LEVIATAN, D. 'On the remainder in the approximation of functions by Bernstein - type operators'.(To appear.)

8. LUPAS, A. and MÜLLER, M. 'Approximationseigenschaften der Gammaoperatoren'. Math. Z., 98 (1967), pp. 208-226.

9. MAMEDOV, R. G. 'The asymptotic value of the approximation of differentiable functions by linear positive operators'. Dokl. Akad. Nauk SSSR, 128 (1959), pp. 471-474 (in Russian).

10. MAMEDOV, R. G. 'On the asymptotic value of the approximation of repeatedly differentiable functions by positive linear operators'. Dokl. Akad. Nauk SSSR, 146 (1962), pp. 1013-1016 (in Russian). English translation in Sov. Math. Dokl., 2 (1962), pp. 1435-1438.

11. MAMEDOV, R. G. 'Some general results on the asymptotic value and the degree of approximation of functions by systems of linear positive operators'. Izvest. Akad. Nauk Azerbaidz. SSR, No. 6 (1962), pp. 3-13 (in Russian).

12. MÜLLER, M. Die Folge der Gammaoperatoren. Dissertation Stuttgart 1967.

13. NATANSON, I. P. Konstruktive Funktionentheorie. Akademie-Verlag, 1955.

14. SCHURER, F. On linear positive operators in approximation theory. Thesis Techn. Univ. Delft 1965.

15. STANCU, D. D. 'Approximation of functions by a new class of linear polynomial operators'. Revue Roumaine de Math. Pures et Appl., 8 (1968), pp. 1173-1194.

16. SZASZ, O. 'Generalizations of S. Bernstein's polynomials to the infinite interval'. J. Res. Nat. Bur. Standards, 45 (1950), pp. 239-245.

17. WALK, H. 'Approximation durch Folgen linearer positiver Operatoren'. Archiv der Math. (To appear in 1970).

RELATED INTERPOLATION PROBLEMS

G. A. Read

(Woolwich Polytechnic, London)

1. Introduction

There is a great deal of literature devoted to the problem of determining uniqueness classes for given sequences $\{L_n\}$ of linear functionals. That is to say, to determine the class of functions C for which $L_n(f) = L_n(g)$ for all n, with f and g in C, implies that f=g. A profitable approach to the problem is to determine an expansion class E for the associated generalised Newton interpolation series (i.e. a class of functions representable by this series), and then to use the fact that an expansion class must also be a uniqueness class.

The linear functionals may be functions of a parameter, and this is indeed the case for certain well known problems. For example, the problem of determining uniqueness classes for the linear functionals

$$L_n(f) = f^{(n)}(\alpha_n) \quad \text{with} \quad |\alpha_n| \leqslant 1,$$

in which case L_n is a function of the complex parameter α_n. In this paper we will show that by applying additional linear functionals with respect to such parameters we may obtain a new sequence of linear functionals $\{T_n\}$ and possibly deduce a uniqueness class for $\{T_n\}$. A similar technique was previously used by the author to improve a result of R. P. Boas on univalent derivatives of entire functions (Read [5]).

2. Related sequences of functionals

Let X be a linear space of complex functions (possibly of infinite dimension) and let $x_0, x_1, \ldots, x_n$ be elements of X. Also let $L_0, L_1, \ldots, L_n$ be linear functionals in the algebraic conjugate space X* of X. If we interpolate a given element $f \in X$ by a linear combination of $x_0, x_1, \ldots, x_n$, say $a_0x_0 + a_1x_1 + \ldots + a_nx_n$, we will require that

$$L_p(a_0x_0 + a_1x_1 + \ldots + a_nx_n) = L_p(f)$$

for $p = 0,1,2,\ldots,n$. The remainder

$$r_n(f,L) \equiv f - a_0x_0 - a_1x_1 \ldots - a_nx_n$$

is uniquely determined by

$$|L_p(x_q)|r_n(f,L) = \begin{vmatrix} f & x_0 & \ldots & x_n \\ L_0(f) & L_0(x_0) & \ldots & L_0(x_n) \\ \cdot & \cdot & \cdots & \cdot \\ L_n(f) & L_n(x_0) & \ldots & L_n(x_n) \end{vmatrix} \qquad (1)$$

provided that the $(n+1) \times (n+1)$ determinant $|L_p(x_q)|$ is non-zero (see Davis [2], p. 75).

We will now assume that each functional L_p is a function of a complex parameter α_p, so that, for a given $f \in X$,

$$L_p(f),\ L_p(x_0),\ \ldots,\ L_p(x_n)$$

are complex functions of the variable α_p which generate a linear function space Y_p, say. We will also assume that $f,x_0,x_1,\ldots,x_n$ are independent of all parameters α_p, $p = 0,1,\ldots,n$; and that L_p is independent of α_q unless $p=q$.

With the above assumptions, we notice that for each value of p, $p = 0,1,\ldots,n$, the expression (1) is an identity between elements of Y_p. (In this context the coefficients $f,x_0,x_1,\ldots,x_n$ are merely constants in Y_p.)

Suppose now that, for each p, Q_p is an element of the algebraic conjugate space Y_p^* of Y_p; then we may apply $Q_0, Q_1,\ldots,Q_n$ successively to both sides of (1) to obtain

$$Q_nQ_{n-1} \ldots Q_0|L_p(x_q)|r_n(f,L) = \begin{vmatrix} f & x_0 & \ldots & x_n \\ Q_0L_0(f) & Q_0L_0(x_0) & \ldots & Q_0L_0(x_n) \\ \cdot & \cdot & \cdots & \cdot \\ Q_nL_n(f) & Q_nL_n(x_0) & \ldots & Q_nL_n(x_n) \end{vmatrix}$$

$$= \begin{vmatrix} f & x_0 & \cdots & x_n \\ T_0(f) & T_0(x_0) & \cdots & T_0(x_n) \\ \cdot & \cdot & \cdots & \cdot \\ T_n(f) & T_n(x_0) & \cdots & T_n(x_n) \end{vmatrix}$$

$$= |T_p(x_q)| r_n(f,T), \tag{2}$$

where $T_p \equiv Q_p L_p \in X^*$ for $p = 0,1,2,\ldots,n$.

Our hope is that (2) will enable us to prove that $||r_n(f,L)|| \to 0$ implies $||r_n(f,T)|| \to 0$ as $n \to \infty$, in certain particular cases. In the applications which follow we will be concerned only with polynomial interpolation so that $x_m = z^m$, $m = 0,1,\ldots,n$.

3. Univalent derivatives of entire functions

Consider the interpolation problem associated with the linear functionals $L_p(f) = f^{(p)}(\alpha_p)$, $p = 0,1,2,\ldots$. The following results are known (there are many others):

Theorem A (S. S. Macintyre [4])

If $|\alpha_p| \leqslant 1$ then the class of entire functions of exponential type less than 0.7259 is an expansion class in the topology of uniform convergence for $|z| \leqslant 1$ (the corresponding interpolation series converging uniformly in all α_p).

The upper bound of all values which can replace 0.7259 to give a corresponding uniqueness class is the so called Whittaker constant W; it is known that $0.7259 \leqslant W < 0.7328$ but the exact value is unknown (S. S. Macintyre [3] and [4]).

Theorem B (S. S. Macintyre [4])

If $H = \{z : |z - t| \leqslant h, -1 \leqslant t \leqslant 1\}$ and $\alpha_p \in H$ for all p, then the class of entire functions of exponential type less than $\frac{\pi}{4} \exp\left(-\frac{\pi^2 h}{8}\right)$ is an expansion class in the topology of uniform convergence in H (the corresponding interpolation series converging uniformly in all α_p).

If h=0, so that $-1 \leqslant \alpha_p \leqslant 1$ for all p, then $\pi/4$ is known to be the best value for the corresponding uniqueness class.

Theorem C (Boas [1] page 173)

If $\alpha_{2p+1} = 0$ and $|\alpha_{2p}| \leqslant 1$ then the class of entire functions of exponential type less than $\log(2 + \sqrt{3}) = 1.31\ldots$ is an expansion class in the topology of uniform convergence for $|z| \leqslant 1$, (the corresponding interpolation series converging uniformly in all α_p).

With the notation of section 1 and the conditions of Theorem A we can put

$$Q_p(\phi) = \begin{cases} \dfrac{1}{b_p - a_p} \displaystyle\int_{a_p}^{b_p} \phi \, d\alpha_p & (a_p \neq b_p), \\ \phi(a_p) & (a_p = b_p); \end{cases}$$

so that for $p \geqslant 1$

$$T_p(f) = Q_p L_p(f) = \begin{cases} \dfrac{f^{(p-1)}(b_p) - f^{(p-1)}(a_p)}{b_p - a_p} & (a_p \neq b_p), \\ f^{(p)}(a_p) & (a_p = b_p), \end{cases}$$

and

$$T_0(f) = \frac{1}{b_0 - a_0} \int_{a_0}^{b_0} f(\alpha_0) \, d\alpha_0 .$$

We also notice that $|L_p(z^q)| = n!(n-1)! \ldots 2!1!$, and therefore from (2) we obtain

$$r_n(f,T) = \frac{\displaystyle\int_{a_n}^{b_n} d\alpha_n \int_{a_{n-1}}^{b_{n-1}} d\alpha_{n-1} \cdots \int_{a_0}^{b_0} r_n(f,L) d\alpha_0}{(b_n - a_n)(b_{n-1} - a_{n-1}) \ldots (b_0 - a_0)} . \qquad (3)$$

(If $a_p = b_p$ for some p, we simply omit the contribution of this value of p in (3).)

If

$$\rho_n(f,L) = \sup |r_n(f,L)|, \quad |\alpha_p| \leqslant 1, \quad p = 0,1,\ldots,n$$

then it is clear that (3) implies

$$|r_n(f,T)| \leqslant \rho_n(f,L),$$

so that the expansion class for $\{L_p\}$ is also an expansion class for $\{T_p\}$, and we therefore have a much shorter proof of theorem 1 of Read [5]; namely:

Theorem 1

If $f(z)$ is an entire function of exponential type less than 0.7259 and only a finite number of its derivatives are univalent in $|z| \leqslant 1$ then $f(z)$ is a polynomial.

The same method gives the other theorems of [5] more easily, but in addition we can deduce the following from Theorem C:

Theorem 2

If $f(z)$ is an even entire function of exponential type less than $\log(2+\sqrt{3})$ and only a finite number of its odd derivatives are univalent in $|z| \leqslant 1$ then $f(z)$ is a polynomial.

In order to prove theorem 2 we take

$$Q_{2p}(\phi) = \begin{cases} \dfrac{1}{b_p - a_p} \displaystyle\int_{a_p}^{b_p} \phi \, d\alpha_{2p} & (a_p \neq b_p), \\ \phi(a_p) & (a_p = b_p), \end{cases}$$

with $|a_p| \leqslant 1$ and $|b_p| \leqslant 1$ for all p. Then

$$T_{2p+1}(f) = f^{(2p+1)}(0),$$

$$T_{2p}(f) = \begin{cases} \dfrac{f^{(2p-1)}(b_p) - f^{(2p-1)}(a_p)}{b_p - a_p} & (a_p \neq b_p) \\ f^{(2p)}(a_p) & (a_p = b_p) \end{cases}$$

$$T_0(f) = \frac{1}{b_0 - a_0} \int_{a_0}^{b_0} f \, d\alpha_0 .$$

The required result follows immediately from (2) as in the previous theorem.

4. Generalized Lidstone series

The Lidstone series is the interpolation series associated with the linear functionals

$$L_{2p}(f) = f^{(2p)}(0), \quad L_{2p+1}(f) = f^{(2p)}(1).$$

It is known that entire functions of exponential type less than π form an expansion class, and that π is the best value in the corresponding uniqueness class. We intend to generalize the problem by considering eventually the linear functionals

$$P_{2p}(f) = f^{(2p)}(a_p), \quad P_{2p+1}(f) = f^{(2p)}(b_p),$$

where $\{a_p\}$ and $\{b_p\}$ are specified sequences of complex numbers.

Theorem 3

If K is a convex set, and the class of functions E is an expansion class for the functionals $L_p(f) = f^{(p)}(\alpha_p)$ with $\alpha_p \in K$ (the corresponding interpolation series converging uniformly in each α_p) then E is an expansion class for the functionals

$$T_{2p}(f) = f^{(2p)}(a_p), \quad T_{2p+1}(f) = \begin{cases} \dfrac{f^{(2p)}(b_p) - f^{(2p)}(a_p)}{b_p - a_p} & (a_p \neq b_p) \\ f^{(2p+1)}(a_p) & (a_p = b_p) \end{cases}$$

with $a_p \in K$ and $b_p \in K$ for all p.

<u>Proof</u>. With the notation of Section 2, we put

$$Q_{2p}(\phi) = \phi(a_p), \quad Q_{2p+1}(\phi) = \begin{cases} \dfrac{1}{b_p - a_p} \displaystyle\int_{a_p}^{b_p} \phi(t)dt & (a_p \neq b_p), \\ \phi(a_p) & (a_p = b_p). \end{cases}$$

The result then follows from (2) exactly as in theorem 1.

Corollary 1

E is also an expansion class for the functionals P_p if $a_p \in K$ and $b_p \in K$ with $a_p \neq b_p$.

<u>Proof</u>. The polynomials θ_n, of degree n, which satisfy

$$T_p(\theta_n) = T_p(f), \quad p=0,1,\ldots,n,$$

clearly satisfy

$$P_p(\theta_n) = P_p(f), \quad p=0,1,\ldots,n,$$

provided that $a_p \neq b_p$; and therefore $r_n(f,T) \equiv r_n(f,P)$ for all n.

Corollary 2

If $|a_p| \leqslant 1$, $|b_p| \leqslant 1$ and $a_p \neq b_p$, then the class of entire functions of exponential type less than 0.7259 is an expansion class for $\{P_p\}$.

Corollary 3

If $a_p \in H$, $b_p \in H$ and $a_p \neq b_p$ for all p then the class of entire functions of exponential type less than $\frac{\pi}{4} \exp\left(-\frac{\pi^2 h}{8}\right)$ is an expansion class for $\{P_p\}$.

Corollary 4

If $a_p = 0$, $0 < |b_p| \leq 1$ then the class of entire functions of exponential type less than $\log(2 + \sqrt{3})$ is an expansion class for $\{P_p\}$.

Corollaries 2,3 and 4 follow immediately from theorems A, B and C respectively. The example $\cos \pi z/2$ shows that the constants in Corollary 2 and in Corollary 3, with $h=0$, cannot exceed $\pi/2$; and the example $\sin \pi z$ shows that $\log(2 + \sqrt{3})$ cannot be replaced by any number exceeding π in Corollary 4.

It would be interesting to know if $\pi/4$ is the best value in Corollary 3, when $h=0$; certainly it does not give the best result when $a_n = -1$ and $b_n = 1$, for in this case the corresponding value is $\pi/2$.

References

1. BOAS, R. P. Entire functions. Academic Press, 1954.
2. DAVIS, P. J. Interpolation and approximation. Blaisdell, 1963.
3. MACINTYRE, S. S. 'An upper bound for the Whittaker constant'. J. London Math. Soc., 22 (1947), pp. 305-311.
4. MACINTYRE, S. S. 'On the zeros of successive derivatives of integral functions'. Trans. Amer. Math. Soc., 67 (1949), pp. 241-259.
5. READ, G. A. 'Univalent derivatives of entire functions'. J. London Math. Soc., 44 (1969), pp. 189-192.

PROBABILISTIC METHODS IN THE THEORY OF APPROXIMATION OF FUNCTIONS OF SEVERAL VARIABLES BY LINEAR POSITIVE OPERATORS

D. D. Stancu

(University of Cluj, Roumania)

1. Introduction

Let $Y_n = \{(Y_{n1},\ldots,Y_{ns})\}$ be a sequence of s-dimensional random vectors and let $F_n(y_1,\ldots,y_s;x_1,\ldots,x_s)$ denote the probability distribution function of Y_n, where $(y_1,\ldots,y_s)$ is any point of the Euclidean space R_s and $(x_1,\ldots,x_s)$ is a real s-dimensional parameter, varying in a parameter space Ω_s, which is a subset of R_s.

We shall assume that $(x_1,\ldots,x_s)$ represents the mean value of this distribution function, i.e.,

$$x_r = \int_{R_s} y_r dF_n(y_1,\ldots,y_s;x_1,\ldots,x_s),$$

where r=1,2,...,s and the s-fold integral is extended over all $(y_1,\ldots,y_s) \in R_s$.

Consider a real-valued function $f(y_1,\ldots,y_s)$ defined and bounded on R_s, such that the mean value of the random variable $f(Y_{n1},\ldots,Y_{ns})$ exists for n=1,2,... . This mean value is given by

$$E[f(Y_{n1},\ldots,Y_{ns})] = P_n(f;x_1,\ldots,x_s)$$
$$= \int_{R_s} f(y_1,\ldots,y_s)dF_n(y_1,\ldots,y_s;x_1,\ldots,x_s). \quad (1)$$

Assuming first that the random vector Y_n is of discrete type, one may observe that its distribution function:

$$F_n(y_1,\ldots,y_s;x_1,\ldots,x_s) = \Pr[Y_{n1} \leqslant y_1,\ldots,Y_{ns} \leqslant y_s;x_1,\ldots,x_s]$$

is a step function so that $Pr[Y_{n1} = y_1,\dots,Y_{ns} = y_s;x_1,\dots,x_s]$ is zero at every point of R_s except at a finite or countably infinite number of points $(a_{r1},\dots,a_{rs})$ $(r=1,2,\dots)$ and every such point (jump point) is taken with a positive probability (jump):

$$p_n(a_{r1},\dots,a_{rs};x_1,\dots,x_s) = Pr[Y_{n1} = a_{r1},\dots,Y_{ns} = a_{rs};x_1,\dots,x_s],$$

satisfying the condition

$$\sum_r p_n(a_{r1},\dots,a_{rs};x_1,\dots,x_s) = 1.$$

The corresponding distribution function is

$$F_n(y_1,\dots,y_s;x_1,\dots,x_s) = \sum_{(r)} p_n(a_{r1},\dots,a_{rs};x_1,\dots,x_s), \qquad (2)$$

where the summation is extended now over all points $(a_{r1},\dots,a_{rs})$ such that $a_{r1} \leq y_1,\dots,a_{rs} \leq y_s$.

Consequently, in this discrete case we are able to write down the following expression for the operator (1):

$$P_n(f;x_1,\dots,x_s) = \sum_r f(a_{r1},\dots,a_{rs})p_n(a_{r1},\dots,a_{rs};x_1,\dots,x_s). \qquad (3)$$

If the s-dimensional random vectors Y_n are of continuous type, having the probability densities $\rho_n(y_1,\dots,y_s;x_1,\dots,x_s)$ $(n=1,2,\dots)$, then we have

$$F_n(y_1,\dots,y_s;x_1,\dots,x_s) = \int_{-\infty}^{y_1} \cdots \int_{-\infty}^{y_s} \rho_n(u_1,\dots,u_s;x_1,\dots,x_s)du_1\dots du_s,$$

and the operator (1) can be written as follows

$$P_n(f;x_1,\dots,x_s) = \int_{R_s} f(y_1,\dots,y_s)\rho_n(y_1,\dots,y_s;x_1,\dots,x_s)dy_1\dots dy_s. \qquad (4)$$

It is easy to see that the operator $P_n(f;x_1,\dots,x_s)$ defined by (1), or in particular by (3) and (4), is a positive linear operator.

2. A limit theorem

We shall henceforth assume that for n=1,2,... the variances of the random vectors Y_n exist and that the components,

$$\sigma_{n,j}^2 = \int_{R_s} (y_j - x_j)^2 dF_n(y_1,\dots,y_s;x_1,\dots,x_s),$$

of these variances are different from zero $(j=1,2,\dots,s)$.

Now we shall state and prove the central result of this paper:

If the real-valued function $f(x_1,\dots,x_s)$ is continuous on a compact subset D_s of Ω_s and we have uniformly on D_s

$$\lim_{n\to\infty} \sigma^2_{n,j} = 0 \quad (j=1,2,\dots,s), \tag{5}$$

then

$$\lim_{n\to\infty} P_n(f;x_1,\dots,x_s) = f(x_1,\dots,x_s)$$

uniformly on D_s.

In order to prove this assertion we first take into account that since

$$P_n(1;x_1,\dots,x_s) = \int_{R_s} dF_n(y_1,\dots,y_s;x_1,\dots,x_s) = 1,$$

we have

$$\begin{aligned} R_n(f;x_1,\dots,x_s) &= f(x_1,\dots,x_s) - P_n(f;x_1,\dots,x_s) \\ &= \int_{R_s} [f(x_1,\dots,x_s)-f(y_1,\dots,y_s)]\,dF_n(y_1,\dots,y_s;x_1,\dots,x_s). \end{aligned}$$

Consequently we are able to write

$$|R_n(f;x_1,\dots,x_s)| \leq \int_{R_s} |f(x_1,\dots,x_s)-f(y_1,\dots,y_s)|\,dF_n(y_1,\dots,y_s;x_1,\dots,x_s).$$

Now it is convenient to make use of the modulus of continuity of f, defined as follows:

$$\omega(f;\delta_1,\dots,\delta_s) = \sup|f(x''_1,\dots,x''_s)-f(x'_1,\dots,x'_s)|,$$

where $(x'_1,\dots,x'_s)$ and $(x''_1,\dots,x''_s)$ are points from D_s such that: $|x''_1 - x'_1| \leq \delta_1,\dots,|x''_s - x'_s| \leq \delta_s$, $\delta_1,\dots,\delta_s$ being positive numbers.

Using the following properties of the modulus of continuity:

$$|f(x''_1,\dots,x''_s)-f(x'_1,\dots,x'_s)| \leq \omega(f;|x''_1-x'_1|,\dots,|x''_s-x'_s|),$$

$$\omega(f;\lambda_1\delta_1,\dots,\lambda_s\delta_s) \leq (1 + \lambda_1 +\dots+ \lambda_s)\omega(f;\delta_1,\dots,\delta_s),$$

where $\lambda_1 > 0,\dots,\lambda_s > 0$, we have

$$\begin{aligned} |f(x_1,\dots,x_s)-f(y_1,\dots,y_s)| &\leq \omega(f;\tfrac{1}{\delta_1}|x_1-y_1|\delta_1,\dots,\tfrac{1}{\delta_s}|x_s-y_s|\delta_s) \\ &\leq (1 + \tfrac{1}{\delta_1}|x_1-y_1|+\dots+ \tfrac{1}{\delta_s}|x_s-y_s|)\omega(f;\delta_1,\dots,\delta_s) \end{aligned}$$

and therefore

$$|R_n(f;x_1,\dots,x_s)| \leq \left(1 + \sum_{j=1}^{s} \frac{1}{\delta_j} P_n(|x_j-y_j|;x_1,\dots,x_s)\right)\omega(f;\delta_1,\dots,\delta_s).$$

In accordance with the Cauchy-Schwarz inequality we have

$$P_n(|x_j-y_j|;x_1,\dots,x_s) \leq \left(\int_{R_s} (x_j-y_j)^2 dF_n(y_1,\dots,y_s;x_1,\dots,x_s)\right)^{1/2} = \sigma_{n,j}.$$

We may therefore write

$$|R_n(f;x_1,\dots,x_s)| \leq \left(1 + \sum_{j=1}^{s} \frac{\sigma_{n,j}}{\delta_j}\right)\omega(f;\delta_1,\dots,\delta_s).$$

If we set $\delta_j = \alpha_j\sigma_{n,j}$ $(j=1,2,\dots,s)$, where $\alpha_1,\dots,\alpha_s$ are fixed positive numbers, we obtain finally

$$|R_n(f;x_1,\dots,x_s)| \leq \left(1 + \frac{1}{\alpha_1} + \dots + \frac{1}{\alpha_s}\right)\omega(f;\alpha_1\sigma_{n,1},\dots,\alpha_s\sigma_{n,s}). \qquad (6)$$

We note that with the aid of the constants $\alpha_1,\dots,\alpha_s$ it will be easy to obtain the desired inequalities corresponding to each concrete case.

Since by our hypothesis (5) the right-hand side of the last inequality tends to zero on D_s for $n \to \infty$, it follows that the sequence of operators $\{P_n(f;x_1,\dots,x_s)\}$ converges uniformly to $f(x_1,\dots,x_s)$ on D_s.

It should be remarked that this result represents an extension to the multidimensional case of a result due to Feller [4], and that in Stancu [13] we established an inequality of the form (6) when s=1.

3. Finite difference representation of operators

Now let us consider a method for representation by finite differences of the linear positive operators of discrete type.

It is convenient to make use of an interpolation polynomial of Newton-Biermann type for several variables (see Stancu [8], [10]):

$$N(f;t_1,\dots,t_s) = \sum_{0\leq i_1+\dots+i_s\leq n} \frac{(nt_1)^{[i_1]}\dots(nt_s)^{[i_s]}}{i_1!\dots i_s!} \Delta^{i_1,\dots,i_s}_{\frac{1}{n},\dots,\frac{1}{n}} f(0,\dots,0),$$

where

$$(nt_k)^{[i_k]} = nt_k(nt_k-1)\dots(nt_k-i_k+1),$$

while

$$\Delta^{i_1,\ldots,i_s}_{\frac{1}{n},\ldots,\frac{1}{n}} f(0,\ldots,0) = \sum_{\nu_1=0}^{i_1}\cdots\sum_{\nu_s=0}^{i_s}(-1)^{\nu_1+\ldots+\nu_s}\binom{i_1}{\nu_1}\cdots\binom{i_s}{\nu_s} f\left(\frac{i_1-\nu_1}{n},\ldots,\frac{i_s-\nu_s}{n}\right) \tag{7}$$

represents the finite partial difference of order $(i_1,\ldots,i_s)$ of the function f, with the steps $h_1=\ldots=h_s=1/n$ and the starting point $(0,\ldots,0)$.

With the aid of the changes of variables $nt_k=y_k (k=1,2,\ldots,s)$ we obtain

$$N(f;\frac{y_1}{n},\ldots,\frac{y_s}{n}) = \sum_{0\leq i_1+\ldots+i_s\leq n} \frac{y_1^{[i_1]}\cdots y_s^{[i_s]}}{i_1!\ldots i_s!} \Delta^{i_1,\ldots,i_s}_{\frac{1}{n},\ldots,\frac{1}{n}} f(0,\ldots,0). \tag{8}$$

Note that this polynomial satisfies the interpolating properties

$$N(f;\frac{k_1}{n},\ldots,\frac{k_s}{n}) = f(\frac{k_1}{n},\ldots,\frac{k_s}{n}) \tag{9}$$

for $k_1=0,1,\ldots,n; k_2=0,1,\ldots,n-k_1;\ldots;k_s=0,1,\ldots,n-k_1-\ldots-k_{s-1}$.

By using the formula (8) we can find for the mean value of the random variable $N(f;\frac{y_1}{n},\ldots,\frac{y_s}{n})$, where $(y_1,\ldots,y_s)$ has the probability distribution function $F_n(y_1,\ldots,y_s;x_1,\ldots,x_s)$, the following representation:

$$\int_{R_s} N(f;\frac{y_1}{n},\ldots,\frac{y_s}{n})dF_n(y_1,\ldots,y_s;x_1,\ldots,x_s) = \sum_{0\leq i_1+\ldots+i_s\leq n} \frac{m_{[i_1,\ldots,i_s]}}{i_1!\ldots i_s!} \Delta^{i_1,\ldots,i_s}_{\frac{1}{n},\ldots,\frac{1}{n}} f(0,\ldots,0), \tag{10}$$

in terms of the factorial moments

$$m_{[i_1,\ldots,i_s]} = \int_{R_s} y_1^{[i_1]}\cdots y_s^{[i_s]} dF_n(y_1,\ldots,y_s;x_1,\ldots,x_s).$$

These moments can be found by means of the corresponding factorial moment-generating function

$$g(t_1,\ldots,t_s) = E(t_1^{y_1}\ldots t_s^{y_s}) = \int_{R_s} t_1^{y_1}\ldots t_s^{y_s} dF_n(y_1,\ldots,y_s;x_1,\ldots,x_s), \tag{11}$$

according to the formula

$$m_{[i_1,\ldots,i_s]} = \left.\frac{\partial^{i_1+\ldots+i_s} g(t_1,\ldots,t_s)}{\partial t_1^{i_1}\ldots t_s^{i_s}}\right|_{\substack{t_1=1\\ \ldots\\ t_s=1}} \tag{12}$$

It should be observed that if the random vector Y_n is of discrete type and assumes the values $(k_1,\ldots,k_s)$ with the probabilities $p_{n;k_1,\ldots,k_s}$, where $k_1=0,1,\ldots,n; k_2=0,1,\ldots,n-k_1;\ldots;k_s=0,1,\ldots,n-k_1-\ldots-k_{s-1}$, then according to (9) the equality (10) reduces to

$$\sum_{0\leq k_1+\ldots+k_s\leq n} p_{n;k_1,\ldots,k_s} f\left(\frac{k_1}{n},\ldots,\frac{k_s}{n}\right)$$
$$= \sum_{0\leq k_1+\ldots+k_s\leq n} \frac{m_{[i_1,\ldots,i_s]}}{i_1!\ldots i_s!} \Delta^{i_1,\ldots,i_s}_{\frac{1}{n},\ldots,\frac{1}{n}} f(0,\ldots,0), \quad (13)$$

where

$$m_{[i_1,\ldots,i_s]} = \sum_{0\leq k_1+\ldots+k_s\leq n} k_1^{[i_1]}\ldots k_s^{[i_s]} p_{n;k_1,\ldots,k_s}.$$

4. Operators for uniform approximation

Let us show next a special method for obtaining concrete positive linear operators suitable for uniform approximation of continuous functions.

Consider a sequence of s-dimensional random vectors $\{X_k=(X_{k1},\ldots,X_{ks})\}$ and let us assume that the components $Y_{n\nu}$ of the random vector Y_n represent the arithmetic means of the first n components $X_{k\nu}$ $(k=1,2,\ldots,n)$ for $\nu=1,2,\ldots,s$, that is

$$Y_{n\nu} = \frac{1}{n}[X_{1\nu}+\ldots+X_{n\nu}] \quad (\nu=1,2,\ldots,s).$$

If we make the further assumption that for any natural number n the random vectors $X_1,\ldots,X_n$ are independent and identically distributed, then the common characteristic function $\phi(t_1,\ldots,t_s)$ of these random vectors, which is given by

$$\phi(t_1,\ldots,t_s) = \int_{R_s} \exp\left(i\sum_{\nu=1}^{s} t_\nu x_\nu\right) dF(x_1,\ldots,x_s),$$

$F(x_1,\ldots,x_s)$ being the common distribution function of these random vectors, can be used for expressing the characteristic function of the random vector Y_n:

$$\psi_n(t_1,\ldots,t_s) = \left[\phi\left(\frac{t_1}{n},\ldots,\frac{t_s}{n}\right)\right]^n, \quad (14)$$

since

$$\sum_{\nu=1}^{s} t_\nu Y_{n\nu} = \frac{1}{n} \sum_{k=1}^{n} [t_1 X_{k1} + \ldots + t_s X_{ks}].$$

5. Examples

For illustrative purposes we shall consider some examples, assuming that the random vectors $X_m (m=1,2,\ldots)$ are independent and identically distributed.

(i) Let us suppose first that the random vector $X_m = (X_{m1},\ldots,X_{ms})$ has at most one component different from zero and

$$\Pr[X_{m\nu}=1] = x_\nu, \quad \Pr[X_{m\nu}=0] = 1-x_\nu,$$

$$\Pr[X_{m1}=0,\ldots,X_{ms}=0] = y = 1-x_1-\ldots-x_s \,,$$

where $0 \leq x_\nu \leq 1 \quad (\nu=1,2,\ldots,s)$.

It follows that the characteristic function of X_m is given by

$$\phi(t_1,\ldots,t_s) = x_1 \exp(it_1)+\ldots+x_s \exp(it_s) + y.$$

Hence the characteristic function of $Y_n = (Y_{n1},\ldots,Y_{ns})$ can be expressed as follows:

$$\psi_n(t_1,\ldots,t_s) = \{x_1 \exp(\frac{it_1}{n})+\ldots+x_s \exp(\frac{it_s}{n})+y\}^n .$$

Clearly, this corresponds (see, e.g., Wilks [16]) to the random vector Y_n, whose components $Y_{n\nu}$ are $Z_{n\nu}/n$, where $Z_{n\nu} = X_{1\nu}+\ldots+X_{n\nu}$ $(\nu=1,2,\ldots,s)$, the random vector $Z_n = (Z_{n1},\ldots,Z_{ns})$ having the multinomial distribution:

$$\Pr[Z_{n1}=k_1,\ldots,Z_{ns}=k_s] = p_n^{k_1,\ldots,k_s}(x_1,\ldots,x_s)$$
$$= \frac{n!}{k_1!\ldots k_s!(n-k_1-\ldots-k_s)!} x_1^{k_1}\ldots x_s^{k_s}(1-x_1-\ldots-x_s)^{n-k_1-\ldots-k_s}.$$

Now referring to (3) we obtain the following operator

$$B_n(f;x_1,\ldots,x_s) = \sum_{0\leq k_1+\ldots+k_s\leq n} p_n^{k_1,\ldots,k_s}(x_1,\ldots,x_s) f(\frac{k_1}{n},\ldots,\frac{k_s}{n}). \quad (15')$$

It is easily seen that this operator may also be written in the form

$$B_n(f;x_1,\ldots,x_s)$$
$$= \sum_{k_1=0}^{n} \sum_{k_2=0}^{n-k_1} \ldots \sum_{k_s=0}^{n-k_1-\ldots-k_{s-1}} q_n^{k_1,\ldots,k_s}(x_1,\ldots,x_s) f(\frac{k_1}{n},\ldots,\frac{k_s}{n}), \quad (15)$$

where

$$q_n^{k_1,\ldots,k_s}(x_1,\ldots,x_s) \equiv p_n^{k_1,\ldots,k_s}(x_1,\ldots,x_s)$$
$$= \binom{n}{k_1}\binom{n-k_1}{k_2}\cdots\binom{n-k_1-\ldots-k_{s-1}}{k_s} x_1^{k_1}\cdots x_s^{k_s}(1-x_1-\ldots-x_s)^{n-k_1-\ldots-k_s}.$$

It is obvious that this linear operator is positive on the s-dimensional simplex

$$\Delta_s = \{(x_1,\ldots,x_s); x_1\geq 0,\ldots,x_s\geq 0, x_1+\ldots+x_s\leq 1\}. \tag{16}$$

Since in this case the factorial moment-generating function is

$$g(t_1,\ldots,t_s) = (x_1t_1+\ldots+x_st_s+y)^n,$$

we have

$$m_{[i_1,\ldots,i_s]} = n^{[i_1+\ldots+i_s]} x_1^{i_1}\cdots x_s^{i_s}.$$

Consequently, with the aid of formula (13) we can give the following representation of the operators of Bernstein type (15), in terms of finite differences:

$$B_n(f;x_1,\ldots,x_s)$$
$$= \sum_{0\leq i_1+\ldots+i_s\leq n} \frac{n^{[i_1+\ldots+i_s]}}{i_1!\ldots i_s!} x_1^{i_1}\cdots x_s^{i_s} \Delta^{i_1,\ldots,i_s}_{\frac{1}{n},\ldots,\frac{1}{n}} f(0,\ldots,0),$$

which enables us to find at once

$$\sigma^2_{n,j} = B_n((t_j-x_j)^2;x_1,\ldots,x_s) = \frac{x_j(1-x_j)}{n} \leq \frac{1}{4n} \quad (j=1,2,\ldots,s).$$

Therefore, in this case the inequality (6) becomes

$$|f(x_1,\ldots,x_s)-B_n(f;x_1,\ldots,x_s)| \leq (1+\frac{1}{\alpha_1}+\ldots+\frac{1}{\alpha_s})\omega(f;\frac{\alpha_1}{2\sqrt{n}},\ldots,\frac{\alpha_s}{2\sqrt{n}}).$$

Now if we choose $\alpha_1=\ldots=\alpha_s=2$ we obtain finally the inequality

$$|f(x_1,\ldots,x_s)-B_m(f;x_1,\ldots,x_s)| \leq (1+\frac{s}{2})\omega(f;\frac{1}{\sqrt{n}},\ldots,\frac{1}{\sqrt{n}}),$$

valid for $(x_1,\ldots,x_s) \in \Delta_s$, f being continuous on the simplex Δ_s. This inequality was given by us in 1960 [9]. In 1962 Schurer [6], using an important result due to Sikkema [7], obtained a better constant which can be used in place of $1 + \frac{s}{2}$ in this inequality.

(ii) Now suppose that the random vector $X_m=(X_{m1},\ldots,X_{ms})$ has an s-variate Poisson distribution, i.e.,

$$Pr(X_{m1}=k_1,\ldots,X_{ms}=k_s) = p(k_1,\ldots,k_s;x_1,\ldots,x_s)$$

$$= e^{-(x_1+\ldots+x_s)} \frac{x_1^{k_1}\ldots x_s^{k_s}}{k_1!\ldots k_s!} \qquad (k_1,\ldots,k_s = 0,1,2,\ldots).$$

The characteristic functions of X_m and $Y_n=(Y_{n1},\ldots,Y_{ns})$ are respectively

$$\phi(t_1,\ldots,t_s) = \exp(x_1 \exp(it_1)+\ldots+x_s \exp(it_s)-x_1-\ldots-x_s),$$

$$\psi_n(t_1,\ldots,t_s) = \exp(nx_1 \exp(it_1/n)+\ldots+nx_s \exp(it_s/n)-nx_1-\ldots-nx_s).$$

It is easily seen that the latter represents at the same time the characteristic function of $Y_n = (\frac{X_1}{n},\ldots,\frac{X_s}{n})$, where $(X_1,\ldots,X_s)$ has an s-variate Poisson distribution with the parameters $nx_1,\ldots,nx_s$.

In the case of this distribution, formula (3) leads us to the operator

$$P_n(f;x_1,\ldots,x_s) = \sum_{k_1,\ldots,k_s=0}^{\infty} e^{-n(x_1+\ldots+x_s)} \frac{(nx_1)^{k_1}\ldots(nx_s)^{k_s}}{k_1!\ldots k_s!} f(\frac{k_1}{n},\ldots,\frac{k_s}{n}), \tag{18}$$

which represents an extension to s variables of an operator studied early by Favard [3] and Szasz [15].

Assuming that x_j depends on n in such a way that for $n\to\infty$ we have $nx_j \to z_j > 0$ $(j=1,2,\ldots,s)$, we can obtain this operator starting from the operator (15). In this limit case formula (17) permits us to find the following representation for the operator (18):

$$P_n(f;z_1,\ldots,z_s) = \sum_{i_1,\ldots,i_s=0} \frac{(nx_1)^{i_1}\ldots(nz_s)^{i_s}}{i_1!\ldots i_s!} \Delta^{i_1,\ldots,i_s}_{\frac{1}{n},\ldots,\frac{1}{n}} f(0,\ldots,0).$$

If we presuppose that f is continuous on

$$D_s:\{(x_1,\ldots,x_s):0 \leq x_j \leq a_j, a_j > 0,\ j=1,2,\ldots s\},$$

then by virtue of (6) we obtain the inequality

$$|f(x_1,\ldots,x_s)-P_n(f;x_1,\ldots,x_s)| \leq (1+\sqrt{a_1}+\ldots+\sqrt{a_s})\omega(f;\frac{1}{\sqrt{n}},\ldots,\frac{1}{\sqrt{n}}),$$

valid for $(x_1,\ldots,x_s) \in D_s$, since in this case $\sigma^2_{n,j} = \frac{x_j}{n} \leq \frac{a_j}{n}$ and we can select $\alpha_j = 1/\sqrt{a_j}$ $(j=1,2,\ldots,s)$.

(iii) We now assume that the random vector X_m has a geometric distribution:

$$\Pr(X_{m1}=k_1,\ldots,X_{ms}=k_s) = \prod_{j=1}^{s} x_j(1-x_j)^{k_j} \quad (k_1,\ldots,k_s=0,1,2,\ldots),$$

where $0 \leq x_j \leq 1$ $(j=1,2,\ldots,s)$.

Since the characteristic function of X_m is

$$\phi(t_1,\ldots,t_s) = \prod_{j=1}^{s} \frac{x_j}{1-(1-x_j)\exp(it_s)},$$

we obtain for the characteristic function of the vector Y_n the following expression

$$\psi_n(t_1,\ldots,t_s) = \prod_{j=1}^{s} \left(\frac{x_j}{1-(1-x_j)\exp(it_s/n)}\right)^n .$$

One observes that this represents the characteristic function of $Y_n = (\frac{X_1}{n},\ldots,\frac{X_s}{n})$, where $(X_1,\ldots,X_s)$ has an s-variate Pascal distribution:

$$\Pr(X_1=k_1,\ldots,X_s=k_s) = \prod_{j=1}^{s} \binom{n+k_j-1}{k_j} x_j^n(1-x_j)^{k_j},$$

where $k_1,\ldots,k_s=0,1,2,\ldots$.

In accordance with (3) we therefore obtain the operator

$$P_n(f;x_1,\ldots,x_s) = \sum_{k_1,\ldots,k_s=0}^{\infty} \left\{\prod_{j=1}^{s} \binom{n+k_j-1}{k_j} x_j^n(1-x_j)^{k_j}\right\} f(\frac{k_1}{n},\ldots,\frac{k_s}{n}). \tag{19}$$

It should be observed that if we replace x_j by $1/(1+x_j)$ $(j=1,2,\ldots,s)$ then we arrive at the operator

$$Q_n(f;x_1,\ldots,x_s) = \sum_{k_1,\ldots,k_s=0}^{\infty} \left\{\prod_{j=1}^{s} \binom{n+k_j-1}{k_j} \frac{x_j^{k_j}}{(1+x_j)^{n+k_j}}\right\} f(\frac{k_1}{n},\ldots,\frac{k_s}{n}), \tag{20}$$

which in the case s=1 has been considered first by Baskakov [1].

Since in this case of operator (19) we have

$$\bar{\sigma}_{n,j} = \left[P_n\left\{\left(\frac{1-x_j}{x_j} - y_j\right)^2;x_1,\ldots,x_s\right\}\right]^{1/2} = \frac{1}{x_j}\sqrt{(1-x_j)/n}$$

assuming that f is continuous on

$$D_s':\{(x_1,\ldots,x_s):a_j \leq x_j \leq 1,\ 0 < a_j < 1,\ \ j=1,2,\ldots,s\},$$

we have on D_s'

$$\left|f\left(\frac{1-x_1}{x_1},\ldots,\frac{1-x_s}{x_s}\right) - P_n(f;x_1,\ldots,x_s)\right| \leqslant \left(1+\sum_{j=1}^{s}\frac{\sqrt{1-a_j}}{a_j}\right)\omega\left(f;\frac{1}{\sqrt{n}},\ldots,\frac{1}{\sqrt{n}}\right).$$

On the other hand, for the operator (20) we have

$$\sigma_{n,j} = \left\{Q_n\left[(x_j-y_j)^2;x_1,\ldots,x_s\right]\right\}^{1/2} = \sqrt{x_j(1+x_j)/n} \quad (j=1,2,\ldots,s).$$

Consequently, if we presuppose that f is continuous on

$$D_s'' : \{(x_1,\ldots,x_s) : 0 \leqslant x_j \leqslant a_j,\ a_j > 0,\ j=1,2,\ldots,s\},$$

we obtain at once the inequality

$$|f(x_1,\ldots,x_s) - Q_n(f;x_1,\ldots,x_s)| \leqslant \left[1+\sum_{j=1}^{s}\sqrt{a_j(1+a_j)}\right]\omega\left(f;\frac{1}{\sqrt{n}},\ldots,\frac{1}{\sqrt{n}}\right).$$

(iv) We shall now consider a case when the random vectors $X_1,X_2,\ldots$ are not independent and identically distributed.

Let us assume that we have an urn which contains N balls : a_o of color $0, a_1$ of color $1,\ldots,a_s$ of color s. A ball is drawn at random and if it is of color k it is replaced with c additional balls of color $k(k=0,1,\ldots,s)$. This procedure is repeated n times. Let X_{ij} be one or zero according as the i-th trial results in a ball of color j or not. The probability that the total number of balls of color $j:X_{1j}+X_{2j}+\ldots+X_{nj}$ be equal to k_j, where $0 \leqslant k_j \leqslant n$ $(j=0,1,\ldots,s)$ and $k_0+k_1+\ldots+k_s=n$, is given by

$$\frac{C_n^{k_1,\ldots,k_s}}{A(n)}\prod_{i=0}^{s}\prod_{\nu_i=0}^{k_i-1}(a_i + \nu_i c),$$

where
$$C_n^{k_1,\ldots,k_s} = \frac{n!}{k_0!k_1!\ldots k_s!} = \frac{n!}{k_1!\ldots k_s!(n-k_1-\ldots-k_s)!}$$

and $A(n)=N(N+c)\ldots(N+\overline{n-1}c)$.

This is the probability function of the s-variate Markov-Polya distribution.

Now let: $a_j/N = x_j$ $(j=1,2,\ldots,s)$, $c/N=\alpha$. Since $a_o/N=1-x_1-\ldots-x_s$, it follows that the probability of

$$Y_{nj} = \frac{1}{n}\sum_{i=1}^{n}X_{ij} = \frac{k_j}{n} \quad (j=1,2,\ldots,s)$$

can be written down at once as

$$w_n^{k_1,\ldots,k_s}(x_1,\ldots,x_s;\alpha)$$

$$= \frac{C_n^{k_1,\ldots,k_s}}{B(n)} \left\{ \prod_{j=1}^{s} \prod_{\nu_j=0}^{k_j-1} (x_j+\nu_j\alpha) \right\} \prod_{\mu=0}^{n-k_1-\ldots-k_s-1} (1-x_1-\ldots-x_s+\mu\alpha),$$

where $B(n)=(1+\alpha)(1+2\alpha)\ldots(1+\overline{n-1}\alpha)$.

It is now easy to see that in this case we obtain the operator*

$$P_n^{[\alpha]}(f;x_1,\ldots,x_s) = \sum_{0\leq k_1+\ldots+k_s\leq n} w_n^{k_1,\ldots,k_s}(x_1,\ldots,x_s;\alpha) f\left(\frac{k_1}{n},\ldots,\frac{k_s}{n}\right), \quad (21)$$

which in the case s=1 was introduced and studied in detail in our papers [11], [12], [13].

It is obvious that (21) represents a polynomial of degree m with respect to $x_1,\ldots,x_s$ and that for $\alpha \geq 0$ it is a <u>positive</u> linear operator on the simplex Δ_s defined in (16). In the special case $\alpha=0$ it reduces to the n-dimensional Bernstein polynomial† (15').

It is easy to verify that if $x_1 > 0,\ldots,x_s > 0$, $x_1+\ldots+x_s < 1$ and $\alpha > 0$, then we can write

$$\frac{1}{C_n^{k_1,\ldots,k_s}} w_n^{k_1,\ldots,k_s}(x_1,\ldots,x_s;\alpha)$$

$$= \frac{B\left(\frac{x_1}{\alpha}+k_1,\ldots,\frac{x_s}{\alpha}+k_s, \frac{1-x_1-\ldots-x_s}{\alpha}+n-k_1-\ldots-k_s\right)}{B\left(\frac{x_1}{\alpha},\ldots,\frac{x_s}{\alpha}, \frac{1-x_1-\ldots-x_s}{\alpha}\right)},$$

by using the s-fold Dirichlet integral

$$B(p_1,\ldots,p_{s+1}) = \int_{\Delta_s} u_1^{p_1-1}\ldots u_s^{p_s-1}(1-u_1-\ldots-u_s)^{p_{s+1}-1} du_1\ldots du_s. \quad (22)$$

By taking this into consideration,we readily arrive at the following representation of the corresponding factorial moment-generating function (11):

---

* In [14] we investigated another operator of this type.

† See Dinghas [2], Lorentz [5] and Stancu [9].

$$B(\frac{x_1}{\alpha},\ldots,\frac{x_s}{\alpha},\frac{1-x_1-\ldots-x_s}{\alpha})g(t_1,\ldots,t_s)=$$

$$\int_{\Delta_s} u_1^{\frac{x_1}{\alpha}-1}\ldots u_s^{\frac{x_s}{\alpha}-1}(1-u_1-\ldots-u_s)^{\frac{1-x_1-\ldots-x_s}{\alpha}-1}(1-u_1-\ldots-u_s+t_1u_1+\ldots+t_su_s)^n du_1\ldots du_s .$$

Consequently, if we take into account formula (12) and that the Dirichlet integral (22) has the value (see, e.g., Wilks [16]):

$$B(p_1,\ldots,p_{s+1})=\frac{\Gamma(p_1)\ldots\Gamma(p_{s+1})}{\Gamma(p_1+\ldots+p_{s+1})},$$

we obtain at once the following expressions for the factorial moments of the s-variate Markov-Polya distribution:

$$m_{[i_1,\ldots,i_s]}=n^{[i_1+\ldots+i_s]}\frac{B(\frac{x_1}{\alpha}+i_1,\ldots,\frac{x_s}{\alpha}+i_s,\frac{1-x_1-\ldots-x_s}{\alpha})}{B(\frac{x_1}{\alpha},\ldots,\frac{x_s}{\alpha},\frac{1-x_1-\ldots-x_s}{\alpha})}=$$

$$=\frac{n^{[i_1+\ldots+i_s]}}{(1+\alpha)(1+2\alpha)\ldots(1+\overline{i_1+\ldots+i_s-1}\alpha)}\prod_{\nu=1}^{s}x_\nu(x_\nu+\alpha)\ldots(x_\nu+\overline{i_\nu-1}\alpha).$$

Now referring to (13) we can give the following representation for our operator (21):

$$P_n^{[\alpha]}(f;x_1,\ldots,x_s)=\sum_{0\le i_1+\ldots+i_s\le n}C_n^{i_1,\ldots,i_s}\frac{\prod_{\nu=1}^{s}x_\nu(x_\nu+\alpha)\ldots(x_\nu+\overline{i_\nu-1}\alpha)}{(1+\alpha)(1+2\alpha)\ldots(1+\overline{i_1+\ldots+i_s-1}\alpha)}\Delta^{i_1,\ldots,i_s}_{\frac{1}{n},\ldots,\frac{1}{n}}f(0,\ldots,0),$$

by means of the finite partial differences (7).

The application of this formula yields

$$P_m^{[\alpha]}(1;x_1,\ldots,x_s)=1,\quad P_m^{[\alpha]}(y_j;x_1,\ldots,x_s)=x_j,$$

$$P_m^{[\alpha]}(y_j^2;x_1,\ldots,x_s)=\frac{1}{1+\alpha}\left\{\frac{x_j(1-x_j)}{n}+x_j(x_j+\alpha)\right\},$$

so that

$$\sigma_{n,j}^2=\frac{1+\alpha n}{1+\alpha}\cdot\frac{x_j(1-x_j)}{n}\qquad(j=1,2,\ldots,s).$$

The inequality (6), where we take $\alpha_1=\ldots=\alpha_s=2$, enables us to write down

$$|f(x_1,\dots,x_s)-P_n^{[\alpha]}(f;x_1,\dots,x_s)| \le (1+\frac{s}{2})\omega\left(f;\sqrt{\left\{\frac{1+\alpha n}{n+\alpha n}\right\}},\dots,\sqrt{\left\{\frac{1+\alpha n}{n+\alpha n}\right\}}\right). \quad (23)$$

Consequently, if $f(x_1,\dots,x_s)$ is continuous on Δ_s and if $0 \le \alpha = \alpha(n) \to 0$ as $n \to \infty$, then the sequence of operators $\{P_n^{[\alpha]}(f;x_1,\dots,x_s)\}$ converges to $f(x_1,\dots,x_s)$ uniformly on Δ_s.

It should be noticed that when $\alpha=0$ the inequality (23) reduces to one established by us [9] for the s-dimensional Bernstein operator (15).

References

1. BASKAKOV, V. A. 'An example of a sequence of linear positive operators in the space of continuous functions'. Dokl. Akad. Nauk SSSR, 113 (1957), pp. 249-251.
2. DINGHAS, A. 'Uber einige Identitäten vom Bernsteinsche Typus'. Norske Vid. Selsk. Trondheim, 24 (1951), pp. 96-97.
3. FAVARD, J. 'Sur les multiplicateurs d'interpolation'. J. Math. Pures Appl., 23 (1944), pp. 219-247.
4. FELLER, W. An Introduction to Probability Theory and its Applications, Vol. II. John Wiley, 1966.
5. LORENTZ, G. G. Bernstein polynomials. Univ. of Toronto Press, 1953.
6. SCHURER, F. 'On the order of approximation with generalized Bernstein polynomials'. Indag. Math., 24 (1962), pp. 484-488.
7. SIKKEMA, P. C. 'Der Wert einiger Konstanten in der Theorie der Approximation mit Bernstein-Polynomen'. Numer. Math., 3 (1961), pp. 107-116.
8. STANCU, D. D. 'On some Taylor developments of functions of several variables'. Revue de Math. Pures Appl., 4 (1959), pp. 249-265.
9. STANCU, D. D. 'On some polynomials of Bernstein type'. Studii Cercet. St. Matem. (Iasi), 9 (1960), pp. 221-233.
10. STANCU, D. D. 'The remainder of certain linear approximation formulas in two variables'. SIAM J. Numer. Anal., 1 (1964), pp. 137-163.
11. STANCU, D. D. 'On a new positive linear polynomial operator'. Proc. Japan Acad., 44 (1968), pp. 221-224.
12. STANCU, D. D. 'Approximation of functions by a new class of linear polynomial operators'. Rev. Roumaine Math. Pures Appl., 13 (1968), pp. 1173-1194.
13. STANCU, D. D. 'Use of probabilistic methods in the theory of uniform approximation of continuous functions'. Ibid. 14 (1969), pp. 673-691.
14. STANCU, D. D. 'Approximation of functions of two and several variables by a class of polynomials of Bernstein type'. Studii Cercet. Matem. (Bucharest)., 11 (1969) (to appear).
15. SZASZ, O. 'Generalization of S. Bernstein's polynomials to the infinite interval'. J. Res. Nat. Bur. Standards, 45 (1950), pp. 239-245.
16. WILKS, S. S. Mathematical Statistics. John Wiley, 1963.

NAME INDEX

Entries refer to pages. In some cases the reference number is also given, e.g. 273:6 means reference [6] occurring on p. 273.

SUBJECT INDEX

CORRIGENDA

Page	Position	For	Read
12	bottom	$<$	$\leqslant$
18	bottom	$\varepsilon_n(y)$	$\varepsilon_n^{\omega}(y)$
25	l. 9	[7]	Sec. 7
"	l. 3 up	"	"
28	l. 12	subsequence	subsequence)
"	l. 14	bounds	bound
36	eq. (5)	$f(x_i^{(n)}$	$f(x_i^{(n)})$
38	eq. (16)	$c_i^{(n)}.....$	$c_i^{(n)}(.....)$
39	l. 6 up	(8)	(8) be
"	l. 3 up	ℓ	i
45	l. 11	Insert (34) at end	
53	ll. 6, 7	T_n	T_n^*
57	l. 6	$\cos n\varphi$	$\sin n\varphi$
61	ref. [2]	59	69
66	l.13	these	there
72	l.17	$E_i(x)$	$E_i(x)$,
73	l. 2 up	$D(x)$	$D_i(x)$
"	bottom	$B_i(x)$	$B_i(x)$,
75	l. 12	$+2\delta_{i+1}^k$	$+2\delta_{i-1}^k$
85	l. 7	[4]	[14]
"	l. 14	[8]	[18]
86	eq. (12)	r_i	r_i^2
89	l. 13	numbers	numbers with sum 1
97	eq. (55)	$\Vert f \Vert$	$\Vert f \Vert^2$
125	eq. (45)	$\lambda_k - \lambda_j x$	$(\lambda_k - \lambda_j)x$
126	l. 5 up	does	does not
127	l. 9 up	large z	large x
"	l. 3 up	y	$\tilde{y}$
140	l. 4	F	$\mathbb{F}$
175	l. 9 up	(19)	(9)
177	l. 3	$\left(.....\right)$	$\left(.....\right)^2$
182	l. 3	The,	Then
203	l. 6	below	opposite
222	l. 14 up	C	B

Page	Position	For	Read
224	l. 16	j-1	j+1
228	l. 2	n_{k-1}	n_k-1
236	l. 7 up	α_n	α_m
244	eq. (8)	S(u-v, w-u)	(S(u-v), w-u)
250	l. 1	u	u_ε
258	l. 8	$(Au_n-Au, {}_{\varepsilon n})$	(Au_n-Au, ε_n)
260	l. 5	$h_1 = h_1$	$h_1 = h_2$
261	l. 14	or	of
264	l. 13 up	Delete "Let" at end	
267	l. 3	Y	$Y^\perp$
270	l. 5	$= 1+n(1+\varepsilon/n)$	$\leqslant 1+n(1+\varepsilon/n)$
"	l. 11 up	$\lambda\|x\|$	$\lambda\|x\|$
"	l. 9 up	$=\lambda\|z\|$	$=\lambda\|z\|$
273	l. 15	[36]	[6]
277	l. 18	$j \leqslant i$	$j < i$
297	l. 3	ration	ratio
301	l. 10 up	k:{	{k:
305	l. 9 up	x_{n+1}	x^*_{n+1}
317	l. 4 up	by the error	be the error
341	l. 6 up	m	n
"	l. 5 up	m	n